AC 7064

D0992111

AMERICAN
MALLEABLE IRON

A Handbook

Malleable Founders' Society
Cleveland
1944

The Rumford Press
Concord, New Hampshire

PREFACE

Malleable iron founding is one of the oldest of our national industries and the product occupies a most important place in the design, the engineering, and the materials of American manufacture.

The bibliography of malleable iron is voluminous, though confined, primarily, to the scientific and trade press. Written by many eminent authorities, it represents a prodigious amount of exhaustive research and practical experience.

No attempt has been made in recent years to assemble and edit the published and other available data in such form as to serve equally well students, teachers, engineers, metallurgists, customers, government agencies, the Army and Navy, and others interested in the subject. Neither the metallurgical textbook nor the technical operating manual could fill this exceedingly diversified requirement.

A handbook seemed to afford the best medium for this purpose. It permits of the presentation of technical data in sufficiently narrative form to be interesting to both the scientific and the lay reader.

Every effort has been made in this volume to reconcile the divergent theories and practices which invariably exist in any metallurgical art. While exceptions doubtless will be taken to the results of that effort, the Editors can only rest on the fact that theirs has been an honest endeavor to offer what appeared to be the most generally accepted opinions and methods.

It is inevitable that some important subject matter will be found to have been omitted and, by contrast, some inclusions may seem inconsequential. What is trivial to the scientist, obvious to the technician, or routine to the operator may be of major importance to the layman. These considerations have been carefully evaluated throughout the editing process.

In our present-day accelerated economy, manufacturing practices do not long remain static; what is impossible today will be routine tomorrow, — new tools, improved techniques and other operating practices engender constant change. Future revisions, it is hoped, will maintain the timeliness of the material in this book.

The Editors have drawn freely on all available sources and most gratefully acknowledge their indebtedness to the many authors concerned. A full measure of appreciation is also expressed to the many individuals and the committees whose research, writing, criticism, and suggestions have contributed to this publication.

If this Handbook can be instrumental in the dissemination of information on malleable iron, its manufacture, and the promotion of its proper use in ever-widening fields of service, it will have served its purpose.

To assure the most faithful reproduction possible, the photographs of castings in this book have not been retouched.

CONTENTS

I

THE BACKGROUND

AMERICAN malleable iron is an alloy consisting principally of iron and carbon which, as cast, is extremely hard and brittle but is rendered tough and ductile by a subsequent heat-conversion process. Because of its unique metallurgical structure, it possesses valuable properties which, by reason of their combination in this one metal, establish it as the ideal material for a wide diversity of applications. Chiefly, these properties are: great toughness; remarkable resistance to heavy and repeated impact; excellent ductility; high resistance to corrosion; easy machinability; and a versatile castability that makes possible sound castings, accurate to pattern, in complicated as well as simple forms, over an extensive range of weights and sizes. A brief review of the evolution of American malleable iron will contribute to one's understanding of how and why it attains its properties.

Iron was known and used in Europe, Asia, and Africa from the earliest times of which any historical records exist. And from evidences that have been found, there can be no question that hundreds of generations before the dawn of recorded history, primitive man had discovered this metal and fashioned it into very simple tools and weapons. He had learned that the red hot mass resulting from the heating of a type of reddish earth could be pounded into shapes of his own designing — and the forging of tools and weapons of "wrought" or "worked" iron had begun. What primitive man did not know was that his reddish earth was iron ore — oxides of iron — and that his wood fire deoxidized it — drove out the oxygen and left essentially pure iron; and what he also did not know was that in addition to supplying heat, the charcoal formed as his fire burned was the ideal agent for so reducing his ore. At any rate, his wood charcoal gave the results he wanted.

From this beginning, the making of iron over the centuries progressed through the stages of reducing ore in Catalan hearths, then in their successors, the early stack furnaces. In these, temperatures were sufficient to produce only an incandescent, spongy mass of iron. This iron, however, was chemically almost pure, for two principal reasons: First, the temperatures were still below the ranges where chemical combination could occur between the iron and any other elements present — notably the carbon of the charcoal; and, second, at the temperatures attainable, the charcoal ash resulting from combustion of the fuel sintered or partially fused with the clay and other minerals found in nature with the ore, to form a slag. Possibly some of the slag worked through and out of the iron, but because of the latter's pasty condition much slag remained trapped in the iron.

The glowing masses with which these early ironmasters worked were called "blooms" and their furnaces, "bloomeries," which in their later built-up forms became the "high furnaces" of Renaissance Europe and were the forerunners of the modern cupola and blast furnace. The blooms were forged by hammering, to shape and form the tools, weapons, and other articles desired, and to force out as much as possible of the trapped slag.

As furnaces and their performances improved, some early ironworkers were surprised to find that their iron was becoming more difficult to work and that when cooled it lacked strength and could be easily broken. Some of them tried the most obvious experiment for overcoming these unwelcome qualities, which was to reheat the iron, and were gratified to find that their material was at least partially restored to the more ductile condition they thought of as natural.

Since the science of metallurgy had not yet even been conceived, these craftsmen could not have known and probably did not suspect what was occurring in their irons. Their practices were based purely on experiment and experience. But unwittingly they were putting to good use the chemical principle that with sufficient temperature, carbon will migrate in iron.

As between the iron itself and the materials or atmosphere surrounding it — if carbon is in excess in the latter, it will enter and migrate through the iron; if the excess of carbon is in the iron, it will migrate toward the surface and out of the iron. The former process of carbon absorption is called "carburization"; the latter process of expulsion is "decarburization." During carburization, carbon combines with iron to form iron carbide, which is a harder and more brittle substance than pure iron. Decarburization frees carbon from the carbide, restoring the iron to a chemically purer, softer state.

Up to this time, iron obtained *direct* by the reduction of the original ore could be wrought, since temperatures had not been high enough to cause any appreciable carburization. But with the improving furnaces of this era and their consequent higher temperatures, the hardening influence of carbon was injected into ironmaking, and made necessary the *indirect* or two-stage process of first producing a carburized, hard material from reduction of ore, then by a later heat-treatment decarburizing this material to prepare it for ultimate forging. In reducing ores with charcoal, this carbon-rich fuel and its gases of combustion provided the excess carbon which carburized the otherwise pure iron of the blooms, making them hard and unworkable. When the blooms were reheated, much less fuel was needed than to reduce the original ore.

Hence, carbon migrated out of the iron, carbide was at least partially broken up, and correspondingly the iron was chemically repurified, its hardness diminished and workability restored.

These early industrialists began to learn, too, that within certain limits, larger heats required no more labor than smaller ones, and that the cost of building larger furnaces did not increase in proportion to expanding capacity. So furnaces grew in size, and with them the columns of the charges of ore and charcoal correspondingly increased, as well as the duration of contact between ore and charcoal. Temperatures grew hotter. Carbon absorption increased. These operators naturally were hopeful that a day would come when they could melt iron and cast it, as other metals were melted and cast, expecting their blooms, like other metals, to soften progressively and ultimately to liquefy.

Then one day in the first decade of the Fourteenth Century the capacity of carbon for lowering the melting point of iron became apparent. For in some furnace, well before seemingly high enough temperatures were reached, iron actually melted! When this furnace was broken into for removal of the expected bloom, fluid metal had run down into the hearth of the furnace, collecting in a molten pool and ridding itself of the lighter slag, which floated on the surface of the iron. Here was an iron rich in hard iron carbide, but relatively slag-free and clean. Since working out slag during forging now became almost unnecessary, the indirect process proved to be more efficient and economical than the direct, which involved a much longer reduction period at lower temperatures to avoid carburization, and then the longer and laborious forging to drive out slag. The introduction of melting, with its marked improvement in quality of product, proved an incalculable boon to forging, and was the greatest single influence in the adoption of the indirect process. This became general practice during the Fourteenth Century.

With an ancient knowledge and skill at hand in the casting of other metals, it was but a very short step to iron founding. But the castings made of this newly available material had to be confined to a very limited field, since they were of a highly carburized iron and therefore very hard and brittle.

Meanwhile, the growing capacities of stack furnaces had made possible blooms which were so large as to be unwieldy to handle and hence were pulled apart into pieces of convenient size. With the advent of molten iron, a similar situation arose; so the metal was run out of the furnace into shallow, thinly connected troughs, making pieces that, when cool, were easily broken apart. These troughs, thinly connected with the main body, had when filled a most realistic resemblance to a sow with suckling pigs; hence the term "pig" iron.

The infant foundry industry of this period, because of the meager demand for its weak, hard castings, required relatively little melting stock. Of the two means for obtaining it — through ore reduction or melting pig iron — the latter was obviously the cheaper and more practical, and where possible was adopted, thus in principle establishing the *indirect* process. No better procedure has since been found, and today pig iron provides the base stock of virtually all foundry melting. No significant amount of gray iron, malleable iron, or cast steel is made by a process which derives its basic iron *direct* through the reduction of ore.

To return to the time when iron was first melted, two contrasting materials had been evolved. The first was wrought iron — strong, durable, and ductile in proportion to its freedom from carbon, but because of the necessary forging with crude and clumsy contemporary tools, adaptable only to articles of simplest and fairly substantial form. The second was cast iron — hard, brittle, and weak because of its high carbon, but castable into fairly complicated shapes from small to really formidable sizes. The utility of a metal in which the desirable properties of both wrought and cast iron might be combined was at once apparent to the ironmasters of this era. Many experiments were undertaken to develop such a metal.

In 1722, the great French scientist and metallurgist, Réaumur, described a process for packing small castings in iron ore and heating them to a bright redness for many days. These castings contained iron carbides, and this protracted heat-treatment in this temperature range brought about a slow decarburization, partial to complete, according to the thickness of the castings and the temperature and length of time of heating.

The chemical affinity of oxygen for carbon at elevated temperatures is stronger than for iron. As Réaumur's carbide gave up carbon, the iron ore released oxygen to combine with the freed carbon to form gaseous carbon monoxide and dioxide, which escaped from the furnace. The packing performed three functions: First, it supplied the oxygen for oxidizing the carbon; second, it supported the castings that would soften and lose shape under the applied heat without such support; third, it acted as a "buffer" shielding the castings from direct contact with the hot furnace atmosphere, which contact in the long period of heating would have caused undue oxidation, of iron as well as carbon, creating a heavy scale on the castings and perhaps even destroying thin sections.

In proportion to the controlling factors of time and temperature of heating, Réaumur attained his sought-for result of materially reducing hardness and brittleness and correspondingly imparting toughness and ductility. His process was in effect an "anneal," or heat-treatment, and produced undoubtedly the first malleable iron castings.

This malleableizing process, with only minor deviations, has been pursued in Europe to the present day, its product being European "whiteheart" malleable iron. To understand this descriptive term it must be remembered that this is decarburized material in the sense that most of the carbon freed from its carbide has been eliminated, though all carbide may not have been broken up into iron and carbon. The constituents of the annealed metal, therefore, are mainly iron and iron carbide; and from the presence of the latter, the grains of the metal under tension stretch to a limited extent or not at all, then shear through and across their sections along minute and fairly flat planes which reflect light. These minute reflecting planes give a whitish or grayish color to the ruptured surface, and hence its description as "white-heart."

The story now comes to more familiar scenes. At Newark, New Jersey, in 1820, Seth Boyden had set up an iron foundry. Knowing of European malleable iron, he foresaw in our rapidly developing industries a potential market for this material. Accordingly, he entered upon a series of experiments by which to acquire the technique of making malleable castings. It was appropriate that these experiments in connection with American malleable iron should have been started in 1826 on the Fourth of July. Between this date and September 1, 1832, he kept a diary of his investigations, and from this record it is plain that he was basing his work on Réaumur's process and had no thought but to produce whiteheart malleable iron.

Constantly, in referring to his early trials, Boyden derogatorily described the fractures of his specimens as "black" and "grey"; and of the eleventh experiment, he wrote, ". . . the iron was tough when broken but rather too dark in color." His iron, as cast, was largely composed of iron carbide — hard, brittle, and easily shattered. At a broken cross-section it showed a white, steely fracture, hence came to be called "white iron." Because of the chemical composition of the pig irons available to them, Boyden's white iron contained less sulphur than Réaumur's, more manganese, and much more silicon.

Fig. 1. This print from the encyclopedia of Diderot and D'Alembert, 1762, shows a small furnace such as was available to Réaumur in his early experiments with whiteheart malleable iron.

Fig. 2. This statue in Newark, New Jersey, honors Seth Boyden, who began there in 1826 the experiments from which American malleable iron originated.

Silicon aids the dissociation of iron carbide into iron and free carbon. When freed carbon remains in the iron, this dissociation is known as "graphitization"; when the carbon is freed and then eliminated as in Réaumur's process, the dissociation is "decarburization." Hence in Boyden's "malleable" iron, for a heat-treatment comparable to Réaumur's, relatively more carbon was precipitated than in Réaumur's and remained in the iron as nodules of free "temper" carbon — simply because Boyden's heat-treatment was not long enough in duration to oxidize away more than a small portion of the carbon.

As his heat-treating experiments proceeded and his malleable approached the strength and properties he was striving for, Boyden must have been continually puzzled at its persistent refusal to show his conception of proper whiteheart fracture. Without realizing it, he was witnessing and recording the results of an entirely new process [1] * — graphitization of hard white iron to malleableize it, rather than decarburization. His iron had no relation to the whiteheart product he was trying to imitate, had much better properties, and was in fact a new creation among ferrous metals — "blackheart" or American malleable iron.

* References are to sources listed in "Bibliography of Sources," page 249.

Boyden evidently assumed that the heating periods applied to European irons were long enough, for he never significantly extended them in his own practice. Had he sufficiently lengthened his anneal — though it would have taken many weeks — he could have eliminated from his malleable most of its free carbon, thus duplicating the decarburization occurring in the lower-silicon irons of Europe. But before such a procedure was thought of or attempted, the better qualities of graphitized "blackheart" malleable with its free temper carbon began to demonstrate themselves, and the malleable industry native to our country struck out upon its own course of development.

Within a decade or two after the successful culmination of Seth Boyden's experiments, the manufacture of American malleable iron had spread from New Jersey throughout New England and New York, and in the 1850's was being established in Ohio and Illinois. Much of the early development of the industry was concentrated in New England. Many plants have been operating for 75 years, and at one site in eastern Massachusetts, malleable iron has been manufactured for over a century.

Seth Boyden is said to have begun his experiments because he wanted to find a way to lower the cost of the harness hardware which was being made by hand in his shop. Logically enough, the malleable iron which his work produced found its first chief application in harness fittings and parts for the covered wagons and stagecoaches of his day.

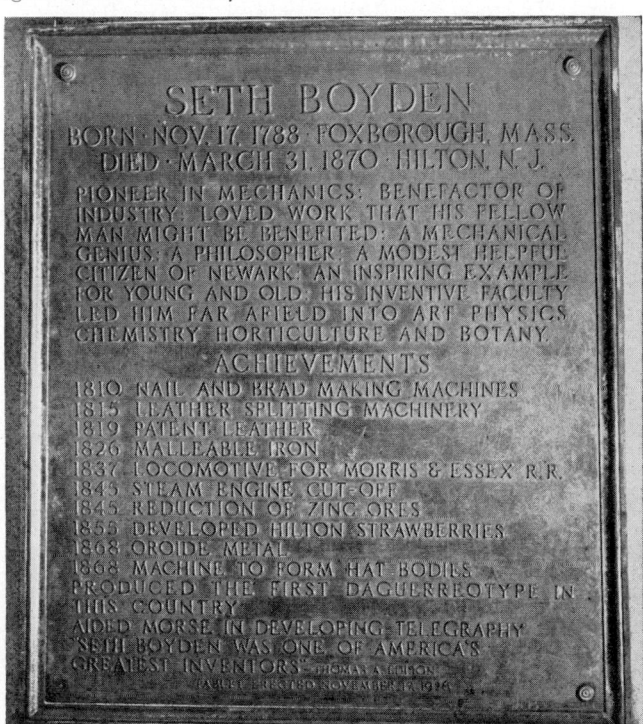

This plaque on the base of his statue records some of Seth Boyden's achievements.

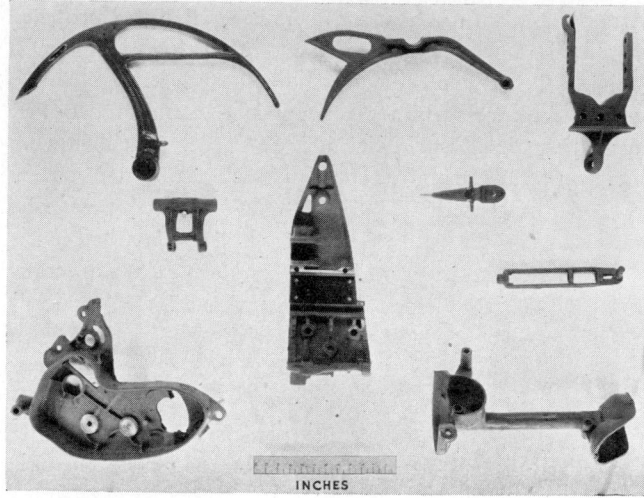

INCHES

Fig. 3. Agricultural castings such as these are among the many applications of malleable iron in the farm implement industry.

The westward expansion of the country brought about widespread building of railroads and a tremendous increase in the manufacture of agricultural implements, all of which created an increasing demand for malleable iron.

The foundry skill to cast malleable iron into pieces of complicated design, and the techniques to take full advantage of its machinability — all these had been acquired through experience in making conveyor chain; pipe and radiator fittings; railroad castings; parts for stoves, machinery, and bicycles; and wagon wheel hubs and flanges, to name only a few of its early applications.

At the turn of the century, the manufacturers of the first automobiles were naturally interested in a material which could be cast to shape in a wide range of sections and sizes, could be machined at relatively low cost, and was strong and tough enough to meet the most severe operating conditions. The wagon builders of the previous decades had found malleable iron eminently suited to their requirements, and the wide use of it in automobiles was a natural consequence. Illustrative of the borrowing of design and material was the adaptation of the malleable iron automobile hub from the malleable wheel hubs and flanges for wagons and buggies. Today the automotive industry is the leading consumer of malleable iron.

It was not only in the manufacture of agricultural machinery and the development of land transportation that the useful properties of American malleable iron were recognized. The swiftly growing communications services of the country employed malleable iron in pole-line hardware, while malleable castings in motors and other applications contributed to the spread of electrification.

American malleable iron, so indispensable as an industrial material, has also a multitude of military applications, as evidenced by widespread use of it in both World Wars. Trucks, personnel carriers, and jeeps rely on it fully as

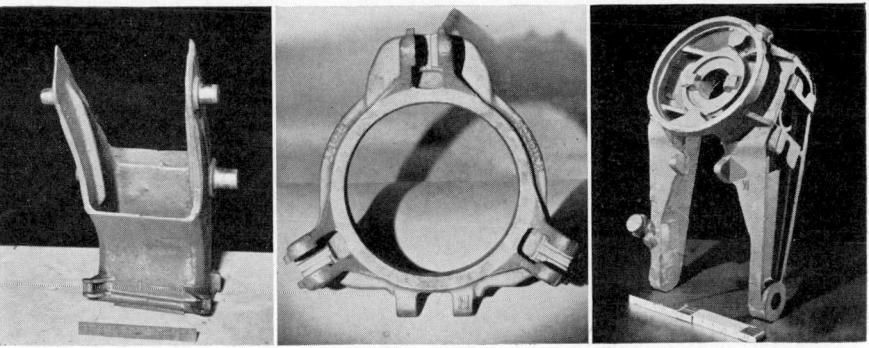

Fig. 4. From left to right, three castings showing the wide range and versatility of malleable iron: a locomotive water scoop, which picks up boiler water from between-the-tracks tanks while the train is under way; a porthole ring assembly, one of the many applications of malleable iron in marine hardware; a part used in the mount of 20-millimeter guns, where the toughness and shock resistance of malleable iron prove their worth.

much as do their civilian counterparts. Malleable iron castings form the bases of antiaircraft guns; reverse-gear housings and other parts in PT boats; steering-gear cases and front and rear axle differential carriers for trucks, jeeps, and command cars; track guides for tanks; parts in the wheel assemblies of bombers and fighting planes; machine-gun mounts; parts in small arms; and many other units.

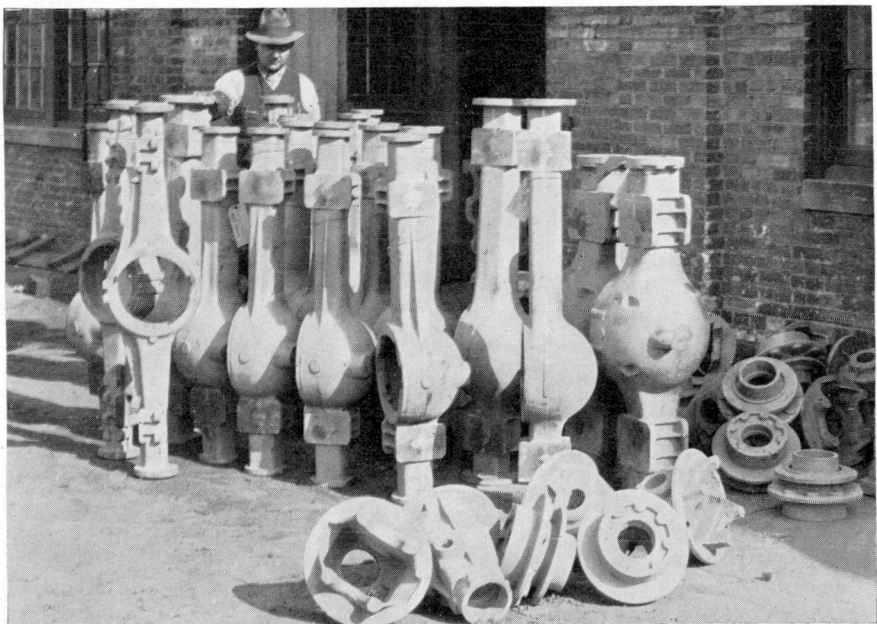

Fig. 5. A suggestion of the extensive use of malleable iron in the automotive industry: a group of three types of truck housings, with differential carriers in the foreground and heavy-duty wheel hubs at the right rear.

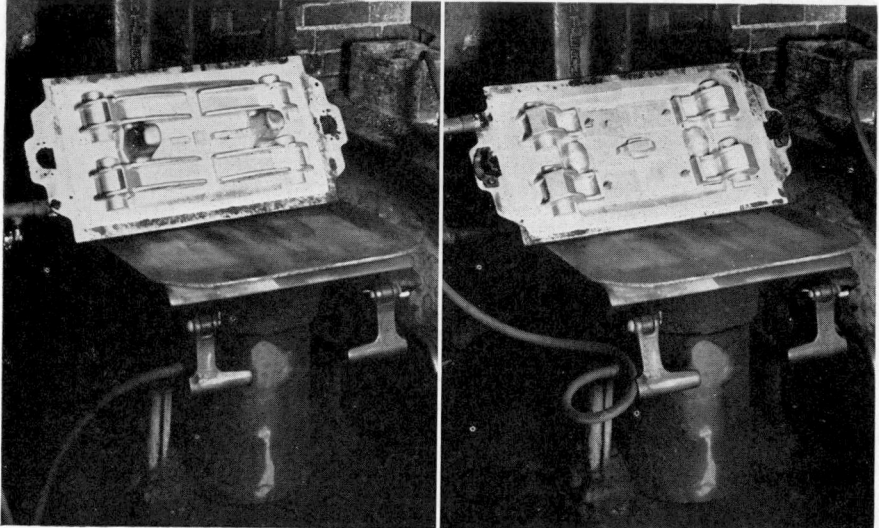

Fig. 6. A casting begins with a pattern. Here at the left is the face of a plate pattern used to form the cope, or upper half of a mold in which four spring hanger castings will be made. At the right is the other face of the plate pattern, which forms the drag, or lower half of the mold.

Malleable iron has been adopted as a primary specification in many military and naval applications where the qualities of toughness, high strength, excellent machinability, and resistance to corrosion have been important considerations. It has also become an alternate specification, frequently at a saving in both weight and cost, for highly critical domestic and imported materials.

Fig. 7. The plate pattern here has been placed between the two halves of a flask, which have not been closed completely on it.

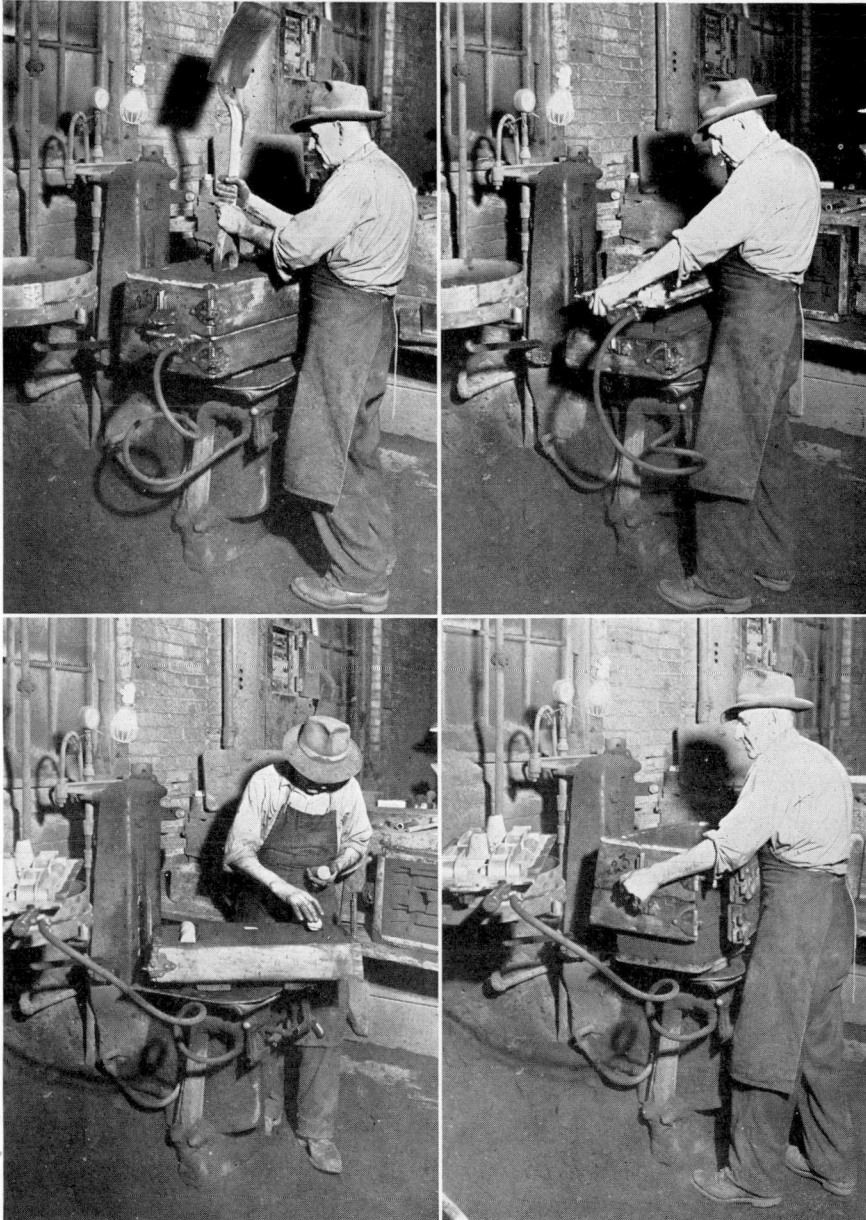

Fig. 8. The flask closed on the plate, the molder here is peening sand in the cope half of the mold.

Fig. 9. The molder is drawing, or lifting, the plate from the drag; the cope is on the bench at the right.

Fig. 10. Cores are being set in the drag. After this, the cope is replaced to make the complete mold.

Fig. 11. The cope having been replaced on the drag, the snap flask is unclamped and removed from the mold.

Boyden's metal, tough and shock resistant to a certain degree, was adequate to the needs of his time. But with the development of American industry there came a widening demand for more and better malleable castings. Spurred by this demand, and as a result of constant experiment, broadening experience, and diligent research, there has gradually been evolved the American malleable iron of today.

The characteristic structure and the mechanical arrangement of its principal elements create in American malleable iron its unique and highly desirable properties. Its toughness, shock resistance, ductility, and corrosion resistance derive from the tightly interlocking granular form of its tough ferrite; its machinability comes from the absence of combined carbon and the presence of free carbon, which functions as a natural machining lubricant.

The reasons for the "blackheart" fracture of American malleable are that when broken in tension its ferrite grains stretch and elongate until they rupture, so that at the point of rupture the cross-section of the end of the broken piece is like a very closely packed bundle of short and very fine needles; between these needles are minute spaces across which the needles throw shadows upon their neighbors; the nodules of free, temper carbon interspersed through the material are black and where exposed darken its color. Thus the general color of the fractured surface is dark, although the tips of the needles — where they sheared at the last instant of parting — are shiny.

American malleable iron is a mixture of iron and carbon, including in its combination smaller amounts of silicon, manganese, phosphorus, and sulphur. From the point of view of structure and chemical composition, the iron is present in the form of ferrite — carbonless iron. The carbon in the structure is free, as temper carbon, rather than chemically combined with iron as cementite (carbide of iron).

Malleable iron is given its unique structure by heat-treatment which converts brittle white iron — a combination of cementite and pearlite (a lamellar aggregate of ferrite and cementite) — into the combination of ferrite and temper carbon which endows it with its highly desirable qualities. Since malleable derives its structure from heat-treatment, it follows that welding, though it can be done, will reconvert the metal to a brittle state. Hence any malleable iron castings which are welded must again be annealed.

The term "malleable iron," as used in this book — unless otherwise specifically stated — refers to the *standard malleable irons* conforming to the American Society for Testing Materials Specification A47–33, Grade 32510 and Grade 35018, these being the malleables in greatest general use and comprising the largest tonnages produced.

In addition to "standard" malleable irons, variants have been developed to meet particular demands. Among these are:

Pearlitic malleable irons for the many services requiring greater strength, hardness, and resistance to wear, but somewhat less ductility than afforded by standard malleables. The distinction resides in the fact that pearlitic malleable

Fig. 12. The gate of four castings at right, seen from the drag side, with the drag side of the plate pattern for comparison.

irons contain definite amounts of carbon in the combined form, whereas the standard malleable irons contain but a trace of combined carbon.

Special malleable irons for a variety of particular applications, their special qualities being imposed by alloying or special heat-treatment, or both. To

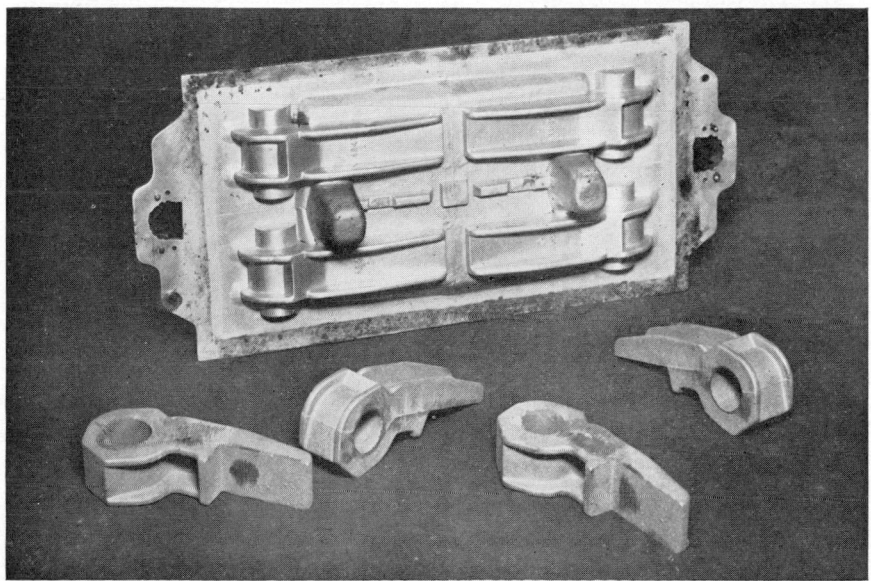

Fig. 13. The four finished castings, and the cope face of the plate pattern from which they were molded.

illustrate — when corrosive action will be encountered, malleable is alloyed
to increase resistance thereto without impairing its other properties.

Cupola malleable iron, so called because of the type of furnace in which it is
melted. It finds extensive application in pipe fittings.

The differences of manufacture, properties, and application of the various grades and classes and their metallurgical aspects are explained in later
chapters.

Although a detailed explanation of the entire process of manufacturing
American malleable iron is given in a later chapter of this book, its funda-
mentals may be here briefly outlined as follows:

Initially, there must be suitable pattern and core box equipment. With
these, sand molds are made. Molten iron of appropriate chemical composition
is poured into the molds. The resulting white iron castings and gating systems
are shaken out of the molds, and the castings are broken away from their
gates and sprues, cleaned, and heat-treated, or "annealed," to be converted into
malleable iron. The malleable castings are cleaned and otherwise prepared
by such finishing operations as grinding and straightening, and then finally
inspected. Irrespective of the methods and equipment employed, these essential operations in this sequence are requisite to all malleable iron manufacturing.

In its principal characteristics and properties, the malleable iron of any
particular grade or class made in any one plant will be essentially like the
iron of the same grade or class made in any other plant. This standardization
is the result of the thorough and continuous control of metallurgical and other
manufacturing processes to which Bradley Stoughton referred when he wrote:
"In no metallurgical process must the conditions of chemical composition,
furnace work, heating temperatures and lengths of operation be adjusted
more delicately than in the manufacture of high-grade malleable . . .
iron. . . ." *

* Stoughton, Bradley: *The Metallurgy of Iron and Steel*, McGraw-Hill, New York and
London, 1934, p. 486. Used by permission.

II

MALLEABLE IRON AMONG THE FERROUS METALS

AMERICAN MALLEABLE IRON ranks high among the ferrous materials in which most engineering and manufacturing is done. In mechanical and engineering properties, it stands well up in the soft-steel range, meeting exacting standards of toughness and machinability and possessing the unique combination of castability and malleability. Starting out as a brittle casting, it gains ductility and toughness through heat-treatment. Thus it avoids the difficulty summarized in the statement that "wrought iron cannot be cast and cast iron cannot be wrought." In physical properties such as specific gravity and in chemical composition, it stands between steel and gray iron.

Steel, American malleable iron, and gray iron, being ferrous metals, are all combinations of iron with carbon, silicon, manganese, phosphorus,

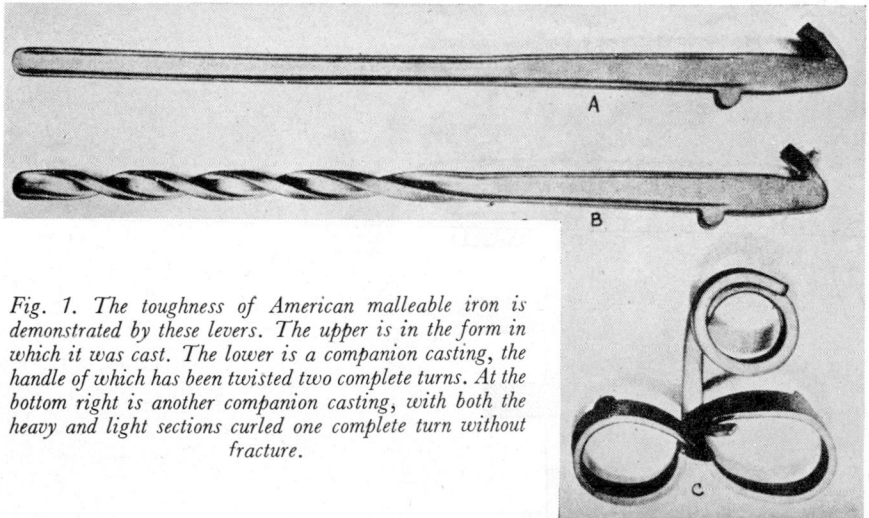

Fig. 1. The toughness of American malleable iron is demonstrated by these levers. The upper is in the form in which it was cast. The lower is a companion casting, the handle of which has been twisted two complete turns. At the bottom right is another companion casting, with both the heavy and light sections curled one complete turn without fracture.

and sulphur. The characteristic properties of each of the three metals result in part from the varying of the proportion of these elements in their composition and in part from the treatment given to the material during the process of manufacture. The chemical composition of the white iron castings which heat-treatment converts into American malleable iron generally falls within the limits shown in Table 1, which may be compared there with the chemical makeup of gray iron and of steel:

TABLE 1. COMPOSITION RANGE OF WHITE IRON, GRAY IRON, AND STEEL CASTINGS

	Standard Malleable Iron (White Iron Analysis)	Gray Iron	Cast Steel
Carbon	2.00–2.70	2.50–4.00	0.10–0.60*
Silicon	1.20–0.80	3.00–0.75	0.60–0.25
Manganese	Less than 0.55	.50–1.20	.50–1.00
Phosphorus	Less than 0.20	.05–0.75	Less than 0.05
Sulphur	Less than 0.18	.05–0.20	Less than 0.06

* Some graphitized steels are manufactured with carbon content as high as 1.70 and silicon running to 1.40.

For malleable iron of either Grade 32510 or Grade 35018, phosphorus up to the range given is not objectionable, as it might be in steel, and the sulphur present is not harmful provided a proper sulphur-manganese ratio is maintained.

PROPERTIES

The mild steels — steel castings with between 0.20 and 0.30 per cent carbon and commercial drop forgings with between 0.10 and 0.20 per cent

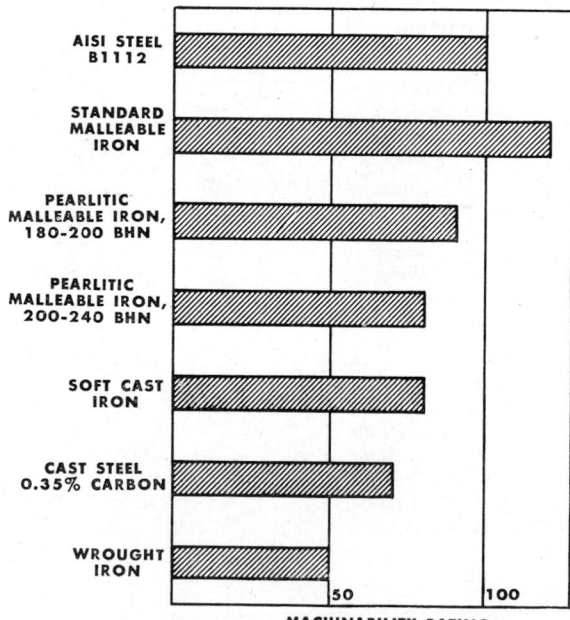

Fig. 2. Machinability comparisons applicable to metal sections in which malleable iron is customarily used.

carbon — are used in applications comparable to those for which malleable iron is specified. Although malleable iron has a slightly lower ultimate strength than comparable steels, it possesses the unique property of a high ratio of yield point to ultimate strength. Yield point is generally considered more important to the designer than is ultimate strength. Since the yield point of malleable exceeds that of a number of steels, the designer often has the option of specifying either material, and may by using malleable secure its inherent characteristics of high fatigue strength, easy machining, excellent corrosion resistance, trueness to pattern, and smoothness of surface.

In estimating the yield point of malleable iron, a figure of 65 per cent of the ultimate strength may safely be used. This figure is reflected in the specification of the American Society for Testing Materials, which provides a minimum yield point value of 35,000 pounds per square inch in conjunction with a minimum ultimate tensile strength of 53,000 p.s.i. and elongation of 18 per cent in 2 inches for Grade 35018 malleable iron. Similarly for Grade 32510, a minimum yield point of 32,500 p.s.i. is specified to accompany ultimate strength of 50,000 p.s.i. and elongation of 10 per cent.

The relation between ultimate strength and elongation is another property of extreme importance to the designer. In most metals, strength and ductility vary inversely, the metal becoming harder and less ductile as its strength increases. When using these metals, therefore, the designer must decide

Fractures of gray iron, white iron, and American malleable iron, from left to right, show the colors characteristic of the three metals.

whether strength or ductility is the more important for a particular application, and then sacrifice one to obtain the other. In standard malleable iron, on the contrary, the higher ultimate strength is accompanied by higher elongation. This relationship between strength and elongation does not hold for the pearlitic malleable irons, which follow the usual rule of the higher the strength, the less the elongation. The fact that malleable iron can be machined with greater ease than any other ferrous metal of comparable mechanical properties [4] is the governing factor which prevails in many applications of it.

SOME DISTINCTIONS

American malleable iron is sometimes called "malleable cast iron," a name giving rise to the erroneous idea that malleable iron is a form of gray iron. Malleable iron, steel, and gray iron are all originally "cast" ferrous metals, just as aluminum, brass, and magnesium are "cast" metals originally, since each is initially formed through the pouring, or "casting," of the molten substance into molds. But with this the similarity ceases; in the manufacturing processes which they undergo, in chemical composition, in microstructure, and particularly in properties, malleable iron [2] and steel, while differing from each other, differ distinctly from gray iron. The term "cast iron" generally means "gray iron." The term "malleable cast iron" is a misnomer and has been replaced by the name "American malleable iron," which is accurate in distinguishing the product both from gray iron materials and from the European whiteheart malleable irons mentioned in Chapter I. It is important to emphasize both distinctions, for American malleable iron is a product wholly apart from both gray iron and whiteheart malleable.

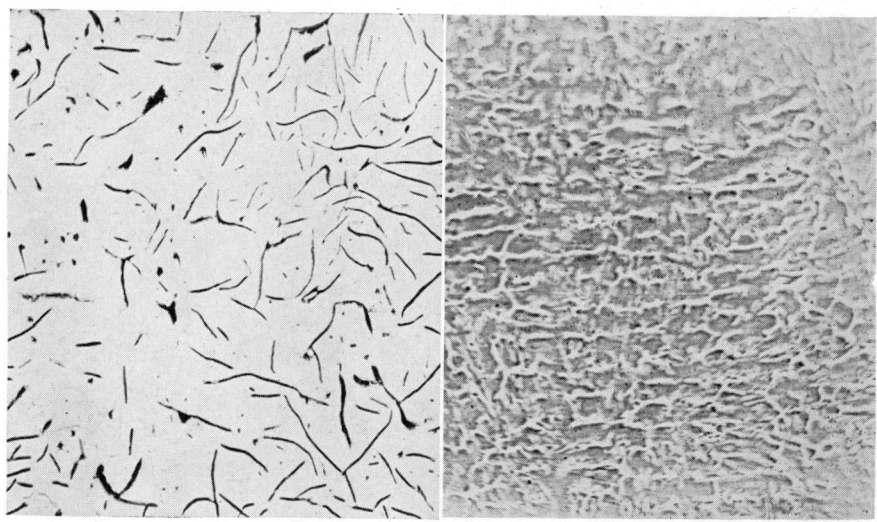

Fig. 3. Microstructure of gray iron, x100, unetched.   *Fig. 4. Microstructure of white iron, x100, unetched.*

The difference between the properties of gray iron and those of malleable iron is due to the fact that when gray iron solidifies, much of its carbon content is present in the form of flaky graphite, as shown in Fig. 3. These graphite flakes, of various shapes and sizes, break up the continuity of the iron. Upon the solidification of the white iron castings which are later to be converted into malleable iron, no flaky graphite — in fact, no free carbon — is present, as Fig. 4 indicates. After the anneal, free carbon appears as the more or less rounded nodules shown in Fig. 5. Such nodular graphite (or temper carbon) does not break up the continuity of the iron.[5]

Usually, gray iron contains appreciable amounts of pearlite, the micro-constituent shown in Fig. 6, which is harder and less ductile than the ferrite that is the principal constituent of malleable iron. The distinction between gray iron and malleable iron, however, is far more than the difference between ferrite and pearlite, for pearlitic malleable irons, even those containing no ferrite, still have such ductility and resistance to shock that they are totally unlike gray iron. Certain heat-treatments will improve the mechanical properties of some gray irons. On the other hand, if a soft gray iron is given heat-treatment such as is used in the production of malleable iron, it may finally consist entirely of ferrite and graphite, but its structure is then greatly weakened, not improved. While gray iron has a distinctly useful field, heat-treatment cannot develop it into a malleable iron. Regardless of annealing cycles, therefore, it cannot attain the properties on which users of malleable iron rely. The extremely ductile nature of malleable iron is shown in Fig. 7.

The essential difference between American malleable iron and European whiteheart malleable iron is that heat-treatment of whiteheart aims at decar-

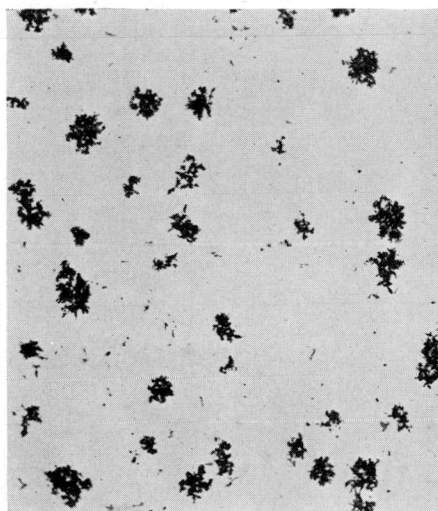

Fig. 5. Microstructure of malleable iron, x100, unetched.

Fig. 6. Gray iron, x1000, etched. White, ferrite; gray, pearlite; black, graphite.

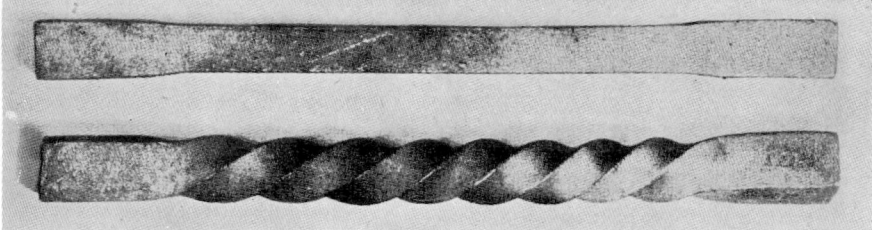

Fig. 7. Torsion test bars of malleable iron show the ductility of the material. The bar is 11 inches long, three-quarters of an inch square. The lower bar has been twisted more than two complete turns without fracture. Note the uniform flow of the metal when it is twisted cold.

burization; heat-treatment of American blackheart effects graphitization. Small whiteheart castings are almost entirely decarburized by the anneal; heavier sections after anneal consist of a white rim and a pearlitic core containing some nodular graphite. Though whiteheart never found much use in America and only one or two foundries were still making it at the end of the nineteenth century, its faults and limitations are sometimes mistakenly considered inherent in American malleable iron.

One misleading idea carried over from whiteheart to American malleable iron is the belief that thick sections will not anneal. This is true for whiteheart malleable, because decarburization proceeds slowly inward from the outer surface. It is not true for American malleable, because graphitization is an internal phenomenon occurring throughout the metal when the graphitizing temperature has been reached. To maintain that, for example, a three- or four-inch section of American malleable iron will not anneal in commercial processes is the same as to argue that it cannot be brought to the minimum graphitizing temperature of about 1450 degrees Fahrenheit and held at this temperature for the proper length of time, a conclusion which is obviously erroneous.

A second major error of this kind is the idea that the strength and ductility of malleable iron castings are in the skin alone. This is largely true for whiteheart malleable, because the decarburized outer section of whiteheart is much like wrought iron, but the center section is often hard and brittle. It is not true for American malleable, because the graphitized structure of American malleable is uniform throughout the casting. Any slight decarburization that may occur in American malleable is limited to the very surface of the casting.

SOME DEFINITIONS

Just as the name "steel" is applied to a considerable variety of forms of metal, the name "malleable iron" is used for convenience to include a number of related forms. The products of malleable iron foundries, as was pointed out in Chapter I, can be broadly divided into (1) standard malleable irons; (2) pearlitic malleable irons; (3) special malleable irons; and (4) cupola malleable iron. These four classes are to be individually discussed in succeeding chapters of this book. At this point, it will be useful to review some of their characteristics, and to state in slightly greater detail the definition of standard malleable iron, the form which is most widely manufactured.

Standard malleable iron is produced in two grades as defined by the American Society for Testing Materials. For general malleable iron castings, material meeting the requirements of Grade 32510, A.S.T.M. Specification A47–33, is used. For applications requiring a high-strength, high-elongation metal, malleable iron which meets the standards of Grade 35018 of that specification is usually selected.

STANDARD MALLEABLE IRON — GRADE 32510

The chemical composition of the white iron from which Grade 32510 malleable iron is produced falls generally within the following limits:

Carbon	2.30 to 2.70 per cent
Silicon	1.20 to 0.80 per cent
Manganese	Less than 0.55 per cent
Phosphorus	Less than 0.20 per cent
Sulphur	Less than 0.18 per cent

During the annealing process, the metal loses some carbon and may gain slightly in sulphur content.

Because of its higher carbon, Grade 32510 malleable iron is extremely fluid and is easily cast into light sections. It is very easily machined and is particularly suitable for castings involving intricate design. Foundries specializing in very light work are successfully producing castings of this grade of malle-

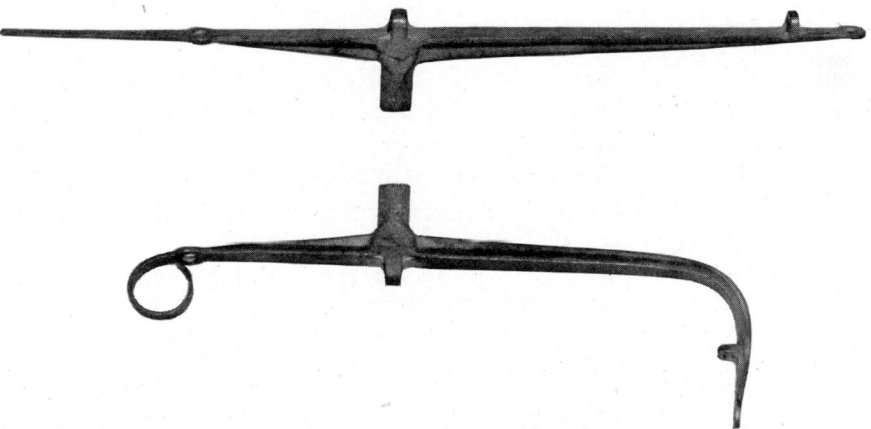

Fig. 8. A knitting machine part of malleable iron demonstrates the punishment the metal can stand. The upper casting is the part as finished; it is 16 inches long, the heavier end being a three-eighths inch section, the lighter end $\frac{1}{16}$. Below it is a companion casting; the heavy ribbed end has been bent 90 degrees and the lighter end has been formed around a one-inch rod without any indication of fracture.

able iron with sections as light as 1/32 inch in limited areas; it is not usually specified for castings having large areas exceeding 1½ inches in thickness. Grade 32510 malleable iron has ample strength for the majority of applications. Its mechanical properties are as follows:

Grade 32510	Minimum Specification Value	Most Probable Value
Ultimate strength (pounds per square inch)......	50,000	52,000
Yield point (p.s.i.).........................	32,500	34,000
Elongation (per cent in 2 inches)...............	10	12.5

This malleable iron is very easily machined, and is particularly suitable for light castings, especially those involving intricate design. The automotive and electrical industries take a large proportion of the Grade 32510 metal produced.[4]

Standard Malleable Iron — Grade 35018

The chemical composition of the white iron from which Grade 35018 malleable iron is made usually falls within the following ranges:

Carbon.......................	2.00 to 2.45 per cent
Silicon.......................	1.20 to 0.85 per cent
Manganese...................	Less than 0.55 per cent
Phosphorus...................	Less than 0.20 per cent
Sulphur......	Less than 0.18 per cent

The malleable iron which is produced from these compositions also loses some of its carbon content and may increase slightly in sulphur content during the anneal.

Because of its lower carbon content, Grade 35018 malleable iron is of higher strength and ductility. Iron of this grade is regularly being cast in sections from 3/32 to 2½ inches in thickness and upon occasion in even larger sections.

The minimum mechanical properties specified for Grade 35018 in A.S.T.M. Specification A47–33, and the most probable values to be expected are:

Grade 35018	Minimum Specification Value	Most Probable Value
Ultimate strength (p.s.i.)............	53,000	55,000
Yield Point (p.s.i.).................	35,000	36,500
Elongation (per cent in 2 inches)......	18	20

Pearlitic Malleable Irons

Irons made from chemical compositions the same as or similar to those given above for standard malleable iron, when so alloyed or heat-treated that some of the carbon in the resultant material is in the combined form, are known as pearlitic malleable irons. They provide high strength and resistance to wear at some cost in ductility and shock resistance. They are fully discussed in Chapter VI.

Special Malleable Irons

Of the various special malleable irons which are produced to meet specialized requirements, the principal are those containing a high silicon content, those alloyed with copper, and those alloyed with copper and molybdenum. High-silicon malleable iron, because of a tendency toward graphitization produced by the high silicon content, can be annealed in an exceedingly short time. Copper as an alloy is used to increase the ultimate strength, the yield point, and the endurance limit of malleable iron, with some sacrifice in elongation. For atmospheres containing sulphurous gases, copper-alloyed special malleable iron is specified because the alloy increases resistance to corrosion. Copper and molybdenum in combination as alloys are used to produce a special malleable iron of superior mechanical properties. Extra high strength and yield point are made possible by the alloying combination, without material sacrifice of elongation or ductility. The special malleable irons are described in greater detail in Chapter VII.

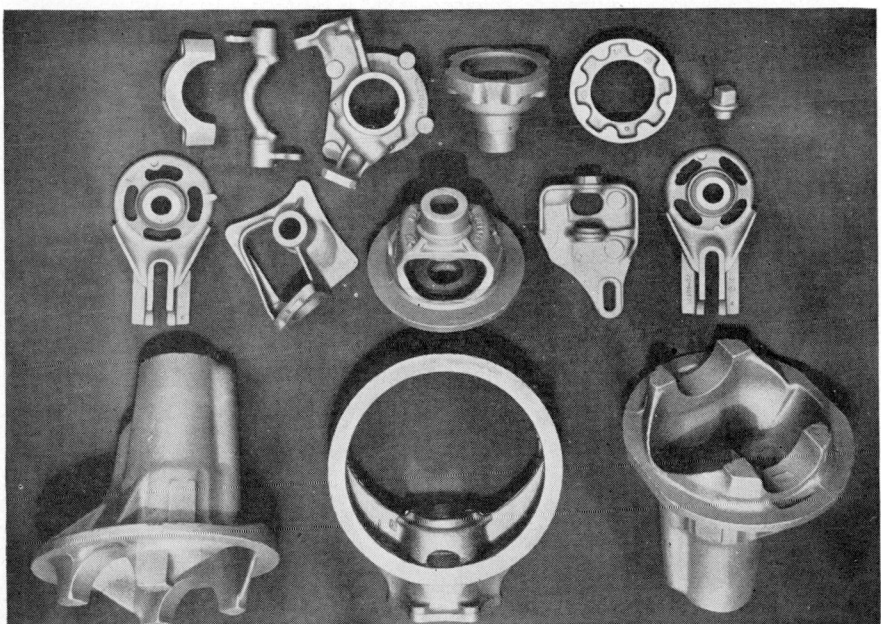

Fig. 9. Typical automotive applications of standard malleable iron.

SPECIFICATIONS

Specifications should include minimum mechanical properties and in addition requirements for good workmanship, soundness of castings, trueness to pattern, and completeness of anneal. It is, however, considered impractical to specify chemical limits, for the reason that the mechanical properties desired are obtainable within such a wide analysis range that the specification would be valueless. Buyers have learned that what they need is performance, which in turn depends upon the qualities of the metal and the design of the casting. The foundryman should be allowed to produce in any way he deems best the properties which will assure performance. Requirements for tension tests, test specimens, finish, inspection, and the like usually follow very closely the American Society for Testing Materials standard. Most American specifications, in fact, parallel those of the A.S.T.M., many simply stating that the iron "must conform to A.S.T.M. A47-33." The mechanical properties specified in this standard appear in Table 2; the complete standard is given in Appendix I. The standard tension test specimen in use in this country is shown in Appendix I, page 231.

TABLE 2. A.S.T.M. AND FEDERAL SPECIFICATIONS FOR MALLEABLE IRON

Organization	Number	Grade	Date	Tensile Strength	Yield Point	Elongation (Per Cent)	Remarks
				(Pounds per Square Inch)			
American Society for Testing Materials	A47-33	32510	1933	50,000	32,500	10	For general malleable iron castings
	A47-33	35018	1933	53,000	35,000	18	For railroad and other work needing high strength and high elongation
United States Army	QQ-I-666	A (Grade 35018)	1943	53,000	35,000	18	Malleable iron melted in air furnace or by other approved process
	QQ-I-666	B (Grade 32510)	1943	50,000	32,500	10	
United States Navy	46-I-8C	A Black (ungalvanized)	1943	53,000	35,000	18	
	46-I-8C	B Zinc coated (galvanized)	1943	50,000	32,500	10	
Pearlitic Malleable Iron Specifications							
American Society for Testing Materials	A220-44T	43010	1944	60,000	43,000	10	Tentative specification
	A220-44T	50007	1944	65,000	50,000	7	
	A220-44T	60005	1944	75,000	60,000	5	
	A220-44T	70003	1944	90,000	70,000	3	
	A220-44T	X	1944	—	—	—	
United States Army Ordnance	AXS-623	A & C	1942	75,000	60,000	5	Brinell 241-187
	AXS-623	B & D	1942	65,000	50,000	8	Brinell 207-163
	AXS-623	E	1942	60,000	43,000	10	Brinell 179-140

III

STANDARD MALLEABLE IRON — ITS PHYSICAL PROPERTIES

THOUGH at one time the physical properties of a metal were taken as including both physical and mechanical characteristics, the term has been restricted, as knowledge has increased, to only those properties closely related to physical changes. Thus it has come to comprise the properties of weight and volume, and thermal, electrical, and magnetic values. This chapter will survey present knowledge of these characteristics of standard malleable iron.

WEIGHT

Weight is a measure of the force of gravity, specifically of the pull of gravitational forces upon a body, and is proportional to the mass of the body, the amount of matter which the body contains.

DENSITY

The density of a substance is the mass of the substance per unit volume· Density is usually expressed in grams per cubic centimeter. At room temperature of 68 degrees Fahrenheit, the density of pure iron is 7.87 grams per cubic centimeter. The density of iron-carbon alloys decreases with increasing carbon and silicon and, to a very slight extent, with rising manganese. For

This malleable iron stair, or catwalk tread, makes good use of the metal's strength, rigidity, and resistance to atmospheric corrosion.

a malleable iron with 2.50 per cent carbon, 0.90 per cent silicon, and 0.35 per cent manganese, recent research gives density values from 7.20 to 7.31 grams per cubic centimeter.[8]

Measurement of the density of molten iron-carbon alloys of varying compositions and at varying temperatures leads to the conclusions that (1) The density of molten iron-carbon alloys decreases with rising carbon content, the temperature being constant; (2) The density decreases with rising temperature, the carbon content being constant.[9]

Specific Gravity

The specific gravity of a body is the ratio of its density to that of some standard substance, usually water at 4 degrees Centigrade (39 degrees F.). The specific gravity of standard malleable iron at room temperature lies between 7.15 and 7.60, depending upon composition. A dependable average figure is 7.32. Since the value reported for specific gravity is a figure indicating the relation between the density of a substance and the density of water, it can be converted to a measure of mass through multiplication by the value for the density of water. If the metric system is employed, density and specific gravity are practically identical, since the density of water in that system is very nearly unity. If values are to be converted from the metric to the British system, the figure for the specific gravity of the substance in question must be multiplied by 62.4,[10] the weight of a cubic foot of water in pounds. Multiplication by 0.0361, the weight of a cubic inch of water, gives the weight per cubic inch of the substance being measured. The specific gravity of malleable iron is compared with specific gravities of other materials in Table 1.[10]

TABLE 1. Specific Gravity of Some Common Materials

	Specific Gravity	Weight per Cubic Inch (Pounds)	Weight per Cubic Foot (Pounds)
Water	1	0.0361	62.4
Cast Aluminum	2.56	0.0924	159.7
Gray Iron	7.20	0.2600	449.2
Malleable Iron	7.32	0.2642	456.4
Cast Steel	7.84	0.2830	488.8
Brass 70–30	8.40	0.3032	524.1
Copper	8.82	0.3184	550.4

VOLUME

The specific volume of a metal is the amount of space occupied per unit mass and is usually expressed in cubic centimeters per gram. For pure iron at 68 degrees F., specific volume is 0.1271 cubic centimeter per gram. Additions of carbon and silicon, which are lighter than iron, increase the

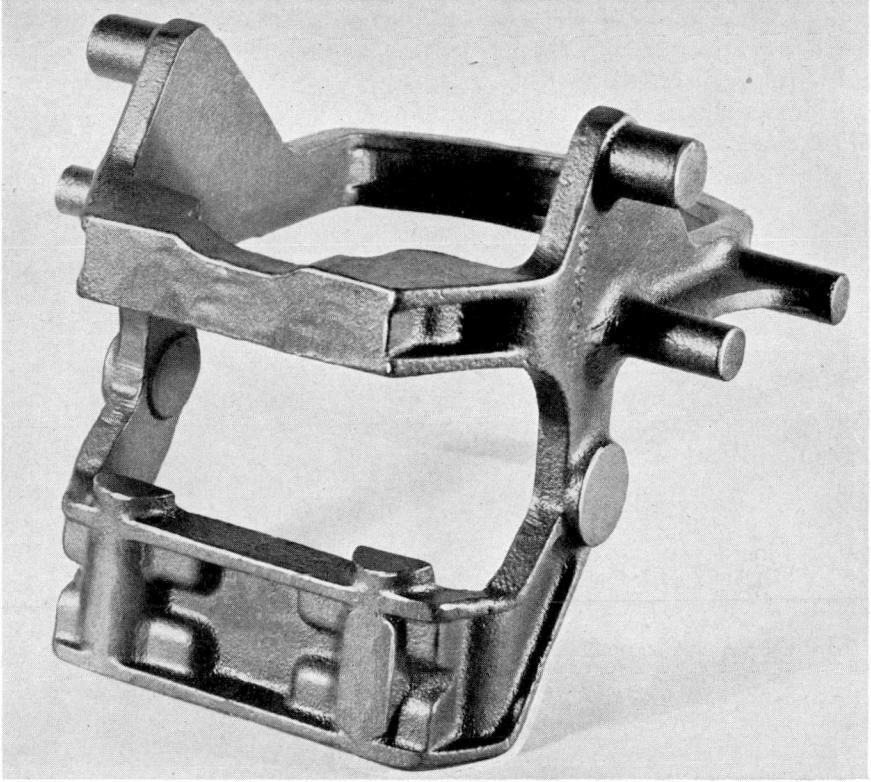

Fig. 1. A malleable iron machine gun cradle.

specific volume. Malleable iron at 68 degrees F. has a specific volume between 0.1316 and 0.1398, usually about 0.1366 cubic centimeter per gram.

Contraction on Solidification

Specific volume falls with decreasing temperature, since the metal becomes more dense as it gets colder. Solid iron castings at 68 degrees F. therefore take up less space than the same weight of metal in the molten condition at 2550 degrees F. On solidification, an especially marked contraction occurs. Foundrymen are most concerned with this, since allowance for it must be made if castings which are dimensionally correct are to be produced.

Experience has shown that all white irons which are suitable for the production of malleable iron have about the same linear shrinkage per foot — approximately one-quarter inch at room temperature.[1]

Expansion During Anneal

Offsetting part of this contraction on solidification is the expansion which takes place during annealing. This is not a thermal expansion due to the high temperature of the malleableizing process, but rather it is a permanent increase in specific volume and is due to changes which take place in the iron during the anneal. Ferrite and temper carbon, the structural components of the malleable iron produced by the anneal, are more bulky than the iron carbide present in the white cast iron when it solidifies. Malleable iron therefore regains in the anneal part of the volume the white iron lost on solidifying.[5, 11] The amount of expansion during annealing is dependent on the percentage of carbon present. The higher the carbon, the more temper carbon is formed and the greater is the increase in volume. Experience has shown this linear expansion to be approximately one-eighth inch per foot for castings of normal carbon content.

Shrinkage Allowance

The net contraction for which allowance must be made is the contraction which occurs when the castings solidify, less the expansion which takes place during the anneal. The net shrinkage is about 1.00 per cent or less, depending on the composition of the melt. Figure 2 shows the effect of carbon content on the net contraction, as determined on 1,000 malleable iron bars one-half inch by one-half inch by 12 inches.[2]

Solid Contraction

After a casting has solidified in the mold and is cooling down to room temperature, it of course contracts to some extent, and when the form of the mold is such as to prevent unhindered contraction, stresses known as "casting strains" are set up in the casting. Proper design and other precautions minimize these strains, but they are in any case removed during the heat-treatment which makes the castings malleable. No malleable iron casting can have casting strains, because the anneal which malleableizes also removes strains.

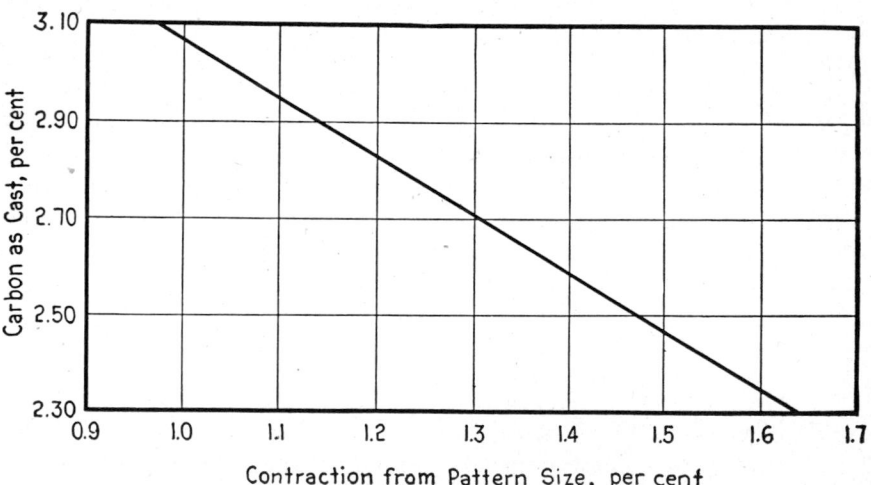

Fig. 2. *Net contraction from pattern size of malleable iron bars, in per cent, as related to carbon content, based on measurements of about 1,000 specimens ½ x ½ x 12 inches.*

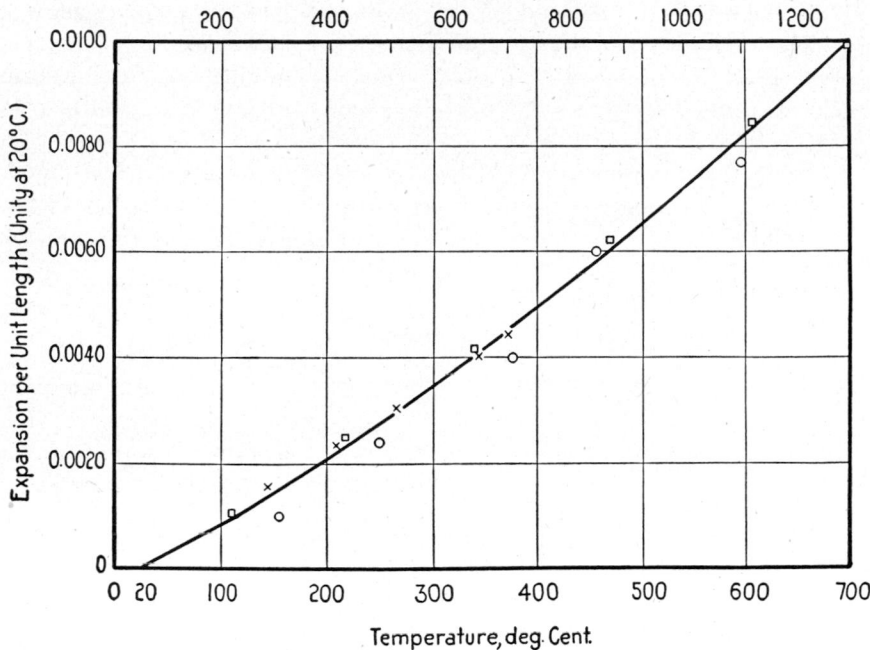

Fig. 3. *Thermal expansion of malleable iron.*[2]

THERMAL VALUES

SPECIFIC HEAT

The specific heat of a material is the quantity of heat required to raise the temperature of a unit mass one degree. It is expressed either as calories required to raise the temperature of one gram one degree Centigrade, or as the number of British thermal units required to raise the temperature of one pound of the substance one degree Fahrenheit.

Specific heat rises with increasing temperature, the range for malleable iron being from about 0.11 calorie per gram per degree C. at room temperature to 0.165 calorie per gram per degree C. at 800 degrees F.[1] Direct determinations give the following values: [2]

TABLE 2. MEAN SPECIFIC HEAT OF MALLEABLE IRON

Temperature Range (Degrees Fahrenheit)	Calories per Gram per Degree Centigrade
70–210	0.122
70–390	0.125
70–570	0.128
70–750	0.133
70–930	0.139
70–1110	0.146
70–1300	0.159

Thermal Expansion

The coefficient of thermal expansion of malleable iron — the expansion in inches per inch per degree Fahrenheit temperature change — like the specific heat, rises slightly with increasing temperatures. For ranges from room temperature to 750 degrees F., an average value is 0.0000066 per degree F. (or 0.000012 per degree C.).[2]

From the curve in Fig. 3 on the preceding page, the coefficient of expansion for different temperature ranges may be determined with greater accuracy.[1]

Thermal Conductivity

Thermal conductivity is the measure in gram-calories per second per square centimeter per degree Centigrade per centimeter of the ability of a substance to transfer heat. Work done some years ago shows that the thermal conductivity of malleable iron decreases with rising temperature, from 0.122 at 80 degrees F. to .095 at 700 degrees F. Results of this study are shown in Fig. 4.[1]

Recent tests conducted on standard American malleable iron of normal analysis give values from 0.151 for a mean temperature of 212 degrees F. to 0.138 for a mean temperature of 800 degrees F.[12] These data are summarized in Table 3.[12]

TABLE 3. THERMAL CONDUCTIVITY OF MALLEABLE IRON

Temperature Range (Degrees Fahrenheit)	Mean Temperature (Degrees Fahrenheit)	K_t*
152–273	212	0.151
163–307	235	0.150
215–400	307	0.149
225–422	324	0.148
273–395	334	0.149
250–476	363	0.147
307–453	380	0.146
278–538	408	0.146
295–585	440	0.145
322–642	482	0.143
400–586	492	0.146
422–628	524	0.144
476–710	594	0.143
538–800	669	0.141
585–883	734	0.140
642–972	807	0.138

* In gram-calories per second per square centimeter per degree Centigrade per centimeter.

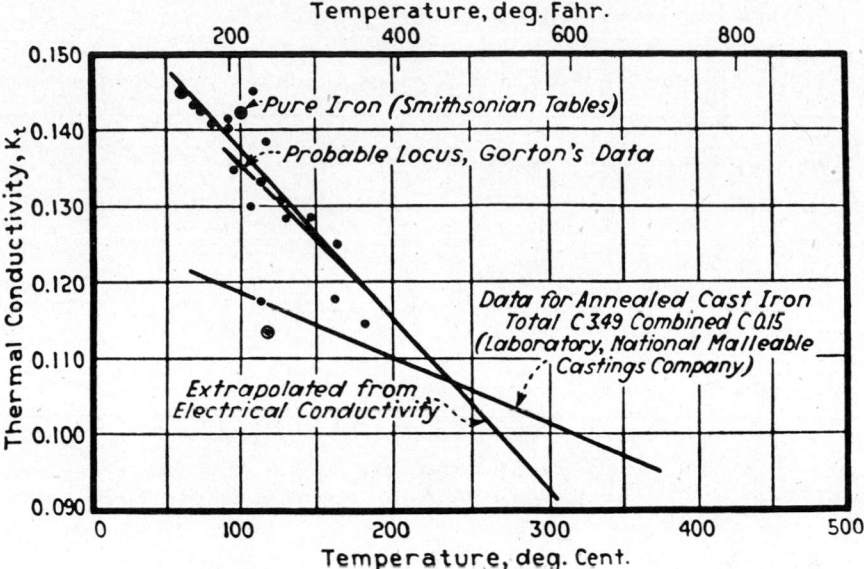

Fig. 4. Thermal conductivity of malleable iron. The constant K_t is in gram-calories per second per square centimeter per degree Centigrade per centimeter.

EFFECT OF TEMPERATURE ON THERMAL PROPERTIES

The thermal expansion of malleable iron also increases with rising temperatures, as shown in Table 4.

TABLE 4. EFFECT OF TEMPERATURE ON THERMAL EXPANSION OF
MALLEABLE IRON

Temperature Degrees Fahrenheit	Linear Expansion Per Cent
75	0
212	0.10
475	0.24
700	0.40
900	0.60
1100	0.77

MAGNETIC AND ELECTRICAL VALUES

RESISTIVITY

Measurements of resistivity on malleable iron with a content of 2.50 to 2.60 per cent carbon and .90 to 1.05 per cent silicon give results from 28.84 to 34.36 microhms per centimeter cube, the average being 32.07.[8] This figure agrees well with other reported data [2, 4, 5, 11] and may be considered accurate for ordinary temperatures. Although theoretically the chemical composition of the iron is of effect on the resistivity, actually so large a proportion of the current is carried through the metal and so slight a proportion through the graphite that different malleable irons are found to show very little divergence in their resistivity.[1]

Effect of Temperature on Resistivity

Electrical resistivity rises with increased temperature. At 800 degrees F., it is twice as great as at room temperature; at 1180 degrees, it is three times as much. Above 1400 degrees F., carbon is redissolved and the resistivity of the metal is permanently increased. The curve in Fig. 5 shows the variation of resistivity with temperature.[2]

Magnetic Properties

Castings used in magnetic-electric equipment should be of high induction and permeability values and low hysteresis loss. Most important, they should show a low value for coercivity, or coercive force, the magnetizing force required to remove residual magnetism. The lower the combined carbon in a casting, the more nearly it approaches these desired properties. With malleable iron, which contains a trace or no combined carbon at all,

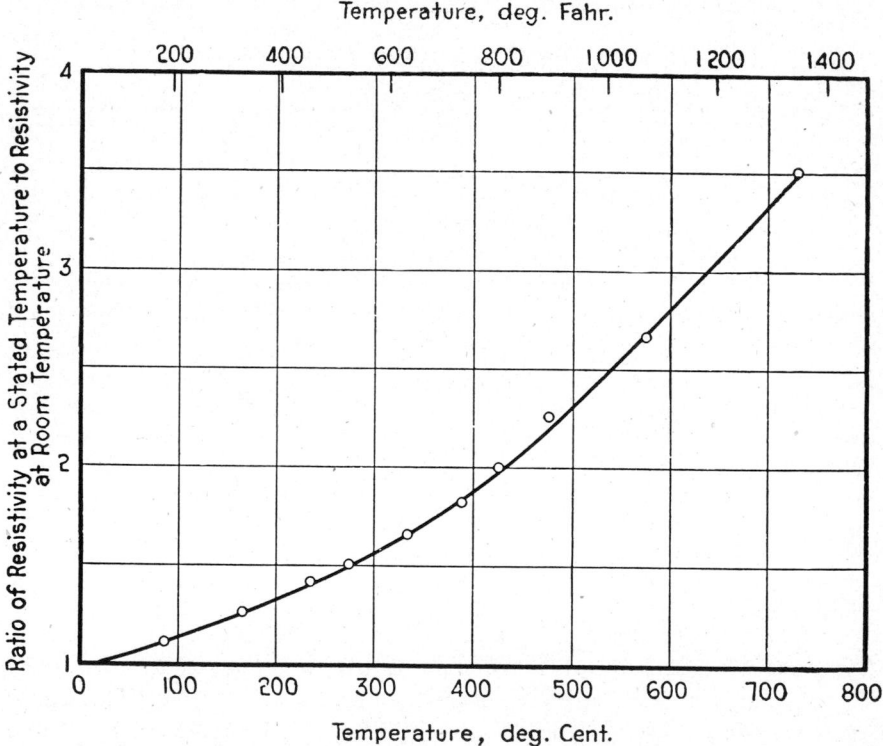

Fig. 5. *Effect of temperature on the electrical resistivity of malleable iron.*

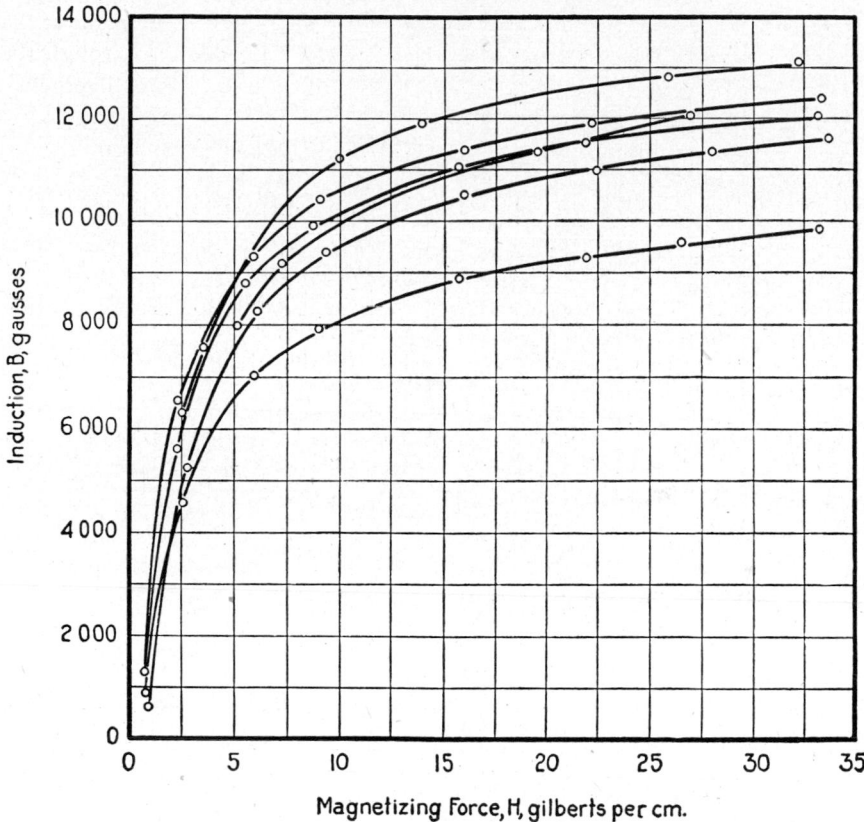

Fig. 6. Magnetization curves for various malleable irons.

hysteresis loss and coercivity are both low.[11] Hence although the electrical properties of malleable iron are not of commercial importance, the magnetic properties are.

The coercivity of malleable iron is from 1.16 to 1.55 ampere turns per centimeter,[1, 8, 11] and increases with increasing combined carbon. Coercivity values for representative American malleable irons are given in Table 5.

TABLE 5. COERCIVITY OF MALLEABLE IRON

Combined Carbon	Temper Carbon	Total Carbon	Silicon	Coercivity
0.02	2.49	2.51	0.91	1.19
0.03	2.50	2.53	1.06	1.16
0.09	2.52	2.61	——	1.21

Magnetization curves for various malleable irons are shown in Figs. 6 and 7.[2] In Fig. 6, the magnetizing force, H, and the induction, B, are recorded in gilberts per centimeter and in gausses. Figure 7 uses ampere turns

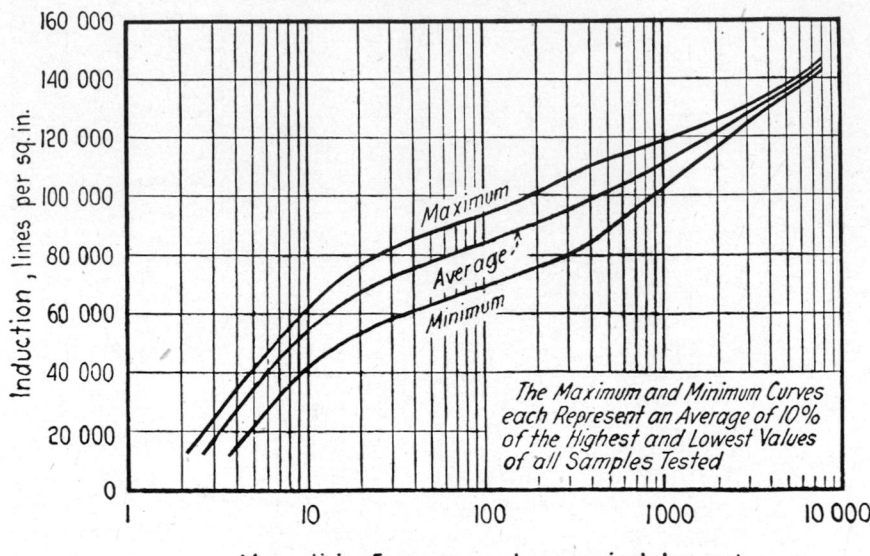

Fig. 7. *Magnetization curves for various malleable irons.*

per inch to measure the magnetizing force, and lines per square inch to measure induction. The permeability, or ratio of induction to magnetizing force, can be determined from Figs. 6 and 7.

IV

STANDARD MALLEABLE IRON — ITS MECHANICAL PROPERTIES

THE mechanical properties of a metal are of decided importance to designer and user alike, for they are the properties involved in its behavior under stress, which indicates the service reasonably to be expected from a part made of it. Hardness, ultimate tensile strength, yield point, elongation, elasticity, fatigue endurance, notch-fatigue strength, damping capacity, shear strength, torsional strength, compressive strength, transverse strength, and impact resistance, all of which are significant of the metal's ductility, toughness, and hardness, constitute its mechanical properties.

Standard tests and standard test specimens make possible the direct comparison of many of these properties for different metals. For certain properties, however, present tests and test specimens can give only approximations. Resistance to impact is one of the characteristics which have not as yet been reduced to a single test equally applicable to all metals. Recent studies have shown that for some metals, including American malleable iron, the notched specimen used for Izod and Charpy impact resistance tests does give a dependable indication of resistance. For some other metals, which are more influenced by the concentration of stress at the notch, these tests are a truer measure of notch sensitivity than of impact resistance.

Though the structure of standard malleable iron is uniform throughout the casting and hence minimizes variations, the properties of any ferrous casting are influenced by the thickness of section. With malleable iron, therefore, as with all other metals, results derived from tests run on specimen bars should be regarded as furnishing a close appraisal of the grade of metal in a casting but should not be construed as meaning that the casting itself will necessarily give exactly the same results.

HARDNESS

The Brinell method of testing hardness is used for American malleable iron because the sphere whose depth of penetration measures the hardness of the material is large enough to cover many grains both of temper carbon and of ferrite.[1] If the indenter rests on too small an area, the test result may possibly show the hardness of the ferrite alone, rather than that of the structure of the material as a whole. The Brinell hardness number [2, 4] for standard malleable iron may run from 110 to 145, usually being in the range from 115 to 135. The hardness is uniform from surface to center of the casting, since even if slight decarburization has occurred in the outermost portion of the casting, the Brinell ball goes through it.[1]

The Brinell hardness of malleable iron, like the tensile strength, increases with lower carbon content, and it bears a fairly close relationship to ultimate strength.

PROPERTIES IN TENSION

The tensile properties of a material are those resulting from its tendency to resist being broken when pulled. The tensile test, commonly used as one of the chief methods of judging the quality of a metal for structural purposes or for service as a machine part, consists of applying a constantly increasing load to a test bar until the bar is pulled apart. Because of its simplicity, this test is widely used even though not many structural parts are subjected to pure tension in service. The load thus applied, measured in pounds, is called

Fig. 1. At left, the cable drum, and below, the worm housing for power winches used on motor trucks built for the Army.

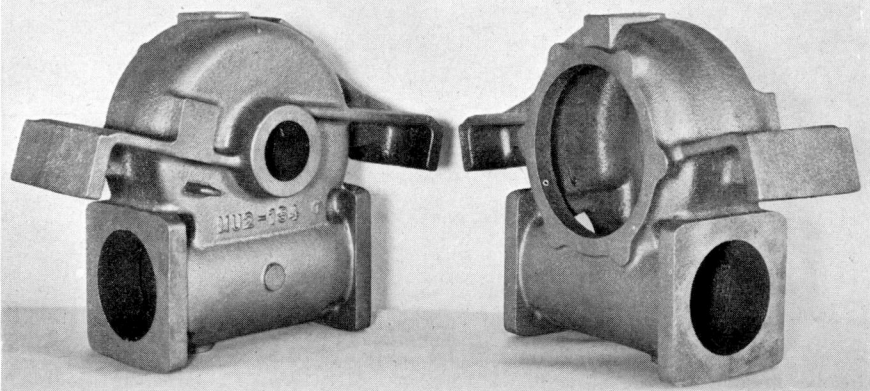

Fig. 2. A group of representative malleable iron castings illustrating the design possibilities of the metal.

"stress." "Unit stress" is the stress per unit area, usually expressed in pounds per square inch. As the stress is applied, it causes some deformation in the test bar, culminating in fracture. Such deformation is called "strain."

Tensile Strength

The load which produces fracture, expressed in pounds per square inch, is the ultimate tensile strength, or ultimate strength, of the material. For standard malleable iron of Grade 32510, minimum ultimate strength is 50,000 p.s.i., and for Grade 35018, 53,000 p.s.i.

Yield Point

The yield point is defined as the stress at which a marked increase in train, or deformation, occurs with no increase in stress. The term "yield strength" is sometimes used as synonymous with yield point. Though this usage is not strictly correct, both terms do designate a particular point or section of the stress-strain curve at which permanent deformation has taken place. Yield strength may be defined as the stress at which a material exhibits a specified limiting set. Some metals such as brass, bronze, and aluminum do not exhibit marked increase in strain without increase in stress, and are therefore considered to have a yield strength, some arbitrary permanent deformation being regarded as defining it. Malleable iron, like steel, does show at a certain point a marked increase in strain without the application of additional stress, and therefore is considered to have a yield point.

The yield point of malleable iron can be observed during tension tests. The deformation of the specimen is at first proportional to the load applied. But as the load is increased, a point is reached at which a marked increase in deformation takes place without additional load. The beam of the testing machine drops abruptly, or the pointer of a dial machine hesitates, when this — the yield point — has been reached.

The minimum yield point of standard malleable iron is 32,500 p.s.i. for Grade 32510 and 35,000 p.s.i. for Grade 35018. Sixty-five per cent of the ultimate tensile strength is the base for applying factors of safety.

Most machine parts are no longer fit for service if they have suffered marked deformation. By indicating the load above which a metal undergoes permanent deformation, the yield point shows the highest stress which the designer can safely plan to impose on a part made of that metal. It therefore is often of far more significance than the ultimate strength of a material. A metal with a yield point of 35,000 p.s.i. can be used in more highly stressed castings than a metal with a higher ultimate strength but a yield point of 30,000 p.s.i.

A good illustration of the value of malleable iron's high yield point is afforded in recent tests made to determine the practicality of substituting malleable iron companion flanges for forged steel companion flanges in low-temperature applications. Physical tests were performed on standard test bars made and annealed with the 4-inch 150-pound malleable flanges, and both the malleable and forged steel flanges were subjected to lever arm bend tests to determine their comparative resistance to thread stripping. Standards of the American Standards Association for the two classes of such forged steel companion flanges are:

	Class 1	Class 2
Minimum tensile strength.....	60,000 p.s.i.	70,000 p.s.i
Minimum yield point.........	30,000 p.s.i.	36,000 p.s.i.
Elongation in 2 inches........	22 per cent	18 per cent
Reduction of area (minimum)..	35 per cent	24 per cent

For the malleable iron flanges, test bars showed a yield point of 41,000 p.s.i. and elongation of 18.5 per cent in two inches. Since the yield point is generally regarded as the essential factor in designing flanges, in view of the fact that leaks occur whenever permanent deformation has set in, it was concluded that with the yield point as criterion, malleable iron flanges can replace forged steel. In the lever arm bend tests, a pipe screwed tightly into the test flange was bent, the load in foot-pounds necessary to break the flange or to

Fig. 3. One of the multitude of applications of malleable iron in conveyor equipment. Shown are two wood-slat conveyors for handling corncobs, for use in a canning plant. Both conveyor chains and one of the drive chains are of malleable iron.

strip its threads being measured. The test thus constituted an exaggerated case of the stresses imposed on companion flanges by misalignment of pipe in installation. It showed the threads of the malleable flange to withstand more bending moment than did the threads of the forged steel flange before "pulling out," the highest loading in foot-pounds being, for steel, 13,900; for malleable iron, 14,500. These tests established that a malleable iron flange will take all the bending moment that a forged steel flange will.

Elongation — Reduction of Area

The amount which the test bar stretches before fracture is the elongation, which is stated in per cent in two inches. Grade 32510 standard malleable iron has a minimum elongation of 10 per cent; Grade 35018 has a minimum of 18 per cent.

When loaded in tension, most ductile materials "neck in" at the location of fracture just before breaking. The amount of this necking-in is called "reduction of area" and is measured in per cent of the original area. For some metals, the reduction of area is used as a measure of ductility. Malleable iron does not exhibit a marked necking-in at the point of fracture, but elongates throughout the entire gauge length and hence has but between 18 and 23 per cent reduction of area at the point of fracture,[2] a favorable characteristic because it indicates that stresses are distributed over a greater area. Elongation is a proper measure of the ductility of malleable iron.

A practical illustration of the ductility of malleable iron is that in addition to its ability to be bent or twisted without fracture, as is illustrated by the twisted bars shown in Fig. 7, Chapter II, the metal can be punched and the punched holes can be drifted to larger size without cracks or fractures. A punched malleable plate is shown in Fig. 4. Holes cored in malleable iron castings can similarly be drifted.

TENSILE TEST VALUES

The representative tensile test values for standard malleable iron in its two grades are given in Table 1.

TABLE 1. TENSILE TEST VALUES

	Ultimate Strength (p.s.i.)	Yield Point (p.s.i.)	Elongation (per cent in 2 in.)
Grade 35018			
Minimum..............	53,000	35,000	18
Most probable value......	55,000	36,500	20
Grade 32510			
Minimum..............	50,000	32,500	10
Most probable value......	52,000	34,000	12.5

MODULUS OF ELASTICITY IN TENSION

The modulus of elasticity, a measure of the rate of stretch of a metal within its elastic limit, is the ratio of unit stress to unit strain. The higher the modulus of elasticity, the stiffer the metal. Stiffness of a casting is of course also affected by design, but, in general, a metal with a high modulus of elasticity has more rigidity than one with a low value. The modulus of elasticity of malleable iron is approximately 25,000,000 p.s.i.

EFFECT OF SECTION ON TENSILE PROPERTIES

With some metals, the diameter of the specimen used in tensile tests is of importance, higher tensile properties being shown if specimens of smaller diameter are used. [1, 13, 15, 16] This situation results from the fact that when the casting is cooling in the mold, light sections cool much more rapidly and consequently have a finer grain. The structure of American malleable iron, however, is determined by the anneal, not by the as-cast condition; specimen diameters therefore do not materially influence tensile test results for malleable.

EFFECT OF MACHINING ON TENSILE PROPERTIES

An earlier chapter of this book pointed out that American malleable iron, by mistaken confusion with European whiteheart, is sometimes thought to have its strength concentrated in the outer portion of a casting. Tensile tests demonstrate the error of this idea; whether a malleable iron test bar is machined or unmachined makes no appreciable difference in the results.[2, 4, 14, 17, 18] A typical study investigating this question involved 48 test bars prepared by eight different foundries.[4] Each plant submitted six bars from the same heat. Three bars from each of the eight sets were tested in the unmachined condition. Three were machined before being tested.

The machined bars in four sets had a slightly higher yield point; the unmachined bars in the other four sets had a slightly lower one. In six of the sets, the machined bars showed a slightly higher ultimate strength, the increase being only .06 to 4 per cent. In the other two sets, the unmachined bars had the higher ultimate strength, by the small differences of .12 to .90 per cent. The machined bars from seven of the eight heats showed slightly higher elongation. Another similar study used bars of five-eighths-, three-quarters-, and seven-eighths-inch diameter from 27 consecutive heats. The five-eighths-inch bars were tested as cast. The larger bars were machined to the standard five-eighths-inch test specimen diameter before being tested. Average test results are summarized in Table 2.

TABLE 2. TESTS OF MALLEABLE IRON TEST BARS
("As Cast" and Machined)

Diameter of Bars as Cast	How Tested	Ultimate Strength (p.s.i.)	Yield Point (p.s.i.)	Elongation (Per cent in 2 in.)
⅝ inch	As cast	54,800	36,500	23.40
¾ inch	Machined to ⅝ inch	53,460	35,950	22.00
⅞ inch	Machined to ⅝ inch	53,530	36,100	20.50

EFFECT OF CHEMICAL COMPOSITION ON TENSILE PROPERTIES

Usually the tensile properties vary inversely with the carbon content of standard malleable iron, which for Grade 32510 is 2.30 to 2.70 per cent and

Fig. 4. Because of its ductility, malleable iron can be punched and sheared like soft steel. On the left, a casting containing five three-fourths inch punched holes, the center one drifted to 1½ inches. At right, a casting five-eighths inch thick, with a large number of three-fourths inch holes, cold-punched, the distance between holes being sometimes as little as one-eighth inch.

for Grade 35018 is 2.00 to 2.45 per cent. Tensile properties also are influenced by the silicon content; however, the silicon should be limited in accordance with the amount of carbon present. As earlier indicated, too high a silicon-carbon total may cause the formation of primary graphite with resultant lower tensile properties.

FATIGUE ENDURANCE

Many machine parts, such as crankshafts, valve parts, piston rods, and shafts carrying rotating elements, are subjected during operation to repeated stress. Cyclic loading of this sort frequently imposes a difficult design problem, because of the fact that a metal cannot withstand a repeatedly applied stress as large as the load which it can stand if that load is applied steadily. Failures resulting from this fact are of the progressive type; that is, the failure originates in the form of a crack at some point in the surface and moves progressively through the piece. Since the final failure, which occurs under repeated loading, takes place suddenly and without warning, the fatigue endurance limit of a metal — the greatest stress which the metal can have repeated an infinite number of times without damage — is among its most important mechanical properties.

The fatigue endurance limit is studied through applying repeated or reversed cycles of stress in tension, in transverse loading, or in torsion. Ten million cycles before failure are considered the standard test. The ratio of fatigue endurance limit to ultimate strength is called the "endurance ratio," and for standard malleable iron may be considered as 0.50, a figure which agrees well with the endurance ratio of wrought ferrous metal.[4] There is some evidence that the endurance ratio increases slightly with increasing ultimate strength.

Thus results quoted in European literature for malleable iron with lower ultimate strength than that of American malleable iron usually show lower endurance ratios of 0.35 to 0.44, [19, 20, 21] while one recent study made in this country on standard malleable iron with the rotating beam machine gave an average value of 0.54.[22] Average values obtained in tests conducted by C. F. Lauenstein of the Link-Belt Company, Indianapolis, and W. M. Murray, Massachusetts Institute of Technology, on standard malleable iron, are as follows:

Ultimate Strength	Yield Point	Elongation	Endurance Limit	Endurance Ratio
54,640 p.s.i.	36,500 p.s.i.	21.5% in 2 in.	31,650 p.s.i.	0.575

Progressive fracture, which usually starts at a notch, scratch, or sharp corner, is indicative that the fatigue limit of the metal has been exceeded. As endurance ratio values would indicate, susceptibility to progressive fracture is much less in malleable iron than in many other metals, an advantage which is attributable to the ferritic matrix and temper carbon nodules in malleable iron.

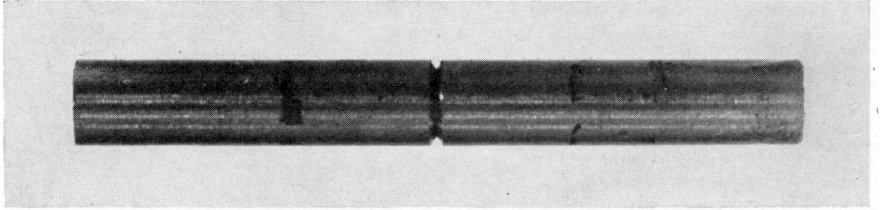

Fig. 5. Notch fatigue strength of malleable iron is determined by studies of bars such as this, which has a 30-degree sharp V notch.

NOTCH-FATIGUE STRENGTH

The relative freedom of malleable iron from progressive or fatigue fracture indicates that it is less sensitive to notch conditions than are most ferrous alloys — a conclusion which recent study has substantiated. Notch sensitivity means the relative ability or lack of ability of a metal to absorb the excess stresses due to notch conditions. Particularly when design requirements limit the practicable size of fillets at sharp corners or when radical section change is involved, low notch sensitivity in the metal being used is of extreme value. Notch-fatigue strength is determined by tests of bars with notches of various kinds in the test section. A bar with a 30-degree sharp V notch, used in studies of the notch fatigue strength of standard malleable iron, is shown in Fig. 5. The notch-fatigue ratio of a metal is the ratio of its notch-fatigue strength to ultimate strength; for standard malleable iron, this ratio is 33 per cent. That is, a malleable iron of 55,000 p.s.i. ultimate strength can be expected to have a notch-fatigue strength of 18,000 to 20,000 p.s.i. This may be compared to cast steel, which has a notch-fatigue ratio of about 20 to 25 per cent or a notch-fatigue strength of 14,000 to 15,000 p.s.i. A malleable iron section thus will withstand a 25 per cent greater load under notch conditions than will an equal cast steel section, or, conversely, a 25 per cent larger metal section is required in cast steel to carry equal loads.

The fatigue ratio and notch fatigue of malleable iron are increased by shot blasting or cold working the surface of the metal at highly stressed areas.

DAMPING CAPACITY

Damping capacity is the ability of a material to resist motion and absorb energy within itself. Standard malleable iron has this quality to a high degree and hence is especially suitable for employment in automotive and vibration applications.

SHEAR STRENGTH

The shear strength of a metal is that property which resists the tendency of one portion to slide over another. It is, for instance, the resistance of the metal to the action of a punching die. The ultimate strength of malleable iron in shear is roughly 90 per cent of the ultimate tensile strength.

The properties of standard malleable iron in shear are as follows: [2]

Shear strength........................ 48,000 p.s.i.
Yield point........................... 23,000 p.s.i.
Modulus of rigidity.................... 10,675,000 p.s.i.

POISSON'S RATIO

The ratio of unit longitudinal deformation to unit lateral deformation of a material under axial stress is called "Poisson's ratio." For malleable iron, Poisson's ratio is 0.17.[23]

TORSIONAL STRENGTH

The resistance of a metal to being twisted about an axis is its strength in torsion. It is calculated from the load applied to produce rotation, the distance from the axis to the point of load application, and the length of the specimen. The properties of malleable iron in torsion are: [2]

Modulus of rupture in torsion   58,000 p.s.i.
Yield point in torsion........   24,850 p.s.i.
Angle of twist at rupture.....   360 degrees, bar 0.9 in. di-
                                  ameter, 5 in. gauge length;
                                  790 degrees, bar 1.0 in. di-
                                  ameter, 10 in. gauge length

COMPRESSIVE STRENGTH

Compression, the force tending to decrease the length of a body, is the reverse of tension. Brittle materials fail under compression by bulging slightly at the center and then shattering, thus giving exact determination of the breaking load. Ductile materials, however, flow indefinitely.[1] Malleable iron, being ductile and capable of great plastic deformation, does not shatter under compression. It takes a permanent set of 1 per cent at about 28,000 p.s.i.,[2] but tests up to 90,000 p.s.i. have not resulted in failure.[1] Practically, there is a limit to the distortion which can take place without interference with the service of the casting. The permissible compressive stress therefore depends on the part itself and on the permanent set which can be tolerated. The modulus of elasticity in compression for standard malleable iron is very close to that in tension, or 25,000,000 p.s.i.[2]

TRANSVERSE STRENGTH

Transverse tests, like tests in compression, are seldom made on malleable iron or other ductile materials because these materials, before they break, will deform to an extent which makes them unserviceable.

The transverse strength of malleable iron was recently determined on six sets of test bars, round and square, approximately 12, 20, and 30 millimeters in thickness. Different lengths of span were also used in the testing. Despite all these variables, the results, with the exception of two high values for the

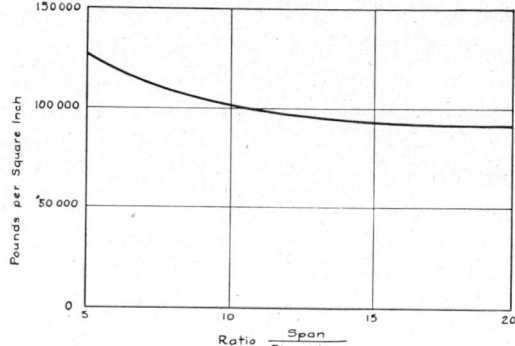

Fig. 6. Transverse strength of malleable iron.

20-millimeter round bars, lie close together. Figure 6 is a graphic presentation of these results, which range from 90,000 to 130,000 p.s.i. The transverse strength decreases with the increase in the ratio of span to diameter. Yield point is about 70 per cent of the transverse strength.[24]

IMPACT RESISTANCE

The resistance of material to impact is an important property and one which has not yet been adequately measured by standard tests. The value of the notched-bar impact tests has often been questioned on the ground that they measure the sensitivity of a metal to stress concentration at a notch, instead of the metal's ability to withstand impact.[14]

This situation does not mean that no importance should be attached to to impact-test results. Generally speaking, more failures occur in metals which have very low Izod or Charpy impact values than in those which have

Fig. 7. A malleable iron bridge railing, bent but not broken by the impact of a heavy truck in an accident.

high ones.[25] But the notched-bar test does not give accurate enough results on metals of different notch sensitivity to be entirely indicative of the metal's resistance to shock. The true test of a metal's ability to resist impact comes in service.

The impact resistance of malleable iron, measured by the Charpy test using a notch, 0.394-inch-square bar, and 0.079 inch depth of notch, is about 16.5 foot-pounds.[4] In tests using a "keyhole" notch with 0.04 inch radius at bottom, a 0.39-inch-square bar, or a test bar with a V notch 0.197 inch in depth, malleable iron shows impact resistance of 6.5 to 8.0 foot-pounds.[4]

As measured by the Izod test, with a V notch, 0.394-inch-square bar, and 0.079 inch depth of notch, the impact value of malleable iron is about 16.5 foot-pounds.[4]

EFFECT OF TEMPERATURE ON MECHANICAL PROPERTIES

A slight, almost unnoticeable, change in structure occurs when standard malleable iron has been heated to 1350 degrees Fahrenheit. When 1400 degrees F. has been reached, however, some of the temper carbon in the iron redissolves, and both the structure and the properties of the metal are entirely altered. For that reason, malleable iron is not generally used at temperatures above 1200 degrees F. Up to that temperature, except under repeated heating, malleable iron does not undergo "growth," or permanent increase in volume, to the extent gray cast iron does.

The tensile strength and yield point of standard malleable iron in general decrease as the temperature rises, a particularly sharp drop being noticed after 800 degrees F.[2] At 1200 degrees F., these properties are approximately 25 per cent of those at room temperature. Elongation decreases slightly until about 600 degrees F. is attained, beyond which temperature it increases rapidly, as does ductility.

Charpy impact values are not appreciably affected by rising temperatures up to 400 degrees F., but if malleable iron castings are heated to about 850 to 900 degrees F., as in the hot-dip galvanizing process, they may be affected by intergranular embrittlement as a result of the heating and quenching. This galvanizing embrittlement can be prevented in two ways: by quenching the annealed castings from 1200 degrees F.[26] or by keeping the phosphorus low.[27] More phosphorus can be tolerated without susceptibility to intergranular embrittlement when silicon is relatively low.

Malleable iron shows no appreciable decrease in impact properties from room temperature to −40 degrees F. Impact tests made on eyebolt lifting plugs, using the standard wedge test machine, showed the material to be quite satisfactory at −40 degrees F. It was possible to deform the original 1¼ inch diameter of the eye of the plug to 1⁄16 inch without fracture, in spite of a relatively heavy section and small-diameter opening. Quenching from 1200 degrees F. aids in reducing low-temperature embrittlement.

V

STANDARD MALLEABLE IRON — ITS ENGINEERING PROPERTIES

To give effective, economical service in a finished part, a metal must possess, among others, certain characteristics made possible by its physical and mechanical properties. These characteristics, for convenience called the metal's engineering properties, include trueness to final dimensions and shape "as cast" or "as formed," freedom from strains, machinability, corrosion resistance, and wear resistance. Since engineering properties such as these have a direct bearing on the cost of the finished part, they are of special importance to the engineer and the production man. As this chapter will show, and as Chapter XI in discussing machining techniques will further explain, much of the wide use of American malleable iron results from its possession of a valuable combination of such characteristics.

CAST TO SIZE

Wherever complexity of design makes forging and machining slow and costly, malleable iron castings are efficient and economical. Widely specified for this reason before Second World War emergencies arose, malleable iron during the period of steel shortages came to be employed in many applications where steel forgings or other strategic materials were formerly used, and was found to give equal or better performance at the same time that it reduced over-all costs. Obviously, coring cavities out of a casting is generally less expensive than machining them out of a forging. Beyond this, however, is the fact that malleable iron can be cast closer to finished dimensions than other materials can generally be forged, thus markedly cutting down the production of machine chips, which in waste of manhours and of machine time are about the most costly product to come out of any manufacturing plant. Moreover, when a single casting can replace an assembly of numerous parts, a more accurate finished product results, since the accumulation of tolerances due to the assembling of individual components each carrying its own tolerance, is eliminated.

The economy that can result from the use of castings is illustrated in the manufacture of the grip for an antiaircraft gun. Fabrication of this part from a forging necessitated removal of 73 per cent of the metal. Replacing the forging with a malleable iron casting reduced the percentage to 32.[28] In another case, 3.75 pounds of bar stock were machined to a finished weight of 1.50 pounds in the manufacture of adapters for antiaircraft shells. A malleable iron casting replaced the bar stock, and the weight of metal removed was reduced from 2.25 pounds to 0.75 pound.[28] Conversion to a pearlitic malleable iron in the manufacture of machine guns, carbines, rifles, and aircraft cannon meant that during a two-year period, 17,400,000 pounds of the pearlitic malleable did the work that would have required 27,000,000 pounds of steel and 700,000 pounds of bronze. As much as 50 per cent saving in manhours in machining was attained by the use of malleable iron in some gun parts. One, for example, had been machined from a piece of steel tubing weighing 20 pounds. The malleable casting which replaced the steel weighed 5.6 pounds. The finished part weighs 4.5 pounds. With the malleable casting 1.1 pounds of metal were removed; with the steel tube, 15.5 pounds.

Machining may sometimes be altogether eliminated if malleable iron is specified, for the ductility of the metal readily allows it to be coin pressed. The passenger-car spring hanger shown in Fig. 1, for example, was originally held to very close tolerances at dimensions A and B through milling. Coin pressing of an unmachined malleable iron casting at the foundry replaced the machining operation but secured the same tolerances. Bolt holes cast in the piece are so accurate that hub boring is the only machining done by the manufacturer.

FREEDOM FROM CASTING STRAINS

Cast metals frequently are subject to internal stresses when the shape of the mold cavity prevents the metal from contracting uniformly throughout during solidification and cooling. These hidden stresses, released or intensified

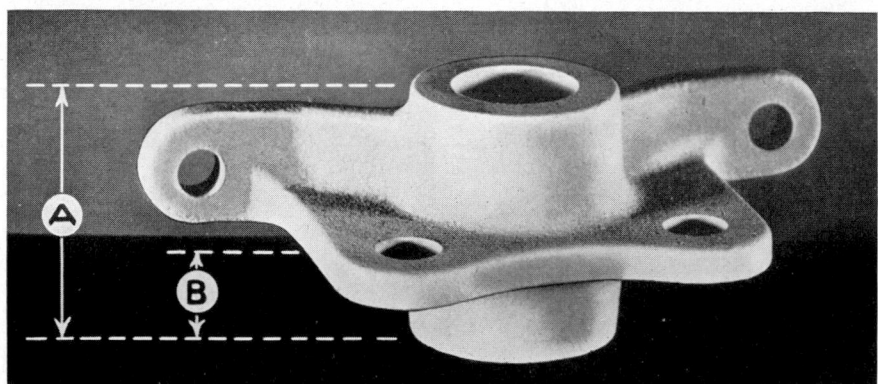

Fig. 1. Coin-pressed malleable iron passenger-car spring hanger.

Official U. S. Navy Photo

Fig. 2. Oerlikon 20-millimeter antiaircraft gun. The pedestal and shoulder rest and hand-grip frame are specified in malleable iron.

by subsequent machining operations, may produce warpage or distortion of the piece — "casting strains," which may render the casting unfit for use as a finished part. Such an occurrence is an impossibility with American malleable iron. The annealing operation which converts white iron castings into malleable iron is not an optional heat-treatment, but an integral part of the manufacture of the iron. It removes any internal stresses which may have been occasioned in the casting process and results in a thoroughly homogeneous stress-free casting.

If a malleable iron casting is bent or twisted by accident, the ductility of the metal permits it to be cold straightened.

MACHINABILITY

Efficiency in the production of finished parts depends to a great degree on the readiness with which machining operations such as turning, drilling, milling, threading, reaming, and so on, are performed, and this in turn depends directly on the machinability of the metal being fabricated. Though it possesses superior toughness and ductility, yet because of its uniformity of structure throughout and because of its nodular temper carbon, American malleable iron is the most easily machinable and free-cutting of ferrous metals of comparable or higher strength. The tables of machining feeds and

Fig. 3. Malleable iron torpedo-warhead protecting rings, a casting in which malleable iron's complete freedom from casting strains is imperative.

speeds recommended by manufacturers of machine tools which appear in Chapter XI reflect this fact, which is evident also in Table 1. This table, developed by a producer of machine tools, assigns relative machinability values to a group of the more readily machined steels and to malleable iron, with S.A.E. No. 1112 steel being rated at the base value of 100. Malleable iron is the most easily machined metal in the group.

TABLE 1. MACHINABILITY VALUES

Malleable Irons	Machinability Value	Brinell Hardness Number
Standard Malleable Iron...............	120	110–145
Pearlitic Malleable Iron...............	90	180–200
Pearlitic Malleable Iron...............	80	200–240

Steels			
S.A.E. Number	A.I.S.I. Number		
1112	B1112........................	100	179–229
1113	B1113........................	135	179–229
1120	——	80	143–179
1118	C1118........................	80	143–179
1137	C1137........................	70	187–229
1022	C1022........................	70	159–192
4130	A4130........................	65	187–229

Since the determination of machinability values involves not only the metal being machined but also the cutting tool used and the machine tool in which the work is done, values are necessarily comparative ratings for a given set of conditions. The amount of energy required to remove a chosen unit of metal, however, is properly regarded as a most significant measure of machinability; tool life per grind, which also takes into account feeds, speeds, and depth of cut, is a second highly reliable value. The rating of malleable iron by the first of these standards, that of power consumption or cutting force, as determined in one study, is conveniently presented in tabular form, as in Table 2.

TABLE 2. ENERGY REQUIRED TO REMOVE ONE CUBIC INCH OF METAL [29]

(VALUES EXPRESSED IN 1,000 INCH-POUNDS)

	Brinell Hardness Number	Feed in Inches per Revolution				
		0.0025	0.005	0.010	0.020	0.040
Armco Iron.................	89	714	536	402	...	...
Hot-rolled Machinery Steel....	109	672	497	405	367	...
Malleable Specimen B *......	112	315	244	221	191	202
High-carbon Malleable †.....	113	256	215	193	173	...
Malleable Specimen A ‡.....	118	315	244	201	179	177
Annealed Cast Steel.........	131	607	432	374	...	...
Soft Gray Iron.............	143	298	237	206	170	...
Cold-rolled Steel............	191	§	§	394	350	...
Special Heat-treated Steel....	223	588	599	511	417	...

* Approximate equivalent of standard malleable iron Grade 32510.
† Air-furnace iron of approximately 3 per cent carbon content.
‡ Approximate equivalent of standard malleable iron Grade 35018.
§ Drill ran out of center.

Explanation of the superior machinability of American malleable iron as resulting from the lubricating action of the nodules of temper carbon in its structure is borne out by this table. It will be noted that, except for soft gray iron, the only metal showing better machinability values than the two standard malleable irons was a high-carbon malleable.

The high machinability of American malleable iron as measured by the second of these standards — tool life per grind — is clearly shown in cases such as the following. Eight machining operations are performed on a mallea-

Fig. 4. A malleable iron agricultural casting of difficult design.

ble iron fan-pulley hub for motor cars, the casting being bored, turned, faced, drilled, tapped, polished, broached, and hand reamed. On the average throughout the operations, according to the manufacturer, adoption of malleable iron trebled tool life per grind and permitted an increase of two and a half times in surface speed. The hub is $2\frac{3}{16}$ inches in diameter with a flange of $3\frac{3}{4}$ inches diameter and a hub hole of $1\frac{15}{32}$ inches.[30] The boring, turning, and facing operations are performed on an automatic machine equipped with Stellite-tipped tools. With 135 feet per minute surface speed, 0.050 inch feed, and $\frac{3}{64}$ inch depth of cut, the production is 125 pieces an hour. Tool life averages 1,000 pieces per tool grind. Second step is the roughing, semifinishing, and finishing of the flange backs, on a similar machine with Stellite-tipped tools. Tool life in this operation is 3,000 pieces per grind.

Eight rivet holes of $\frac{7}{32}$ inch diameter are drilled on 20-inch drill presses; production is 9,000 pieces per drill grind. Two draw-screw holes of $\frac{5}{16}$ inch diameter are drilled in the flange. Average life for the taps used is 45,000 pieces. For the slot on the hub hole, which is one-quarter inch by one-eighth inch deep, a double broaching machine with high-speed cutter is used. Production averages 2,900 pieces a day, and the broach-cutter bars have cut as many as 300,000 pieces before being reground. To finish the hole size to within a tolerance of 0.001 inch, hand reaming with high-speed steel is done. Reamers keep up production of 2,850 pieces a day for two or three weeks per grind if the cutting edge is stoned slightly each day.

Comparable machinability in terms of tool life is shown by malleable iron in the manufacture of a differential gear case. The casting is machined on an automatic lathe hydraulically fed, at 205 revolutions per minute, with cemented carbide cutting tools. Feeds are 0.004 inch per revolution for front tools and 0.003 inch per revolution for rear tools. Production is 53 an hour. Another example is a magneto-drive body made of malleable iron, machined at 275 feet per minute, with a feed of 0.015 inch, $7\frac{1}{2}$ minutes being taken for the first operation and $5\frac{1}{2}$ for the second.

RESISTANCE TO CORROSION

The wide use of American malleable iron in outdoor installations such as pole-line hardware, bridge railings and panels, street signs, railroad tie

Fig. 5. These fan pulley hubs illustrate the machinability of malleable iron explained in the text.

Fig. 6. Boring, turning, and facing operations are performed on the fan pulley hubs at 135 f.p.m., 0.050 inch feed, and ³⁄₆₄ inch cut. Production is at the rate of 125 pieces per hour and 1,000 pieces per tool grind.

plates, and so on, is practical demonstration of the high resistance of the material to atmospheric corrosion. A case in point is that of malleable iron pole mountings at Bridgeport, Conn., which are placed so that for 10 years they have been subjected to alternate wet and dry salt-water corrosion. The pole is located so that the base of the mount is submerged at high tide. Though they were merely painted when installed, the malleable iron castings show no appreciable corrosion after 10 years of service. The malleable iron coupling shown in Fig. 7 was in service for 13 years on a pier in Lake Erie, exposed to water, moist air, and ice. The malleable iron is noticeably less corroded than the steel on which it is mounted. The self-adjusting pad tree

Fig. 7. The malleable iron coupling in place at the right end of this fixture shows notably less corrosion than the steel on which it is mounted. It had been in service on a Lake Erie pier for 13 years.

shown in Fig. 8 is a design patented in 1847. Production of the unit was discontinued about 1865. Some 60 years later, during excavations at the foundry, the one pictured was dug up. Although pitted, it is still whole in spite of about 60 years' exposure to soil corrosion.

Corrosion Tests

A corrosion test which duplicated actual service conditions in so far as possible was run to determine the resistance of various ferrous metals to locomotive smoke. Specimens were suspended in the smokejacks of a roundhouse which were in continuous use. Comparison of such specimens with identical ones in railroad service led to the conclusion that corrosion progressed as far in one month on the specimens in the smokejacks as it did in two years on metals in service.[31] Every two months specimens were removed, cleaned, and weighed, and the loss of weight was recorded.

Table 3 gives the average loss per month in ounces per square inch of original surface. Malleable iron with 1 per cent copper showed the lowest loss, standard malleable iron next. Commercial pure iron and basic open-hearth steel suffered the greatest losses.

TABLE 3. RESULTS OF SMOKEJACK CORROSION TEST [32]

Material	Shape of Specimen	Average loss per month (Ounces per Square Inch)
Standard malleable iron	Flat	0.00545
Standard malleable iron	Round	0.00650
Malleable iron with 1 per cent copper	Flat	0.0044
Malleable iron with 1 per cent copper	Round	0.0058
Wrought iron	Flat	0.0076
Wrought iron	Round	0.00716
Basic open-hearth steel	Flat	0.00855
Basic open-hearth steel	Round	0.00777
Commercial pure iron	Round	0.0087

Stress accelerates corrosion, and in such conditions American malleable iron shows greater freedom from cracking than some corrosion-resistant irons formerly used. This property is of particular value in pipe fittings. Malleable iron is not stainless, however, and it should be determined whether those corrosion products that will form are objectionable. This should be done for other metals in similar service.

Protective Coatings

For some service conditions, a coat of paint is sufficient protection to enable malleable iron castings to give good performance. Other more severe conditions need more effective protection. The many commercial processes for rustproofing ferrous metals may in general be divided into two classes: nonmetallic and metallic.

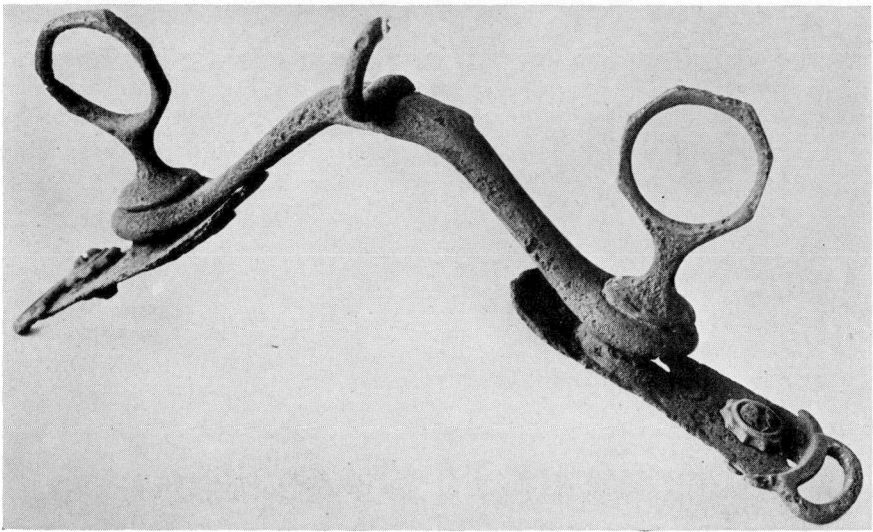

Fig. 8. A malleable iron self-adjusting pad tree, made about 1865, after being buried 60 years in moist ground.

The two types of nonmetallic treatments available and in general use are (1) that which forms a thick skin of iron oxide, and (2) that which forms an iron phosphate coating. Although the iron oxide coating is a protection against rust, it is brittle and will crack if the part is bent, and so is not suitable for castings subjected to bending or twisting. The iron phosphate coating is flexible enough to avoid the development of cracks but may occasionally have pinholes. For this reason, castings with iron phosphate coating are customarily painted or given an oil or wax treatment, to act as a seal. Castings given the iron oxide treatment should likewise be painted or lacquered.

The metallic coatings most commonly used are zinc, tin, and cadmium. Processes for applying aluminum and lead have recently been developed commercially. In very particular circumstances, chrome, nickel, and silver have been employed. Zinc, cadmium, aluminum, and lead can be deposited electrolytically. The most common method of coating with zinc is the hot-dip galvanizing process. Since any possibility of embrittlement can be eliminated by quenching from 1200 degrees Fahrenheit or by chemical composition adjustment, this galvanizing is the most generally used coating for malleable iron. Tests have shown that under identical conditions, malleable iron takes a heavier iron-zinc alloy layer than does wrought iron or steel.[32] The type of casting and the use to which it is to be put should determine the kind of coating to be specified.

For protection and for better appearance, various other finishing processes may be employed, such as lead flashing, chromium plate, and nickel and aluminum plating. Typical of the possibilities are recommendations of two companies, which are given in detail in Appendix II.

EFFECT OF COPPER ON CORROSION RESISTANCE

Addition of copper to the melt in amounts from 0.25 to 0.75 per cent increases the resistance of malleable iron to atmospheric corrosion. In alloyed malleable iron, up to 2.00 per cent copper aids materially in reducing loss due to corrosion by flue gases. The effectiveness of 0.25 per cent copper in reducing corrosion caused by an industrial city atmosphere is shown in Fig. 9.

WEAR RESISTANCE

The resistance of a metal to wear as a result of friction must be considered from the standpoint of three possible types of wear: (1) lubricated bearing, (2) dry bearing, (3) abrasion.

In the case of lubricated bearing wear, malleable iron, like other metals, shows excellent performance as long as the bearing pressures are not high enough to break through a lubricating film and abrasive particles larger than the thickness of the film are not present. Should the film break down, the temper carbon present in malleable iron aids in the lubrication.

In bearings where neither lubricating films nor abrasives are present, and where relative surface speed is high, galling or welding of the mating bearing parts may occur. Because of the soft ferrite matrix of malleable iron, it is not suitable for such applications.

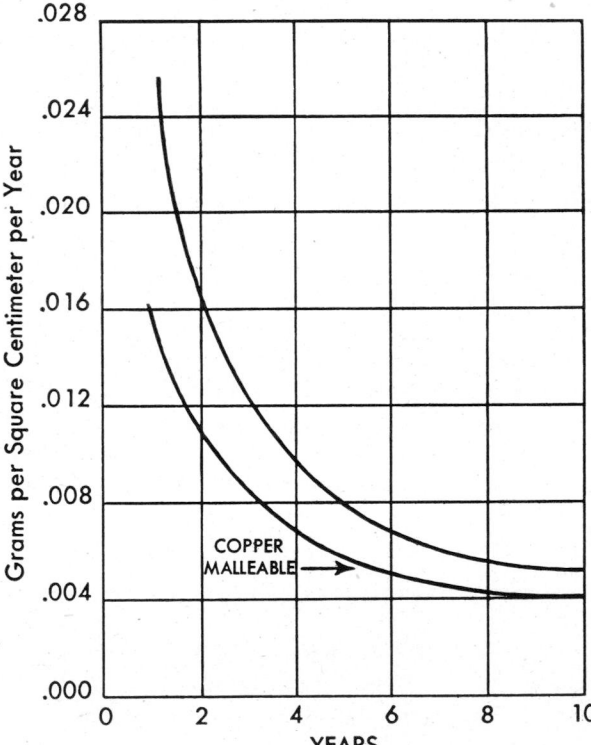

Fig. 9. Effect of 0.25 per cent copper on the resistance of malleable iron to atmospheric corrosion.

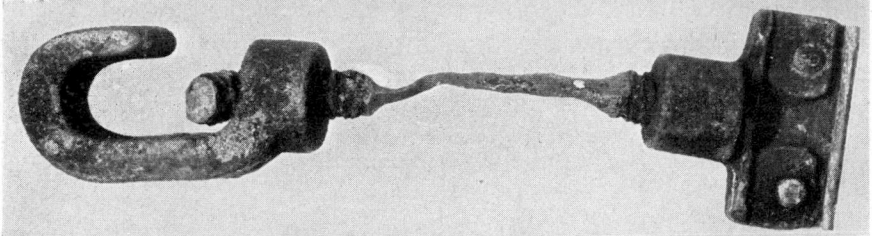

Fig. 10. Another illustration of the comparative corrosion-resistance of steel and malleable iron: Note that the suspension clamp and fixture, both of malleable iron, are virtually as good as new, while the steel link between them is corroded beyond usefulness.

Its ferrite matrix likewise makes malleable iron unsuitable where bearing parts are subjected to the cutting action of hard abrasive particles, such as rough grit, under relatively high speeds and pressures.

In some farm machinery, malleable iron gears have been used for years with great success. Malleable iron bearings are highly suitable in installations where pressures and speeds are low, the bearing being lined with a thin layer of bronze or other bearing metal for higher pressures. In these applications it has been found that even should the lining layer wear through, the malleable iron bearing will not score the shaft.[33] Malleable iron is replacing a large amount of bronze in the backing castings of railroad-car journal bearings.[28]

LOCALIZED HARDENING

The fact that when malleable iron is heated to above 1350 degrees F., some of the temper carbon is redissolved and the metal becomes hard makes possible the surface hardening or spot hardening of malleable castings for particular applications. Heating for surface hardening or spot hardening can be done by either electric induction or oxyacetylene flame, but care must be taken with the latter to have an excess of acetylene in order to avoid decarburization.[34] The flame hardening of malleable iron is similar to case hardening in that it involves recarburization of the ferritic matrix. When flame or induction hardening is properly

Fig. 11. Caster wheels of malleable iron, running on angle floor tracks, speed production in aircraft factories, where they are used to carry cradles in which planes travel the production line.

done, a piece with a hardened, wear-resistant surface and a tough, ductile core is obtained.[35] The main problem in surface hardening malleable iron is that the time element is so short as to make satisfactory reabsorption of the carbon difficult to secure.[36] For this reason, pearlitic malleable iron is generally more adaptable to surface hardening than is standard malleable.

WELDABILITY

Fusion welding of malleable iron is not recommended for stress-carrying parts, because of the resultant formation of a brittle structure. There are applications, however, where tensile stresses are low or stresses are compressive only, in which welded malleable irons, even though lower in ductility and impact value at the weld, may be employed. Welding may be used in the foundry as a means of repairing small surface defects in castings;[38] in such cases, care should be exercised that the heat of welding does not penetrate into stressed sections, unless re-annealing is done after welding.

Malleable iron is very satisfactorily brazed if a suitable low-temperature brazing rod is used and a brazing temperature no higher than 1350 degrees F. is maintained.

Low-temperature solders or the silver solders, which will flow at temperatures under 1350 degrees F., may be used to excellent advantage with malleable iron. In either brazing or soldering, a suitable flux is necessary.

VI

PEARLITIC MALLEABLE IRONS

THE pearlitic malleable irons are harder, stronger, and more resistant to abrasive wear than standard malleable iron, but generally are less ductile and resistant to shock. They are made from hard-iron compositions the same as those used in standard malleable iron, or with various alloy additions, but their characteristic properties result from the fact that they are so heat-treated that some of their carbon content is present in the combined form. The name "pearlitic malleable iron" is a generic term,[39] used to differentiate such metals from standard malleable, not to describe their microstructure, and is applied to them regardless of the form in which the combined carbon appears. It may be in pearlite — a mechanical mixture of ferrite and cementite in alternate layers — it may be in one of the forms such as sorbite or martensite intermediate between pearlite and austenite, or it may be spheroids of cementite.

MANUFACTURE

Processes employed in the manufacture of pearlitic malleable iron do not differ from those used in producing standard malleable, except for the variation in annealing treatment which gives pearlitic malleable its characteristic structure. This may be secured by the following methods: (1) by preventing or retarding second-stage graphitization through adding to the composition a suitable alloy such as those discussed in Chapter VII or through quenching and reheat-treatment or through a combination of alloy and quench; (2) by arresting graphitization before it is complete during heat-treatment, through reduction of the time of second-stage graphitization; (3) by heat-treatment of a completely graphitized malleable iron.

PHYSICAL PROPERTIES

The specific gravity of pearlitic malleable irons is slightly higher than that of standard malleable — 7.35 to 7.44 [8, 39] as against an average 7.32 for standard malleable iron. The thermal conductivity of some pearlitic malleable irons, however, is appreciably higher, being 0.0000109 per degree Fahrenheit.[39] The magnetic and electrical properties of pearlitic malleable irons, because of the combined carbon present in their structure, differ considerably from those of standard malleable. The electrical resistivity of some pearlitic malleable irons is 38.19 to 41.17 microhms per centimeter cube, and their coercivity is 7.87 to 12.55 ampere turns per centimeter.[8] Magnetic permeability, or ratio of induction to magnetizing force, of these irons, at 200 ampere turns per inch, is 78.[39]

MECHANICAL PROPERTIES

The mechanical properties available in pearlitic malleable irons range from those of irons closely similar to standard malleable, with 60,000 pounds per square inch minimum ultimate strength, yield point of 43,000 p.s.i., and 10 per cent elongation, to those of heat-treated metals with 85,000 p.s.i. ultimate strength, 67,500 p.s.i. yield point, elongation of 2.5 per cent, and a Brinell hardness number of 227. The larger part of the tonnage of pearlitic malleable used today is in the range of 5 to 10 per cent elongation and 65,000 to 85,000 p.s.i. ultimate strength.

Fig. 1. A sampling of the many kinds of gears and blanks made of pearlitic malleable iron.

Since 15 to 20 different kinds of pearlitic malleable iron are produced in this country and many of them are made in several grades, complete listing of their mechanical values is beyond the scope of this discussion. Table 1 therefore presents mechanical values for a representative group of commercial pearlitic malleable irons now available.

TABLE 1. SPECIFICATIONS FOR PEARLITIC MALLEABLE IRON AND MECHANICAL TEST VALUES OF COMMERCIAL PEARLITIC IRONS

	Grade	Ultimate Strength	Yield Point	Elongation	Brinell Hardness
United States Army Ordnance Specification AXS-623, 1942	A & C	75,000	60,000	5	241–187
	B & D	65,000	50,000	8	207–163
	E	60,000	43,000	10	179–140
American Society for Testing Materials Specification A220-44T	43010	60,000	43,000	10	——
	50007	65,000	50,000	7	——
	60005	75,000	60,000	5	——
	70003	90,000	70,000	3	——
	X	——	——	——	——

MECHANICAL TEST VALUES OF COMMERCIAL PEARLITIC MALLEABLE IRONS *

Commercial Pearlitic Irons	Ultimate Strength		Yield Point		Elongation		B.H.N.
	Min.	Ave.	Min.	Ave.	Min.	Ave.	Range
Z-Metal	70,000	75,000	50,000	55,000	10	12	170–190
Promal	70,000	75,000	50,000	55,000	10	12	170–190
Lancastalloy	68,000	80,000	50,000	60,000	6	10	180–200
Jewell Alloy	85,000	90,000	55,000	60,000	6	8	183–235
Jewell Alloy No. 42	60,000	70,000	45,000	50,000	12	15	166–196
Jewell Alloy "V"	80,000	85,000	65,000	70,000	4	5	207–255
Special Metal A	60,000	65,000	40,000	45,000	2	5	175–200
Gunite K	85,000	95,000	67,500	80,000	2.5	4	227
Graphitic Steel	70,000	75,000	40,000	50,000	10	12	165–200
Belmalloy	70,000	85,000	47,000	52,000	5	8	179–217
Gensteel	70,000	75,000	45,000	50,000	5	6	170–190
Armasteel		108,000		95,000		1.5	285
Armasteel		105,000		90,000		2.5	269
Armasteel		95,000		82,000		4	241
Armasteel		80,000		50,000		5	187

* These values are stated by the manufacturers for the material as commonly furnished. For special applications, material of higher or lower strength and lower or higher elongation is produced.

Pearlitic malleable iron differs from standard malleable principally in its greater ultimate strength, higher yield point, and greater resistance to abrasive wear. As the strength of pearlitics is increased through alloying and heat-treatment, elongation will be reduced, but the percentage of increase in strength will not necessarily agree with the reduction in elongation, so that a prospective user should carefully study the increase in one resistance factor against the required remaining measure of shock resistance. The relations of ultimate strength, yield point, and elongation to the Brinell hardness of certain commercial pearlitic malleable irons are shown in Fig. 2.[39]

The ratio of yield point to ultimate strength for pearlitic irons in the lower strength range is approximately 0.70. As strength values rise toward 90,000 and 100,000 p.s.i., the ratio of yield point to ultimate strength increases to 0.75 to 0.88.

Effect of Composition on Tensile Properties

Combined carbon in pearlitic malleable iron varies from 0.30 to 0.60 per cent. Since it is the combined carbon which brings about the high strength of these irons, any change in composition which increases the content of combined carbon results in increased strength and hardness, and, to a certain extent, in decreased elongation. The structural form of the combined carbon — whether it is present as pearlite, sorbite, or martensite — has more influence on the elongation of the iron than it has on the metal's strength. Generally, for the same amount of combined carbon, irons with a spheroidized matrix have the best ductility, those with a sorbitic matrix are found to stand next, and then those with a coarsely lamellar pearlitic matrix.[39]

ENGINEERING PROPERTIES

The importance of the engineering properties of pearlitic malleable irons is illustrated by such typical applications as conveying and elevating chains, rocker arms, Diesel pistons, and similar installations where strength and resistance to wear are essential. The usefulness of pearlitic malleable iron in such castings is influenced by the effect of the combined carbon in its structure upon its engineering properties such as machinability and wear resistance. The fact that pearlitic malleable iron can be selectively hardened further widens the field of application for which it offers special suitability.

Machinability

Pearlitic malleable irons, because of their combined carbon content, machine less easily than standard malleable does. But since a wide

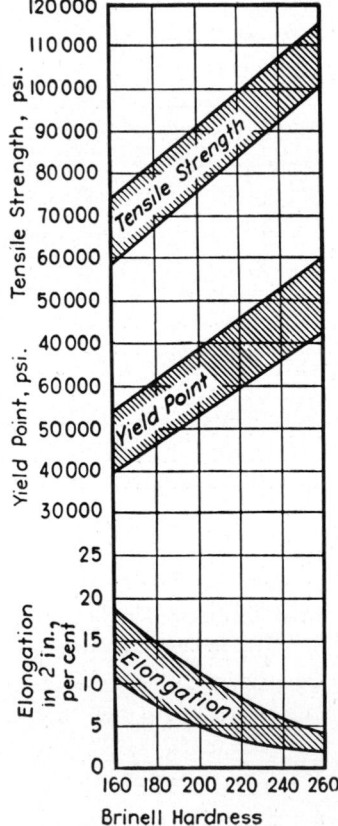

Fig. 2. Relationship of tensile properties of commercial pearlitic malleable iron to Brinell hardness.

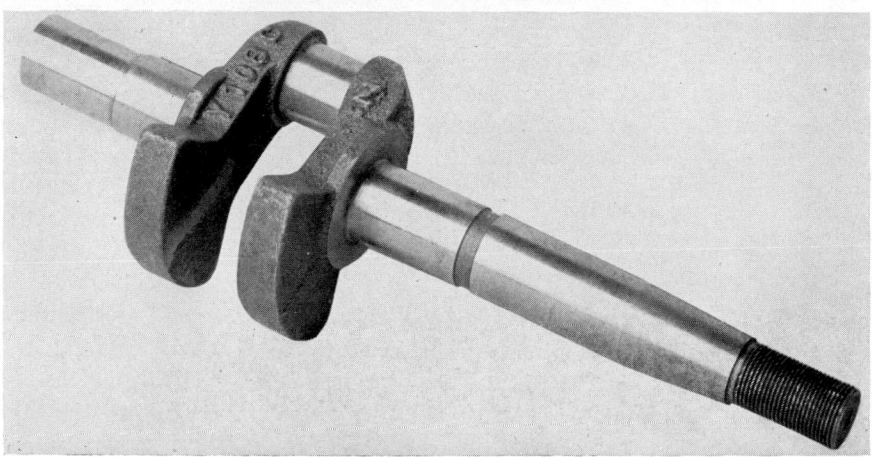

Fig. 3. A pearlitic malleable iron crankshaft, showing the fine finish obtainable in machining pearlitic malleable iron.

range of hardness and structures is available in pearlitic malleable irons, the degree of machinability suitable for a particular requirement is generally to be had. The Brinell hardness number is a reasonably reliable measure of the comparative machinability of pearlitic irons.

The machining of malleable iron is discussed in detail in Chapter XI. In general, the best results in machining pearlitic irons are obtained through using greater feeds and lower speeds than for standard malleable iron,[41] thus taking a fairly heavy cut.[39] The experience of one of the large motor companies has been that when this plan is followed, the pearlitic malleable irons are 20 to 40 per cent more machinable than steel bar stock or drop forgings of the same Brinell hardness number, and that tool life per grind is 20 to 100 per cent longer.[42]

This practice is illustrated in the manufacture of a two-piece differential case of pearlitic malleable iron with ultimate strength of 80,000 p.s.i. The case is machined on a turret lathe with J-Stellite tools. A roughing cut of one-eighth to $\frac{3}{16}$ inch is made at 100 surface feet per minute with a feed of 0.040 inch per revolution. Finishing cuts are made at 128 to 165 surface feet per minute.[43] Another type of pearlitic malleable iron with Brinell hardness number of 170 to 180 is regularly machined dry at higher cutting speeds than can be used for S.A.E. 1020–1030.[39]

A series of tests to determine the average watt-hours per cubic inch of metal removed showed that a pearlitic malleable iron of 211 Brinell had 73 per cent of the machinability of standard malleable iron with a Brinell hardness number of 137. The addition of 1 per cent copper increased the machinability of the pearlitic to 85 per cent of that of the standard malleable iron.[39] The finish obtainable on machined pearlitic malleable iron is shown in Fig. 3.

WEAR RESISTANCE

Pearlitic malleable irons are generally preferred for applications in which any of the three types of wear described in Chapter V is an important factor. Though not all pearlitic irons have equal resistance to wear, the higher indentation hardness and stronger structure available through proper composition and heat-treatment produce excellent performance in such parts as gears, camshafts, chain links, stoker parts, and rolls. The pearlitic malleable iron tank tread roller bodies shown in Fig. 4 illustrate the use of this material in severe service conditions. For gears such as those shown in Fig. 1, hardened pearlitic malleable iron is often specified. When brought by heat-treatment to the file-hard state (about 56 to 58 Rockwell "C" as against 60 Rockwell "C" minimum for steel), pearlitic malleable iron is reported as equalling or excelling carburized steel in wearing qualities.[41] Of the various pearlitics available, several are particularly well adapted for use as bearings, where their excellent nongalling properties in metal-to-metal wear have made possible the elimination of the bronze bushing formerly used.[44]

DAMPING CAPACITY

The high damping capacity noted in Chapter IV for standard malleable iron is also possessed by pearlitic malleable. The ability of this material to absorb energy within itself and thus to restrict vibration has led to the adoption of it for many highly stressed parts such as camshafts.[45]

HARDENABILITY

Pearlitic malleable irons are easily hardened, satisfactory results being obtained either with induction or oxyacetylene heating for differential hardening, with immersion in a lead or[42] salt bath for differential or complete hardening, or with furnace treatment for complete hardening. An example of complete hardening is a crankshaft of the eccentric type, formerly made of a steel forging, either S.A.E. 1020 or 1112, carburized and hardened to Rock-

Fig. 4. Pearlitic malleable iron tank tread roller bodies illustrate the use of this metal under severe service conditions.

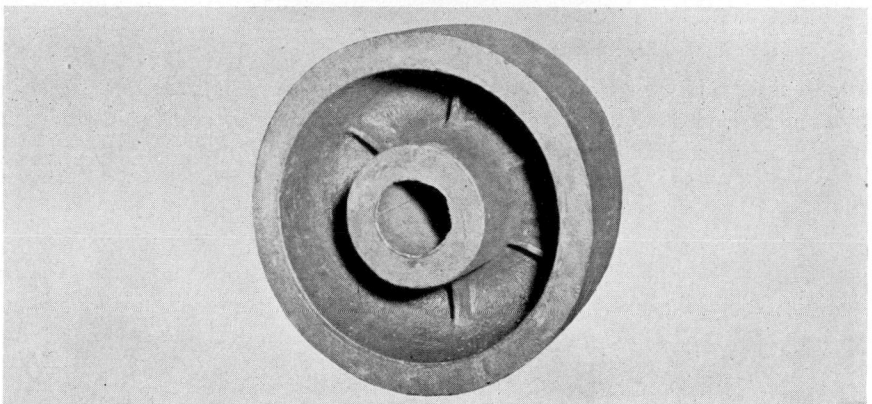

Fig. 5. Important among the uses of pearlitic malleable iron is the manufacture of gears. The gear blank here shown is 12½ inches in diameter, with a flange thickness of 1¼ inches. The cored hole is 2⅝ inches in diameter. The casting weighs 128 pounds.

well "C" 60, now made of a high-strength, low-elongation pearlitic malleable of 170–207 Brinell hardness, which machines readily. After being machined, it is heated to 1550 degrees F., and then is held 30 minutes, oil quenched, and drawn back to 700 degrees F., to give Rockwell "C" 40–45.[44] For hardening pearlitic malleable irons, the lowest temperature and the shortest time possible should be used. The pearlitics can be drawn back to any desired hardness, the temperature being higher and the time longer than for steel. Oil quench is often specified for complicated castings because it gives less distortion, fewer cracks, and shallow hardening.

WELDABILITY

Welding of pearlitic malleable irons is not generally recommended. Those who use welding on pearlitic malleable should follow the practice discussed in Chapter V.

Fig. 6. A heavy pearlitic malleable iron gear blank sectioned to show the manner of gating and the soundness of the casting throughout.

CORROSION RESISTANCE

In sugar factories and in other industries where corrosion of pump parts, chain links, elevator buckets, valve bodies, and rolls is involved, pearlitic malleable irons are widely specified. The inclusion of copper in pearlitic malleable increases its resistance to corrosion[41] and to impact.

USES

Pearlitic malleable irons are used in many of the applications which are discussed in detail in Chapter XVI. But since the pearlitics generally are employed where their superior wear resistance and relatively high yield point are necessary to meet severe service conditions, it is useful to list representative applications as part of the present chapter. Railway castings of pearlitic iron include carry irons, spring retainers, hinges and brackets, and brake shoes and heads. In the automotive field, the pearlitics are used in motorcycle parts, axle housing parts, camshafts and crankshafts, and differential housings. High-pressure unions, valve bodies, and hose couplings are made of pearlitic malleable. Hardened machine gears, cranks, levers, chain links, chain sprockets, rolls, pump parts, nozzles, cams, connecting rods, elevator buckets, drive spiders, hydraulic jack bodies, rocker arms, and universal joints are among the machine parts for which the pearlitic irons are being specified. Ordnance material made of pearlitic malleable iron comprises gun mount parts, pistol parts, gun parts, shell castings, and tank parts. Wrench handles, hammer heads, clamps, shears, snips, and pipe wrenches are some of the tools made of pearlitic malleable, which also is used in highway devices, pipeline couplings, and tractor treads.

VII

SPECIAL MALLEABLE IRONS

THREE TYPES are classified as special malleable irons: (1) high-silicon malleable iron, (2) copper-alloyed malleable iron, (3) copper-molybdenum-alloyed malleable iron, all of which are commercially produced to meet particular requirements. Extra silicon content is employed in high-silicon iron chiefly for the purpose of shortening the necessary annealing time. Copper is used as an alloy in malleable iron to increase resistance to corrosion and to increase ultimate strength and yield point at very slight reduction in elongation. Copper and molybdenum are used in combination as alloys to produce a malleable iron of superior corrosion resistance and mechanical properties. These special irons differ from the pearlitic malleable irons discussed in Chapter VI in that the special irons are completely annealed, deriving their particular characteristics from the effect of the special chemical composition on the ferritic matrix of the casting.

Fig. 1. The "invasion" freight cars built for the United States Army carry standard as well as special malleable iron in many parts. Hand-brake wheels, ratchet wheels, brake shoe heads, and air hose coupling and uncoupling levers are of standard malleable. The buffers at each end of the car are of alloy malleable.

[69]

HIGH-SILICON MALLEABLE IRON

Silicon is not usually regarded as an alloy in ferrous metals such as gray cast iron and malleable iron. Yet in view of the fact that even a moderate change in the percentage of silicon in the melt appreciably affects the properties of the casting, malleable irons containing more than the standard proportion of silicon are regarded as a special type. Though as a result of its composition high-silicon iron is malleableized by a shorter heat-treatment than is used for standard malleable, its physical and mechanical properties in general meet the requirements for Grade 32510, Specification A47-33, American Society for Testing Materials.

COMPOSITION

The chemical composition of high-silicon malleable iron is summarized as follows:

Carbon	2.00 to 2.50 per cent
Silicon	2.00 to 1.40 per cent
Manganese	Less than 0.50 per cent
Phosphorus	Less than 0.12 per cent
Sulphur	Less than 0.10 per cent

A general rule governing the composition of high-silicon malleable iron is that the total percentage of carbon and silicon shall be about 3.90.[46] For example, if the carbon is on the low side — say 2.10 per cent, a silicon percentage of 1.80 can be tolerated without graphitization on solidification in medium sections. On the other hand, an iron with a moderately high carbon content of 2.50 per cent would probably not tolerate more than 1.40 per cent silicon without graphitizing on solidification.

Fig. 2. A close-up view of the alloy malleable buffer for invasion freight cars.

MANUFACTURE

Naturally, the relatively high percentage of silicon gives this iron a much greater tendency toward the formation of primary graphite — graphitization at the time of casting, before heat-treatment — than is found in standard malleable iron. To counteract this tendency, raw materials with a relatively low carbon content are used, and pouring temperatures and cooling rates are carefully controlled. Since the tendency toward primary graphite is influenced by the section of the casting, each foundry in determining the proportions of its charge is

Fig. 3. The buffer stem, buffer lock key, and buffer housing of the invasion freight car, all of alloy malleable iron.

guided by the type of casting to be produced. When it is poured hot and cooled rapidly, such iron is usually free from primary graphite in a bar one inch square.[46]

PROPERTIES

The properties of high-silicon malleable iron closely approximate those of standard malleable of Grade 32510. The particular advantage of high-silicon iron is that it may be annealed in a relatively short time. Some plants regularly use a 15-hour cycle for complete malleabilization.

COPPER-ALLOYED MALLEABLE IRON [51]

Copper in small percentages — 0.25 to 0.50 per cent — is added to standard malleable iron to increase its resistance to corrosion, and in such small amounts has no appreciable effect on the mechanical properties of the casting. In larger amounts, the alloy raises the ultimate strength and yield point of the iron, reducing elongation only slightly. Since copper aids graphitization, it is advisable that the silicon content of the melt be dropped 0.10 per cent for every 1 per cent of copper added,[52] to avoid the formation of primary graphite.

The influence of copper is greater on irons with greater carbon content, but in general copper in amounts of about 1.25 per cent produces in standard malleable iron an ultimate strength of 52,000 to 60,000 pounds per square inch and a yield point of 38,000 to 45,000 p.s.i., and increases the endurance limit. An increase in Brinell hardness number is noted after additions of copper and is due to the copper's dissolving in, and strengthening, the ferrite of the malleable iron. Copper improves the resistance of malleable iron to atmospheric corrosion, especially that produced by atmospheres containing sulphurous gases. The resistance of malleable iron to acid electrolytic corro-

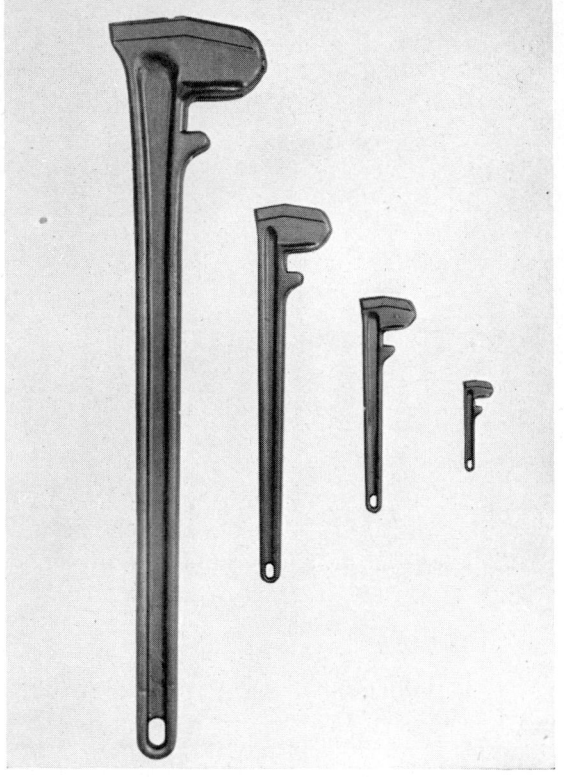

Fig. 4. Illustrated are four of ten sizes, ranging from 60 to six inches, of alloy pipe wrench handle castings.

sion is raised by copper in amounts up to 0.75 per cent.

The strength properties of malleable iron containing 0.75 per cent or more copper can be further increased by a precipitation-hardening treatment. When copper-bearing malleable iron is reheated to 1300 to 1375 degrees Fahrenheit for one hour, then air cooled and tempered at 940 degrees F. for three to five hours, the copper is precipitated out as submicroscopic particles. Yield point and ultimate strength both rise, often 10,000 to 15,000 p.s.i., but elongation falls. The resistance of the metal to overstress is also improved by this treatment.

COPPER-MOLYBDENUM-ALLOYED MALLEABLE IRON

Some foundries regularly alloy malleable iron with copper and molybdenum together in the production of castings of extra high strength and high

Fig. 5. A flask clamp and a gear blank of special malleable iron.

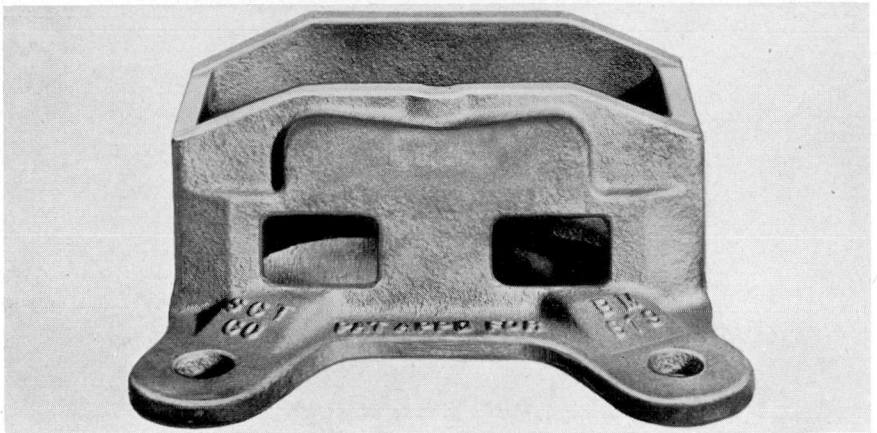

Fig. 6. This roller retainer for a railroad car side bearing is of special malleable iron.

elongation for highly stressed parts. The machinability of this high-strength malleable iron is approximately the same as that of Grade 35018 standard malleable; the manufacturing processes parallel those for the production of standard malleable. The tensile properties of copper-molybdenum-alloyed malleable iron are as follows:

Brinell hardness number..................	135–155
Ultimate strength (p.s.i.).................	58,000–65,000
Yield point (p.s.i.).......................	40,000–45,000
Elongation (per cent in 2 in.).............	15–20

EFFECT OF ALLOYS

Though copper and molybdenum are the alloys principally in use in the manufacture of special malleable irons, the effect of some 20 alloying elements on malleable iron has been studied. Alloys are customarily divided into two classes, graphitizers and retarders, depending upon their effect on graphitization, which may be summarized as follows:

RETARDERS [11, 47, 48, 49]

Slight: Cerium or lanthanum in the presence of sulphur; selenium; tellurium in minute quantities.

Moderate: Molybdenum, tungsten, manganese.

Strong: Boron above 0.10 per cent, vanadium, sulphur, chromium, tin, zinc.

GRAPHITIZERS [11, 50]

Slight: Antimony, cobalt, copper, phosphorus, uranium, zirconium.

Moderate: Boron up to 0.10 per cent, nickel, calcium.

Strong: Aluminum, silicon, titanium, traces of boron.

Some alloys affect the graphitization when the molten metal is cast; others have more effect in the annealing operation. Several patented com-

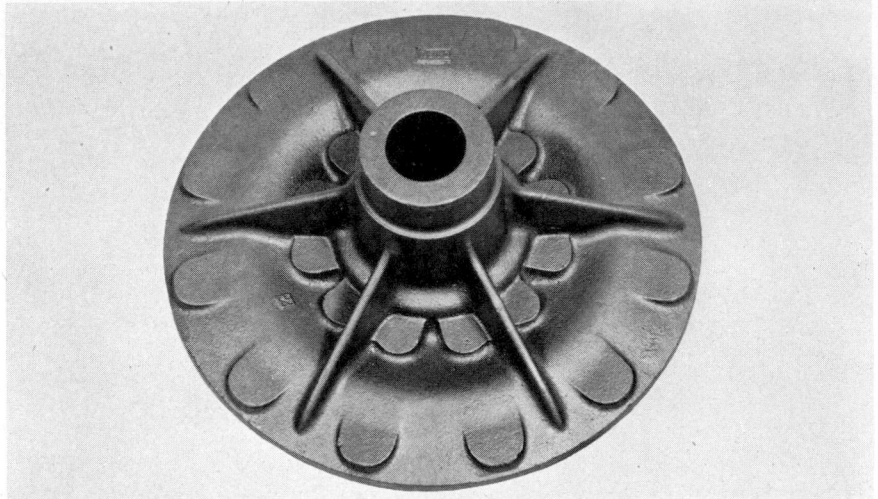

Fig. 7. An alloy malleable differential case casting for a heavy duty truck.

binations of alloys take advantage of this fact by incorporating a retarder to make the iron solidify without primary graphite and a graphitizer to make it anneal more quickly. A bibliography of articles on the effect of alloys on malleable iron is given in Appendix III.

VIII

CUPOLA MALLEABLE IRON

CUPOLA malleable iron is made much as gray iron is, being melted in the cupola and taken directly to the mold. It differs from gray iron in chemical composition and in properties, and from standard malleable iron in chemical composition, in properties,[2] and in the method followed in its manufacture. A cupola necessitates only a low installation cost, produces a quick melt, has higher thermal efficiency than the air furnace, and permits continuous operation,[94] but its product is not so high in strength and elongation as standard malleable iron. In the cupola, the metal is not refined after the initial melt, while equipment used in producing standard malleable iron provides for refining.

COMPOSITION

In general, the raw materials used in the cupola are the same as those used in the air furnace, but the proportions followed in making up the charges are different. The chemical composition of white iron suitable for conversion into cupola malleable iron is as follows:

Carbon............................ 2.80 to 3.30 per cent
Silicon............................ 1.10 to 0.60 per cent
Manganese........................ 0.40 to 0.65 per cent
Phosphorus....................... Less than 0.20 per cent
Sulphur.......................... Less than 0.25 per cent

Cupola malleable iron is characterized by its inherently high carbon content, but a carbon content on the lower side of the cupola malleable range can be obtained by skillful operation during the melting cycle. The high carbon results from direct contact with the fuel, plus the fact that in a cupola the melt cannot be held for refinement before it is poured. As another consequence of the contact with fuel, there is a sulphur pick-up, the amount depending on the fuel. This pick-up can be counteracted by maintenance of a suitable manganese balance and, if necessary, by partial desulphurization just before pouring.

MANUFACTURE

The melting procedure, including the charge, the melt, and possibly refinement in the ladle, is controlled through the checking of samples at frequent intervals throughout the melting period, special attention being given to maintaining a proper balance between the carbon and silicon contents. It is general practice to shake malleable castings from the sand soon after they are poured; it is especially important to do so with cupola malleable castings at the earliest possible moment in order to avoid the formation of primary graphite.

ANNEALING

Annealing practice, except for time, is essentially the same for cupola malleable iron as it is for the standard types. The cupola product graphitizes slowly because of its low silicon content, and consequently the annealing time must be lengthened up to and during the maximum temperature range of 1600–1700 degrees Fahrenheit to allow for complete first-stage graphitization. Likewise the cycle is lengthened through the secondary phase, with a reduced rate of decreasing temperatures below 1400 degrees F. while the castings are passing through the lower critical range.

PHYSICAL PROPERTIES

Since the fluidity of white iron increases as the carbon content is raised, cupola malleable may be used advantageously in castings with very light sections. The average specific gravity of cupola malleable is about 7.15 as compared with 7.32 for standard malleable, and the shrinkage is about one-eighth inch per foot in comparison with slightly less than $\frac{3}{16}$ inch per foot for standard.

MECHANICAL PROPERTIES

The modulus of elasticity in tension for cupola malleable iron is from 22,500,000 to 23,800,000 pounds per square inch. Brinell hardness number ranges from 100 to 120. Izod impact value is from 7 to 9 foot-pounds; Charpy impact value, 4 to 6. The tensile properties of cupola malleable iron are:

TABLE 1. TENSILE PROPERTIES OF CUPOLA MALLEABLE IRON

	Minimum (A.S.T.M. Specification)	Most Probable Value
Ultimate strength (p.s.i.)	40,000	47,000
Yield point (p.s.i.)	30,000	31,000
Elongation (per cent in 2 in.)	5	6

Fig. 1. Cupola malleable iron fittings and valve parts.

The machinability of this type of iron is very good. It is free-cutting because of its high carbon content and other physical characteristics.

As all malleable iron reaches the critical point in the range of 1350 to 1400 degrees F., special consideration must be given to applications where high temperatures are met. Above the critical point, the temper carbon in malleable iron is redissolved and the properties of the metal are completely changed. Iron of this type, therefore, should never be used above the range of 1200 to 1300 degrees F. At 1200 degrees F. the tensile value is about one-third that at room temperature, but it increases rapidly as the temperature drops, and is up to normal at 600 degrees F.

Studies of the creep of cupola malleable iron show that at 800 degrees F. it has two-thirds the creep strength of silicon-killed carbon steel, with a minimum tensile strength of 70,000 p.s.i., and unless that temperature is exceeded no creep occurs at stresses in the order of those generally considered in design. On this basis a figure of 5600 p.s.i. at 775 degrees F. is considered a satisfactory allowable working stress for specification grade cupola malleable iron.

USES

Certain factors favor the use of cupola malleable iron in spite of its relatively low strength values. It is employed in large-volume or low-cost

Fig. 2. Cupola malleable iron pipe fittings with heat-dissipating handles on valves.

products which are of a type requiring metal of mechanical properties superior to those afforded by the regular grade of gray cast iron. This field includes items which will not be subjected to severe service or which are not intended to withstand more than a limited amount of distortion. Although by far its greatest use is in the pipe fittings industry, certain classes of parts for toys, and some types of building hardware and small tools are made of cupola iron. In the manufacture of repetition products of this character, especially those which run into considerable quantities, the factors favoring the cupola process are the rapid and continuous melting schedule which is obtainable and the small amount of floor space needed.

Mechanical test values place limitations on the use of cupola-type iron, and where high strength, ductility, and impact resistance are desired the standard malleable grades are the preferable ones to use. A typical example of this selection appears in the "Marine Engineering Regulations and Material Specifications" issued by the United States Coast Guard to govern the purchase of material for use on United States merchant-type ships. These regulations allow specification grade cupola iron to be used in castings which will be exposed to steam pressures not in excess of 125 p.s.i. Above this and up to 250 p.s.i. high strength air-furnace metal — standard malleable iron — is required. Cupola malleable iron can be galvanized satisfactorily by the hot-dip process, can be electroplated, or can be coated with the various finishes commonly used on commercial castings as described in Chapter V.

IX

MALLEABLE CASTING DESIGN

GOOD design is essential to produce castings which make full use of the adaptability and dependability of malleable iron, are economical to manufacture, and will perform most satisfactorily under service requirements. Close co-operation between the engineer and the foundryman is fundamental. By consultation between them while the work is in the formative stages, design can often be simplified, casting difficulties can be avoided, production costs can be reduced.

The fact must be recognized that design restrictions or other requirements may often dictate the shape of critical pieces or critical sections. In cases of this sort, the engineer has little choice of how he may construct the casting, what clearances he may use, how strengthening ribs may be arranged, and so on. But since one of the greatest advantages of malleable iron is its comparative freedom from design restrictions, the engineer in co-operation with the foundryman generally can arrange even a very complex piece for satisfactory production.

True for malleable iron castings as well as for most other products is the general principle that pleasing appearance is basic to good design. If a piece appeals to the eye, it has an excellent start. Of equal significance, however, are several specific principles which apply directly to design in malleable iron. These may be summarized thus:

1. Provide ample fillets.
2. Seek uniformity of section.
3. Taper gradually at junction of unequal sections.
4. Keep plates in tension, ribs in compression.
5. Provide ample section for gating and feeding.
6. Eliminate cores when possible.
7. Allow sufficient pattern draft.

Since most engineers and designers have many times heard foundrymen say, "Use generous fillets; avoid sharp corners; keep the section as uniform as possible," these principles may seem nothing new. And they are not new. Rather, they are mainly warnings against overdesigning, or warnings that, for good results, metal must be properly distributed. Proper distribution means that low-stressed sections will not be unnecessarily built up and that high-stressed sections will by the provision of ribs or some other form of strengthening be insured against failure. Detailed discussion of the principles will show that, although familiar, they cannot merely be taken for granted.

FILLETS

Fillets calculated to avoid sharp corners are by far the most important consideration in malleable casting design, and being generous with them usually pays dividends. An excellent over-all rule is never to use a fillet radius less than the thickness of the section being poured, and if unequal sections are being joined, to make the fillet radius at least equal to the average of the thickness of the sections.

Sharp inside corners are to be avoided because they tend to develop weaknesses. For example, a competent design engineer would at once reject a design for a shaft, whether cast or machined, if it called for sharp corners at the junctions of different sections, and he would reject it even though the shaft was to be only moderately stressed. Rejection would be caused by his knowledge that unless the sections of the shaft were blended by generous fillets, failures would probably occur because of tears starting in the sharp corners and eventually progressing through the entire shaft. Even a small scratch or notch will often cause such a failure. The same reasoning should rule with malleable iron castings, which are often highly stressed: Design them only as you would design a shaft.

The basic reason for filleting is the fact that a casting cools at right angles to the surface and a stress therefore is developed in any sharp inside corner during cooling, as is illustrated in Fig. 1. If the stress exceeds the strength of the material — as it easily may since the metal is weak immediately after solidification — a heat check or hot tear may form. Very often such flaws are small and unnoticeable, and frequently they are not harmful. But since the tendency for them to form is present in any sharp inside corner, better design is accomplished when they are prevented through the use of a proper fillet. Figure 2 illustrates how the stress line is thus avoided. The cooling being perpendicular to the surface, there is no spot for concentration of stress.

SECTIONS AND TAPER

Absolutely uniform section naturally cannot be maintained throughout any but an extremely simple casting. Hence in practice the rule "Seek uniformity of section" is expressed in two principles:

1. Keep the metal section as uniform as practicable.
2. In going from one thickness of metal to another, do so as gradually as possible.

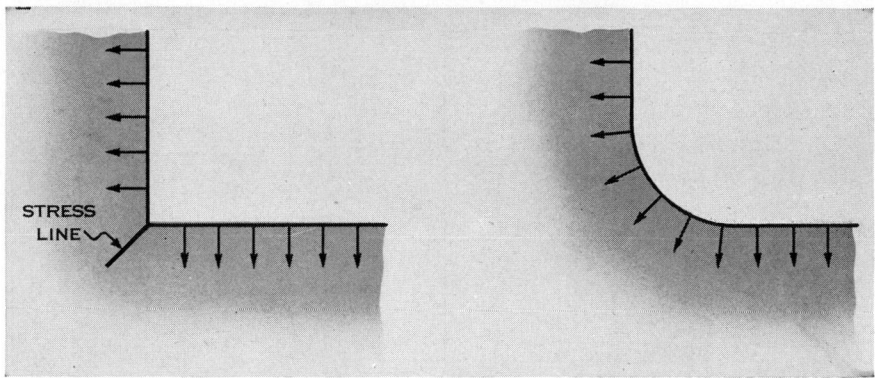

STRESS
LINE

Fig. 1. Diagram showing schematically how stress develops in a corner as a casting cools.

Fig. 2. Diagram showing schematically how proper filleting insures against stress concentration in a corner.

The logic underlying these principles of blending or tapering is based on what happens in a mold that has been filled with any molten metal. Wherever the liquid mass is in contact with the sand surface of the mold, a solid layer forms. As the liquid cools, the layer grows thicker, solidification progressing inward toward the center of the mass at about the same rate — regardless of whether the piece is thick or thin — until the entire mass is solid. Hence of two unequal joining sections, the thinner will solidify in a fraction of the time required for the thicker to do so. Such differences in mass and consequently in solidification time would not cause any problem except for the fact that malleable iron like all other ferrous metals contracts or shrinks in size during the cooling period immediately following solidification.

Because the solidification rate is virtually the same regardless of thickness of the casting, the thinner section will have solidified completely and will be in the process of cooling and therefore contracting while the massive section is still solidifying. A drawing action will result where the thin and thick sections join, and will set up stresses that seek out the weakest spot in the piece, in all probability the spot where the contrasting sections meet. If the stress thus set up is greater than the low strength of the material immediately after solidification, a crack or tear will result. Obviously, the logical way to bridge this weak joining section is to blend from the thick section down to the thin section as gradually as is practicable. This tapering distributes the stresses and disperses their concentration, thereby removing the tendency toward cracking. The outlines shown in Fig. 7, page 84, can be used as a guide when a design requires section changes.

The working application of these principles is embodied in Figs. 3, 4, 5, and 6, on the two following pages. These charts show recommended fillet sizes as well as suggested design practice to be followed when sections of dif-

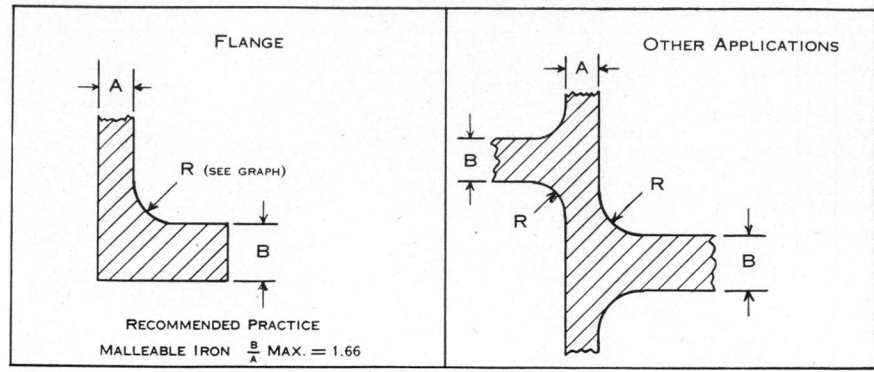

Fig. 3. Recommended filleting procedure
when the flange B is not more than 1.66
times as thick as the supporting wall A.

Fig. 4. Recommended filleting procedure for
joining walls approximately at right angles
to each other.

ferent thickness must be joined. Figure 3 shows a procedure advisable when
a flange B is not more than 1.66 times as thick as its supporting wall A. The
value of R is obtained from the graph in Fig. 6.

Figure 4 illustrates the corresponding procedure to be followed in joining
walls approximately at right angles to each other. The walls shown are of
usual thickness. For the construction indicated in Fig. 4 to be practicable,
B should not exceed 1.66 times A. Values of R are again obtained from the
graph, Fig. 6.

When B is more than 1.66 times as great as A, a bevel or taper design,
such as that illustrated in Fig. 5, should be used, since it permits proper
blending of sections. The value of R for this application is also determined
from Fig. 6.

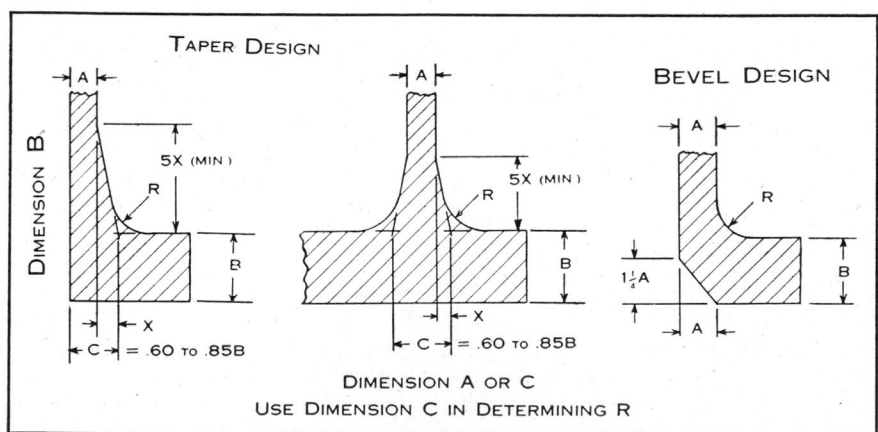

Fig. 5. Recommended filleting procedure when the flange B is more than 1.66 times as great as
the supporting wall A.

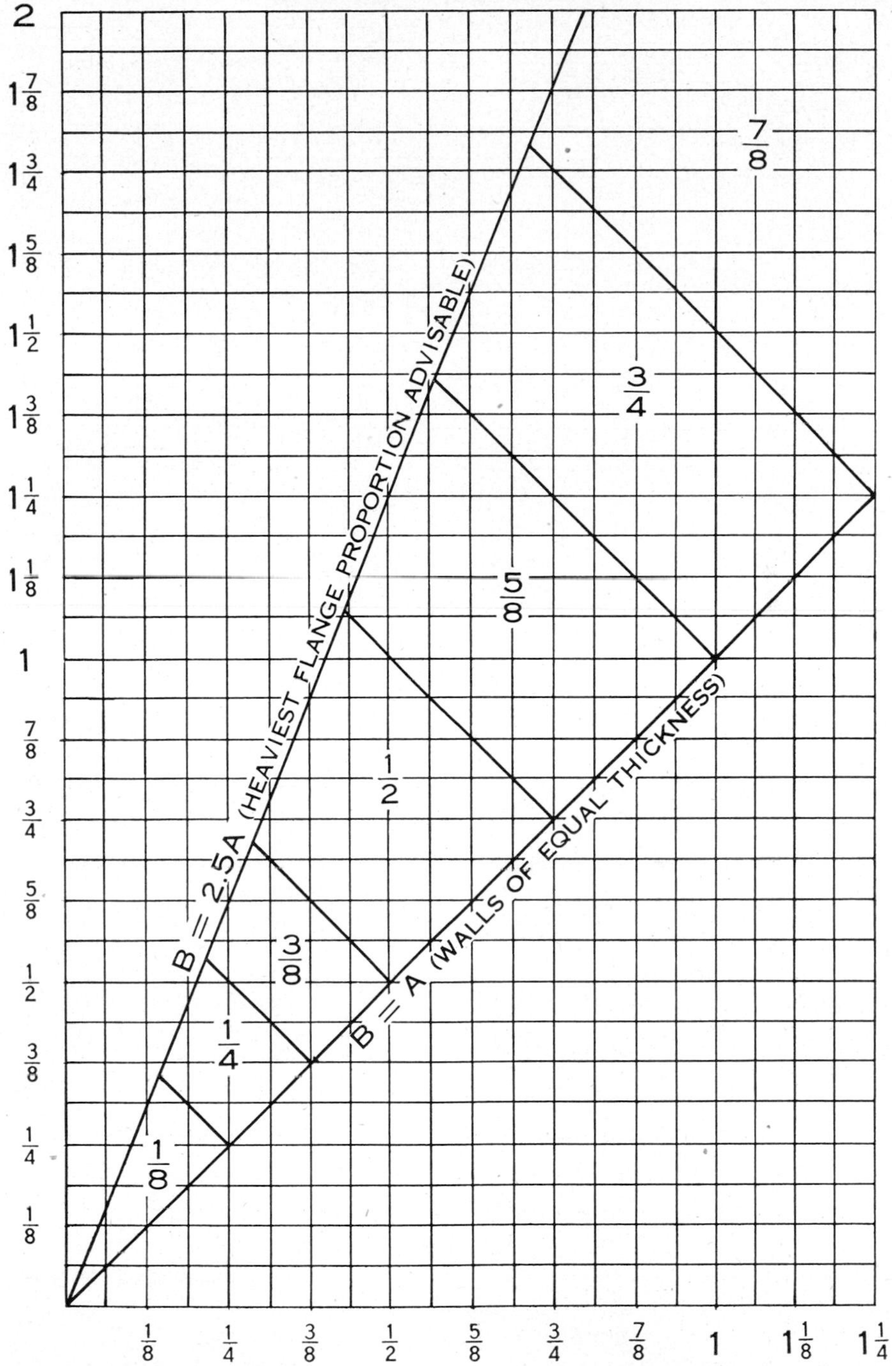

Fig. 6. Recommended fillet radius to be used in casting design for all joints with walls at right angles to each other and for walls of all usual thicknesses and combinations of thicknesses.

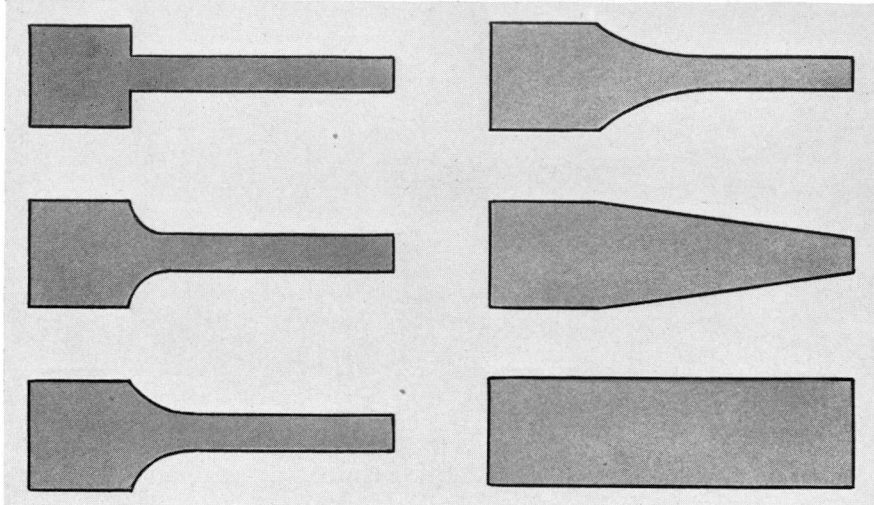

Fig. 7. Tapering to join sections of different thickness in order to prevent concentration of stresses. Left, top, poor design; center, not recommended; bottom, fair design; right, top, good design; center, recommended design; bottom, no change of section, recommended design. In some cases, the taper shown in right center is to be preferred even to unchanged section.

This characteristic of contraction may also be the cause of difficulties when massive sections are involved. As the molten metal in such a section solidifies, the solid layer at the outside of the mass forms a shell, the wall thickness of which increases as additional metal solidifies. The shell tends to hold its shape, and hence to pull molten metal toward the outer walls from the center. The last bit of liquid near the center of the mass may therefore not be of sufficient volume to fill the remaining space, so that when it solidifies a partial void or porous spot will be left in the center of the mass. Such porous spots are avoided by "feeding" — attaching a reservoir of molten metal at the place where trouble may be expected, in order to provide a pressure head which will cause metal to flow into the heavy section to replace that which is drawn out by the outer layer during solidification.

For the reasons which have been suggested above, the combination of a substantial boss surrounded by a thin plate section, often required in malleable iron castings, is likely to present a problem. When such a casting must be designed, consideration should be given to removing the heart of the mass by using a core and thus obtaining a more nearly uniform metal section. The boss can be cored in either of two ways, depending upon the metal section involved and upon the purpose of the finished hole. If bearing throughout the boss is necessary, the coring illustrated in Fig. 8 must of course be used. The coring shown in Fig. 9 is practicable for other designs.

Wheels also illustrate the design principle under discussion here. The rim and hub must usually be heavier in section than the spokes of an open

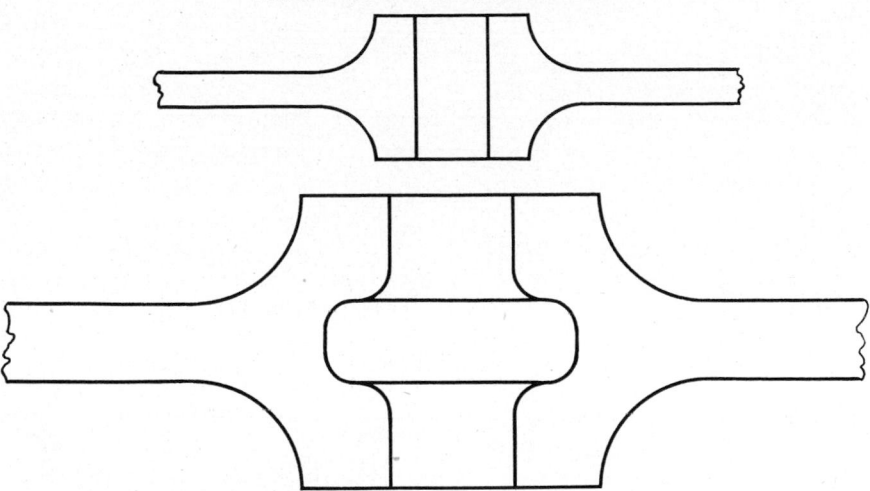

Fig. 8 (upper) and 9. Methods of coring to give substantially uniform metal section when a boss and a thin plate section must be combined.

wheel such as a hand wheel, or than the web in a solid wheel. The necessary difference in masses and consequent difference in cooling rates lead to the establishment of stresses which may cause heat cracks in the spokes or web adjacent to the rim or the hub. If the designer will plan the spokes to be slightly S-shaped and slightly tangential to the hub and will make the design dish-shaped whether it uses spokes or a solid web, the cracking tendency can be minimized. These concessions give the different sections of the wheel enough flexibility to adjust themselves and to withstand the cooling strain without cracking. The use of staggered ribs helps to maintain uniform sections.

PLATES IN TENSION, RIBS IN COMPRESSION

Malleable iron castings in many applications are subject to high stresses in use and to serious shock loads. When designing for such an application, the engineer should bear in mind what may be called the "Plates in tension, ribs in compression" rule. To visualize the necessity for it, consider what happens to a piece with its rib section in tension rather than compression, as shown in Fig. 10.

Assume that the load is variable and pulsating and that at times severe

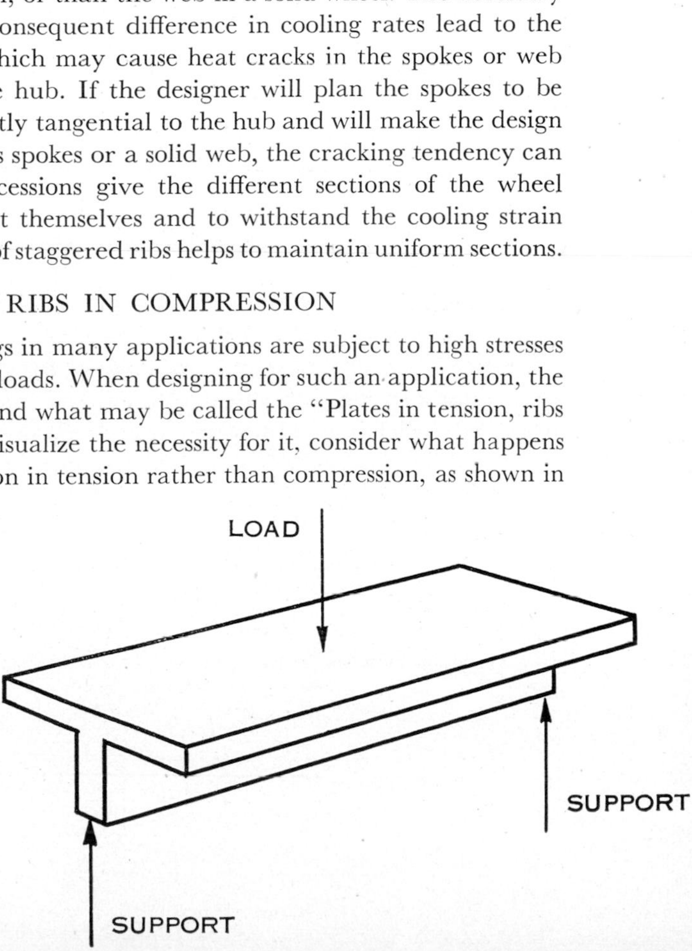

LOAD

Fig. 10. Diagram showing rib section in tension.

SUPPORT

SUPPORT

impact or shock throws extreme stresses into the piece. These stresses will be greatest directly under the load point, at the bottom of the rib, and in the outer structure of the rib. Under extreme shock, when the stress exceeds the strength of the material, the rib is bound to crack or tear open. Though the tear may be very small at first, once it has been started additional shock loads will cause it to progress until the entire piece is torn. Turning the piece upside down, as in Fig. 11, putting the plate in tension and the rib in compression, greatly improves matters. Distributed over the plate, which is many times wider than the rib, the stress does not tend to concentrate in a very narrow metal section, and no tear starts. Though the grains of the metal in the rib are squeezed together, no harm results.

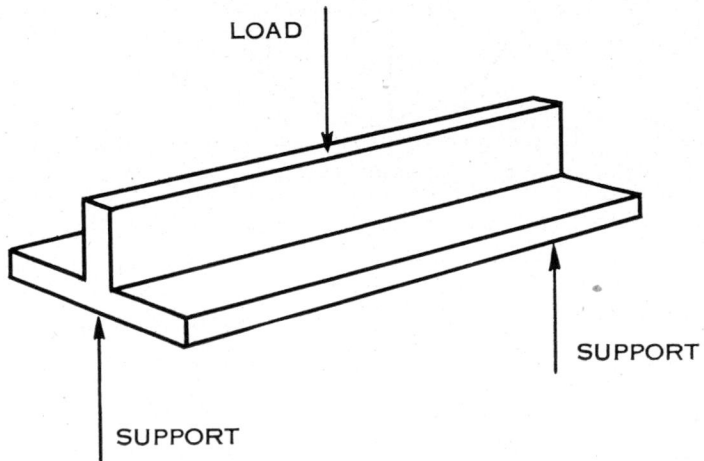

Fig. 11. Diagram showing rib section in compression.

Application of the "Plates in tension, ribs in compression" rule is well illustrated in Fig. 12, showing the original and redesign of an axle clamping plate which fits under a truck axle and by means of U-bolts holds the axle up against a spring. It is subjected to severe stresses in service. The original design, at the left in Fig. 12, was fundamentally a single curved plate, strengthened by four ribs. Redesign was necessitated by failures, all of which were found to start in the ribs, where high tension stresses in the outer fibers under the edges of the axle at the two sides of the casting started small tears that progressed until the strength of the part was gone. Putting the ribs in compression and the plate in tension in the redesign resulted in satisfactory performance. The three weep holes in the redesigned plate were cast in the piece to permit drainage of moisture collecting in the pockets of the casting in service.

In many designs, additional strength can be secured through the addition of a bead to the outside edge of a rib or plate section. Since it increases the stiffness of the edge, the bead is particularly useful when thin sections are

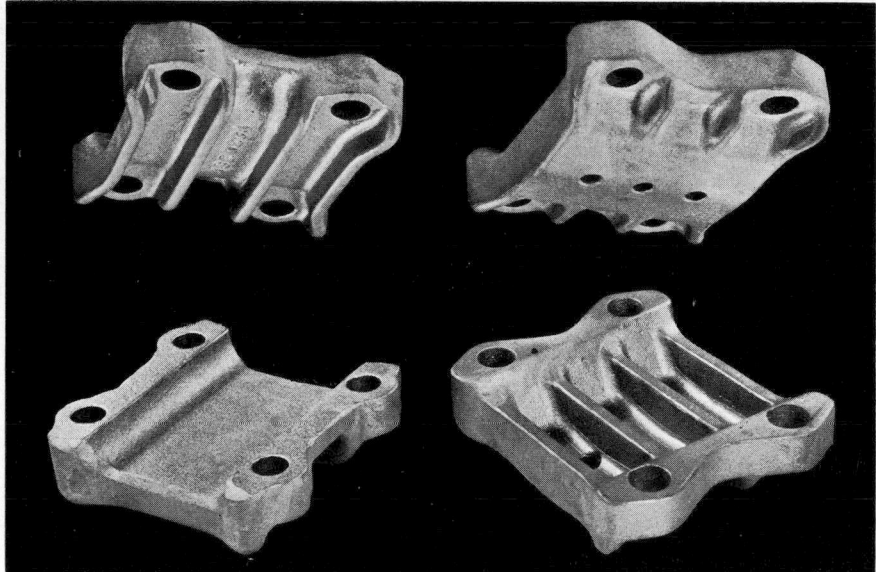

Fig. 12. Upper and lower left, axle clamping plate as originally designed; upper and lower right, redesign.

involved. In planning for beads at edges or around windows in castings, the designer should thoroughly understand that for economical casting production the bead should not interfere with drawing the pattern from the sand. Beads placed at the mold parting line are conveniently handled in the molding, as are those beads which are on the upper or lower pattern surfaces in the mold. If such arrangements cannot be provided, the beads may be made at least partially by a core. The bead should not be too heavy, since too much mass will make feeding of the section necessary. A good rule to follow is to make the over-all thickness at the bead approximately twice that of the section which the bead edges, as in Fig. 13. For example, if the metal section is one-quarter inch thick, a bead one-eighth inch high should be used on each side. Figure 14 shows a malleable iron socket wrench, on which a bead has been added to increase strength, build up stiffness, and improve appearance.

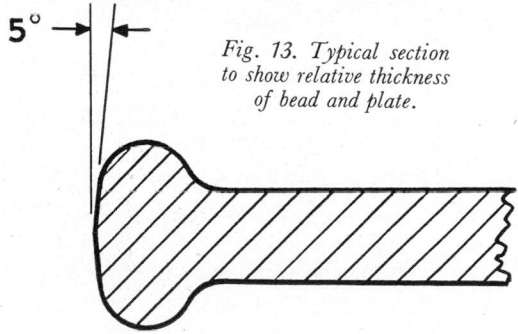

5°

Fig. 13. Typical section to show relative thickness of bead and plate.

GATING

To insure soundness in castings, design at a point on the parting line should provide for a gate of such width and thickness as will permit satisfactory feeding of the metal through all sections. Figure 15 shows

Fig. 14. Malleable iron socket wrench, showing use of bead.

an original and a redesign dealing with this problem. In the original, the thin metal section around the boss was not sufficient for proper gating; in the redesign, the thin section was eliminated to permit gating to be done directly to the boss. Another example of increasing the metal section to assure ample gating area is shown in Fig. 16 where the bosses are extended at their full width to the edge of the casting.

A related gating problem arises in the design of castings having a thin flange surrounding a heavy hub. Since metal must be fed to the hub in such castings, the flange must be thickened at some point or points by a pad or pads extending from the edge to the hub, as in Fig. 17. If possible, the design should permit retention of the pad, for removing it by grinding or machining will increase the cost of the casting. The pad may usually be placed on either face of the flange.

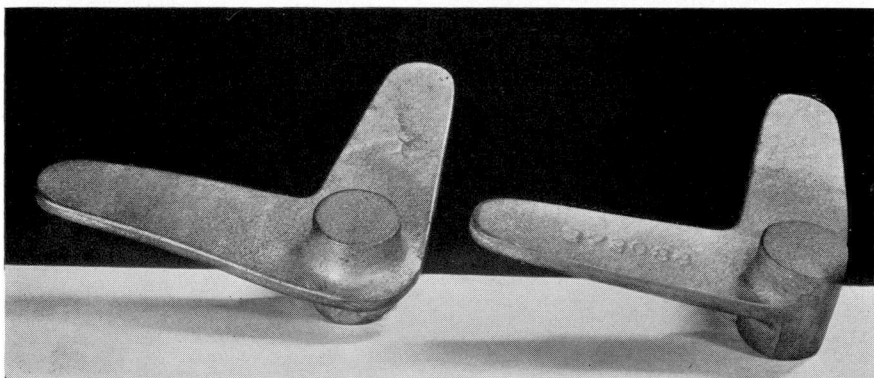

Fig. 15. Original and redesign to provide proper gating area.

Fig. 16. Bosses extended in order to allow sufficient gating area.

Levers of many sizes and types are made of malleable iron, and they offer various special design problems, one of which is illustrated in Fig. 18 on the following page. Here the pinch bolt boss has been filled out slightly, not only to permit better gating but also to simplify grinding. Grinding the gate off this casting to leave a flat finished shape is quicker and cheaper than attempting to obtain a rounded end. In view of the fact that the grinding operation on a small lever is often the most expensive single operation in the manufacture of the piece, design of the kind shown in Fig. 18 has distinct advantages.

CORES

Avoiding the use of cores as far as he can, the designer will reduce the cost and improve the appearance of castings. Cores used to cut down the mass of a section, of course, are justified and often necessary. In considering designs involving cores other than these, however, the designer should visualize how the foundry will make the part. He may then find that a slight change in design will eliminate cores. A simple pan-shaped casting having an internal

Fig. 17. These flanges show built-up gating pads to assure ample supply of metal to the hub. The gate on the flange shown at the right has been ground.

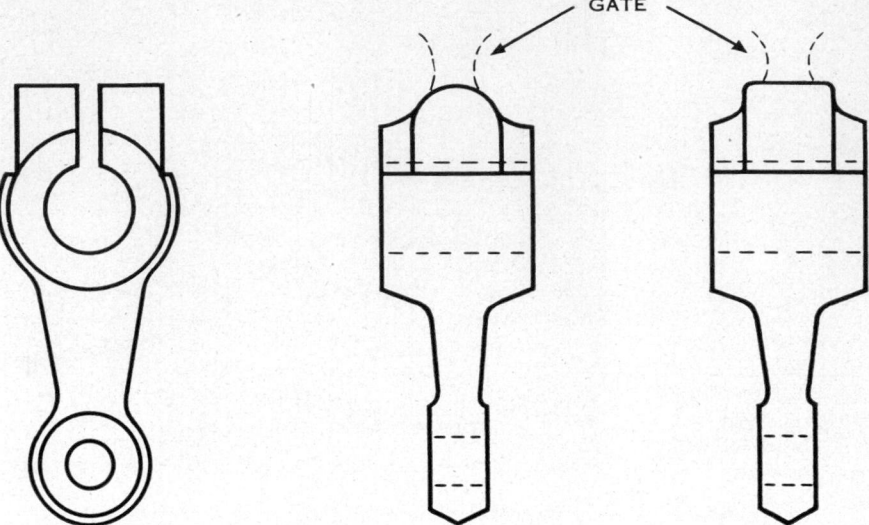

Fig. 18. Lever, showing preferred design for gate removal at the right.

flange, as shown in Fig. 19, calls for the use of a core, with consequent increase in cost, loss in accuracy, and poorer inside appearance. Redesigned as in Fig. 20, the casting has the flange on the outside and can therefore be made entirely in green sand.

The raised pads or bosses required for lubrication holes in many castings offer opportunity to eliminate cores. If the bosses will interfere with the drawing of the pattern from the sand, metal should be added underneath them to

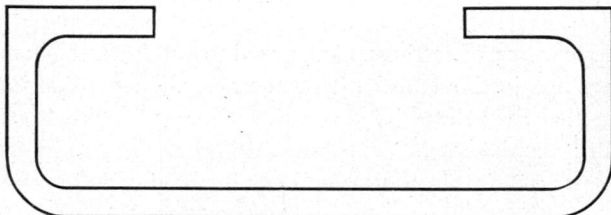

Fig. 19. Casting with internal flange requiring the use of a core.

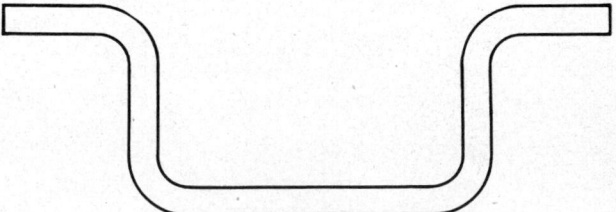

Fig. 20. Casting redesigned, moving flange to outside, to eliminate core.

Fig. 21. Gun cradle casting as originally designed, requiring two side cores.

remove this objection. Figures 21 and 22 illustrate this fact, and show as well how the appearance of a casting is improved by the elimination of cores. The original design (Fig. 21) required two side cores, one at each side of the center cylindrical section. Because of the design, these cores leave sharp corners where the cylindrical section joins the mounting ears of the casting. Corners such as these are weak and especially liable to cracking or tearing under shock or impact loads. As redesigned (Fig. 22) the casting is made without the side cores, providing metal walls tangent to the cylindrical section which join it to the ears by which it is to be mounted and also permit the addition of metal between the lubrication boss and the plate section.

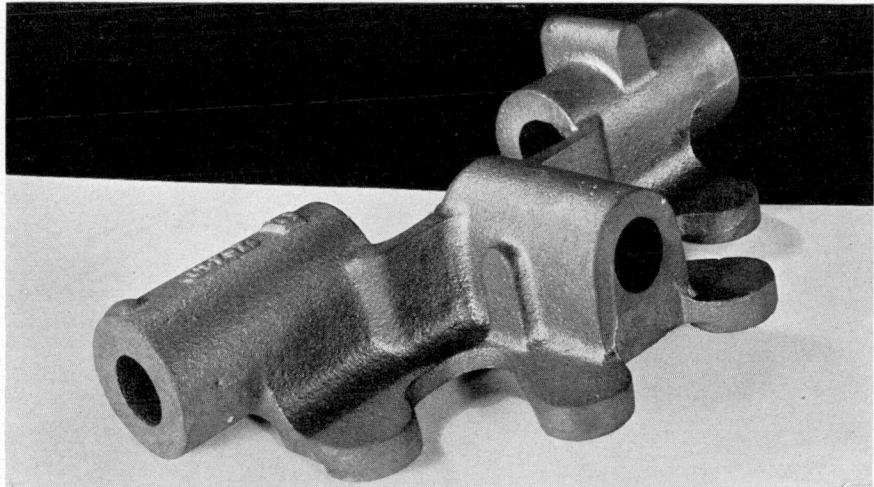

Fig. 22. Gun cradle casting redesigned to eliminate cores.

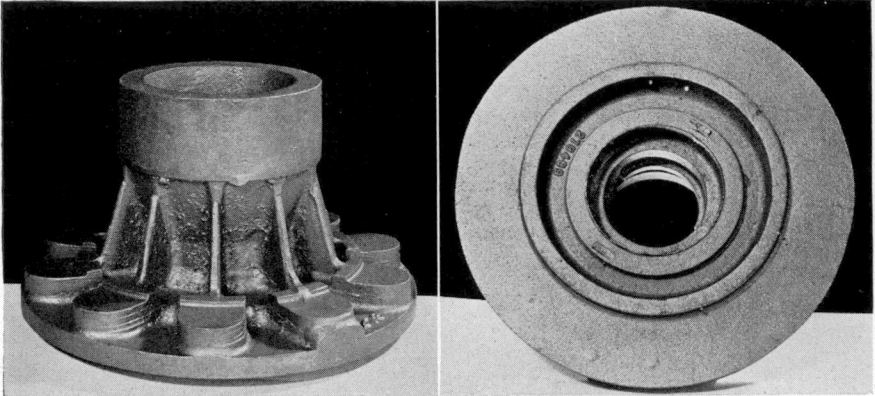

Fig. 23. Wheel hub casting as originally designed.

Frequently, cores must be used in the design of a casting because the piece cannot be so shaped as to avoid them. The designer then should make one core do just as much work as possible. Wheel hub designs are of this type; since they require a center core, they should be so designed that the center core alone is enough. Figures 23 and 24 illustrate the point. In Fig. 23, both an inside and an outside core are required. The redesign in Fig. 24 requires only the inside core. Another advantage of the redesign is that it brings the plate on the outside. The ribs cast inside are therefore in compression and provide stiffness and strength to withstand the severe shock loads to which a wheel hub is subject. In the redesign, the unavoidable center core has been made to do its full job, including both the bearing seats and the strengthening ribs, and, in addition, the "Plates in tension, ribs in compression" rule has been followed, with consequent gain in the dependability of the casting.

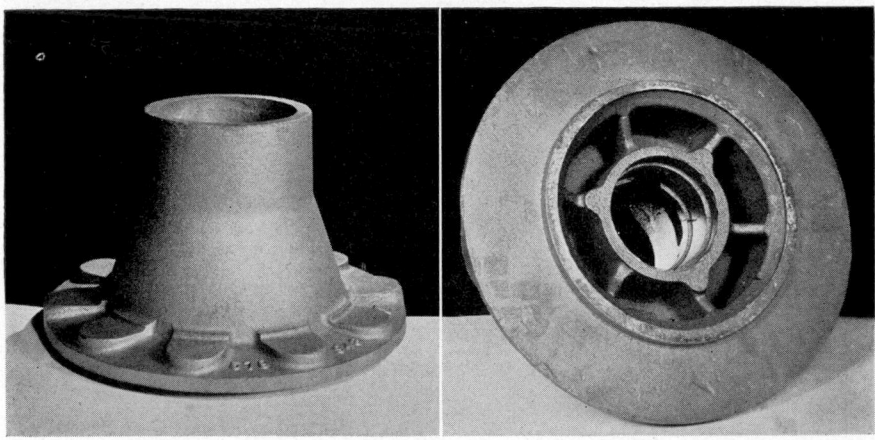

Fig. 24. Wheel hub casting as redesigned.

Fig. 25. Use of slots to provide anchorage for core.

Naturally, when a core must be used, the design must provide proper anchorage, for the core cannot be permitted to move in any direction. Figure 25 shows the use of slots or windows to anchor the core.

For the many cases when the designer must make a choice between coring a hole or casting the piece solid, several factors can aid his decision, but they should be regarded as designing guides only, for they will not apply in exceptional cases. They may be summarized as follows:

The hole should be cast in the piece:

1. When machining time will be saved. It is usually quicker and consequently cheaper to machine a cored hole, because less material is to be removed. A drill will follow a cored hole. If subsequent machining operations are to be located from the finished hole, accuracy in machining the hole should be secured through piloting the drill with a jig, or through boring.

2. When it would not be possible to machine the hole because of its location or shape, and the accuracy of the cored hole satisfies the requirements of the design.

3. When the hole can be cast with sufficient accuracy and machining can be eliminated or reduced.

4. When it will be impractical to make the casting without it.

5. When the section will be made more uniform and at the same time the design will not be adversely affected.

6. When a massive section is so located that it cannot be fed and it is surrounded by a thin section.

The hole should not be cast in the piece:

1. When it will interfere with machining operations.

2. When several holes are required which can be gang-drilled, punched, or put in the piece more accurately or more economically from the solid.

3. When several holes are required which must be in accurate relation to each other.

4. When it will be more practical to make the casting solid.

5. When the hole is too small for foundry production.

6. When the hole is of such a size or in such a location that cleaning it is impracticable.

If the diameter of the hole is equal to or greater than its depth, and if sufficient draft is permitted, the hole can be made in green sand. Otherwise a dry-sand core should be used.

Holes can be made in malleable iron castings by punching or drilling, as well as by coring. Punching a hole through a section has some limitations and is not recommended when the thickness of the metal to be punched is greater than the diameter of the hole. Since malleable iron is ductile, holes may be sized by a drift forced through a cored hole. The drift, which expands the hole slightly and leaves the surface fairly smooth, is usually about .005 inch greater in diameter than the cored hole.

PATTERN DRAFT

A liberal allowance of pattern draft is of great assistance to the foundry in making a casting; the designing engineer therefore should plan on it. The standard advisable for production patterns is $\frac{1}{64}$ inch per inch, this being less than one degree as compared with seven degrees for forgings. Approximately one-quarter inch per foot should be allowed for loose patterns with a deep draw. At all events, the specification should be clear: If a minimum of taper is required, it should be specified; when a reasonable draft can be permitted, it should be noted. Figure 26 illustrates the reasonable minimum. Liberal draft produces the smoothest casting surface.

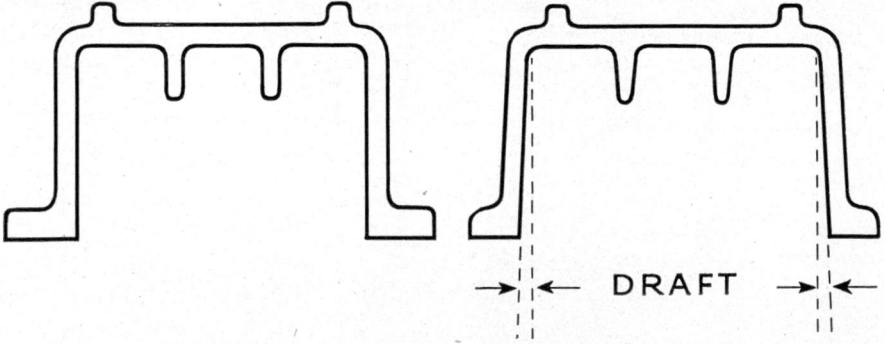

Fig. 26. Recommended minimum of pattern draft is shown at the right. Note that all verticals in the undesirable pattern at the left have been given draft allowance in the drawing at the right.

ACCURACY IN CASTINGS

In considering the degree of accuracy obtainable in malleable iron castings, the designer must realize the possibility of some misalignment between the top and the bottom half of a mold. Though many precautions are taken to keep these discrepancies to a minimum, they cannot be entirely avoided. Hence if the relationship of certain casting surfaces is particularly important, the designer should try to plan the pattern so that the foundry can make all these critical surfaces in the same part of the mold. Their relation to each other will then be more accurate. Surfaces approximately parallel to the parting plane will be the most accurate.

When it is necessary to use a core, a similar condition arises, since the location of the core in the mold is subject to some variation. A core print must be slightly larger than the core used with it, for otherwise the core would not fit into the core print impression. Though with accurate pattern equipment and sound foundry practice the variation will be small, the relationship between the two surfaces will not be so accurate as that between two made in green sand. Likewise, the use of cores usually leaves a mark on the casting at the junction line where the cored surface blends into the molded sand surface. Machining or finishing operations obviously should never be located from these spots.

When extreme accuracy is necessary, malleable iron castings are furnished die-straightened, the straightening being done either by means of a press or by means of a drop hammer. Highly satisfactory results can be obtained by either method when the quantity in production justifies the cost of the necessary dies. The straightening can be carried beyond the point of merely assuring uniformity for jigging or chucking, to actually coining the casting to finish dimensions.

FINISH ALLOWANCES

The type of finishing operation to be used on a casting determines the finish allowance which must be incorporated into the design. Since malleable iron machines more easily than most other ferrous metals, it is advisable for the designer to be generous with the finish allowances he makes. The following are recommended for castings that are not press-straightened:

For milling: $1/16$–$3/32$ inch for small castings
$1/8$–$3/16$ inch for medium castings and more for larger castings

For reaming: $3/32$ inch on the diameter for cored holes under 1 inch
$1/8$–$3/16$ inch on the diameter for medium holes and more for larger holes

For castings which are press-straightened, allowances may be considerably less than those listed. In turning or boring diameters larger than five inches, it is well to allow one-quarter to three-eighths inch on the diameter. If locating points are a considerable distance from the machined surface, additional allowance should be made.

How the castings are to be jigged or chucked is of importance when the amount of finish allowance is being established. The foundry should be given this information. Jigs should never be located from a point where a gate or feeding head has been ground off, and preferably should not be located at the parting line. If the producing foundry is given the proposed machining setup, it can recommend the most practical amount of finish on all machined surfaces. By all means, the drawings should show what surfaces will be machined, for this fact will govern the design of the pattern equipment.

SIMPLIFICATION

Because of its fluidity, malleable iron can be cast in complicated sections, so that intricate castings incorporating numerous flanges and different types of section are readily made of it. Occasionally, however, complication can be carried so far as to affect the cost of the casting. Then it is advantageous to redesign the piece in several simpler components for later assembly by riveting or bolting.

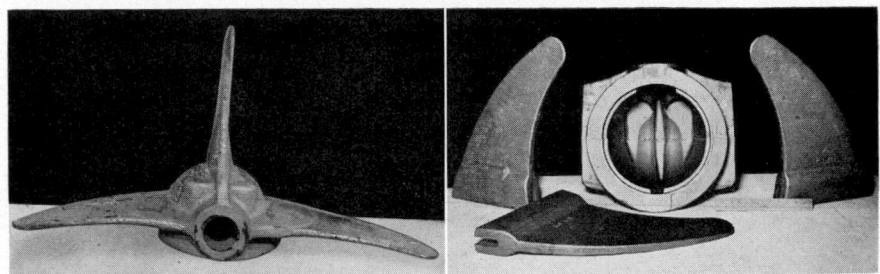

Fig. 27. On the left, a large complicated casting five feet in horizontal dimension, as it was originally designed. On the right, the casting redesigned in four simple components.

The casting shown in Fig. 27 illustrates this kind of simplification in design. It was first designed in one piece, weighing approximately 350 pounds, requiring a large flask, and because of its size being difficult to handle and pack in annealing. Daily production hence was limited and insufficient for the demand. Redesigned into four separate components — the bowl or gear carrier and three wing castings — it was produced at a higher rate and a lower cost.

THICKNESS OF SECTION

Malleable iron is being cast in sections from $\frac{1}{16}$ inch or even less to two inches or more. As a general rule, it will be found that a metal thickness of $\frac{3}{16}$ or one-quarter inch with strengthening ribs well designed and properly located is extremely practical in work with malleable iron. The majority

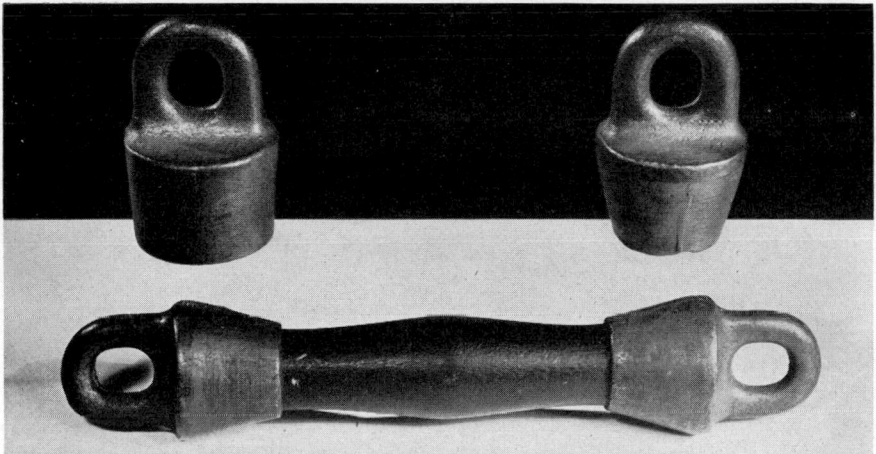

An electrical transmission line strain clamp with malleable iron caps crimped over a headed wood insert. At the left, the cap as cast; at the right, the cap as formed in the crimping operation. The high ductility of malleable iron is demonstrated in this application.

of small castings may well be made in this general dimension. For castings of medium size, section of one-half to three-quarters inch is likewise very practical. The thinness of section that can effectively be cast in malleable iron depends on the design of the part itself and on the type of pattern equipment that will be made available. Quality patterns are vitally important on thin-section intricate castings. Castings of this sort, if possible, should be made without cores. When extremely thin sections are used it is most important that the sections be kept uniform, for there is little opportunity to feed a heavy boss through a thin section.

In designing large flat plates, the engineer should bear in mind that the mass of sand at the top half of the mold tends to sag. This fact will affect the minimum practical thickness of the plate. A plate eight inches square can be $3/16$ inch thick, but in a larger plate the thickness must be increased.

In the design of an ear or lug for bolting or riveting a malleable iron casting to another part, recommended policy is to have the radius of the ear at least equal to the diameter of the bolt-hole. For example, if a $9/16$ inch hole is required, for a one-half inch bolt, the radius of the outside of the lug should be at least $9/16$ inch. A radius of five-eighths or even $11/16$ inch would be preferable.

Sections should be of ample thickness to allow the metal to flow freely to all parts of the casting without chilling and preventing an area from filling up completely. Failure to fill is referred to as a "misrun." If there is a core at the opposite side of a casting from the gate, there must be ample metal section around the core so that the metal will fill the mold properly. If the section is so thin that the metal becomes unduly chilled and does not fuse, an imperfection known as a "cold shut" will occur.

DRAWINGS

Drawings of castings should be made to cover several details which are of assistance to the foundrymen who must arrange the manufacture of the castings. They should show surfaces which are to be machined, finish allowance, tolerances, and jigging points. Any dimension which must be closely held in the rough casting should be indicated. If the casting is to be subjected to pressure, this fact should be stated. The drawing should include the type of final treatment or coating to be applied, such as painting, galvanizing, plating, or other type.

Points that should be covered by the designer in drawings to be submitted to the foundry are:

1. Dimensioning drawings
    A. Dimension the parts clearly and completely
    B. Give all over-all dimensions
    C. Show dimension lines lighter than the outline of the casting
    D. Keep dimension lines outside the area of the casting outline, if possible
    E. Indicate clearly where all surfaces are to be machine-finished and indicate type and amount of finish allowance to be provided
    F. Provide sufficient tolerance for cast finish
    G. Indicate if draft is to be added to or taken from drawing dimensions
    H. Indicate any highly stressed section
    I. Indicate jigging points, if possible

2. Marking
    A. Indicate how and where the pattern number is to be shown
    B. State whether lettering is to be raised or impressed
    C. Keep lettering in a location where it can be readily molded
    D. Keep raised lettering off any surface used for locating and machining the casting
    E. Keep lettering out of deep recesses
    F. Place lettering on sections which are the least stressed

It is advisable to include an estimated rough casting weight on a drawing. The proper procedure in estimating the weight of castings is to find the volume in cubic inches and multiply this figure by .26 for standard or .27 for pearlitic malleable iron to give the weight in pounds. An actual weight will usually exceed an estimated weight by 5 to 10 per cent because of fillets and the fact that castings tend to come slightly oversize.

DESIGN KINKS

Many ideas have been developed to reduce costs, improve designs, and simplify parts, some of them dating from years ago, others much more recent. A few are listed and illustrated in this section in the hope that designers will find them useful. Here ingenuity has taken full advantage of the properties of malleable iron.

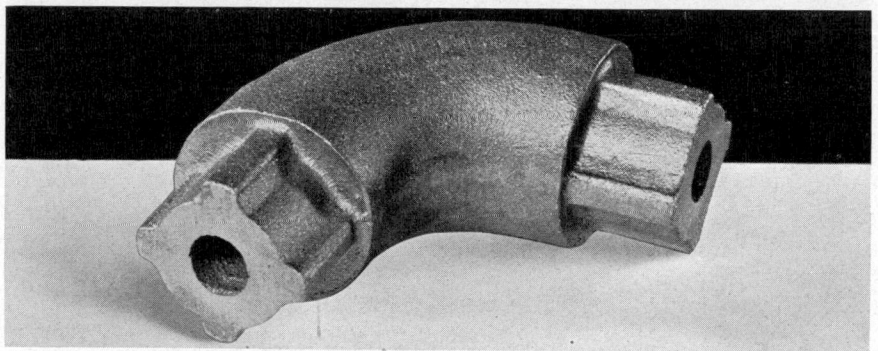

Fig. 28.

1. When making a casting to fit into a tube or pipe, arrange three or four narrow flutes on the surface of the casting, as shown in Fig. 28. Have these be the fitting points, rather than machine the castings to secure the desired fit. Good pattern equipment should be used, and the proper size and fit should be worked out with the foundry.

Fig. 29.

2. The casting of drill-spotting holes, as in Fig. 29, provides a starting point for drilling; and where the hole does not require an exact location, it is a practical way to eliminate a drill jig.

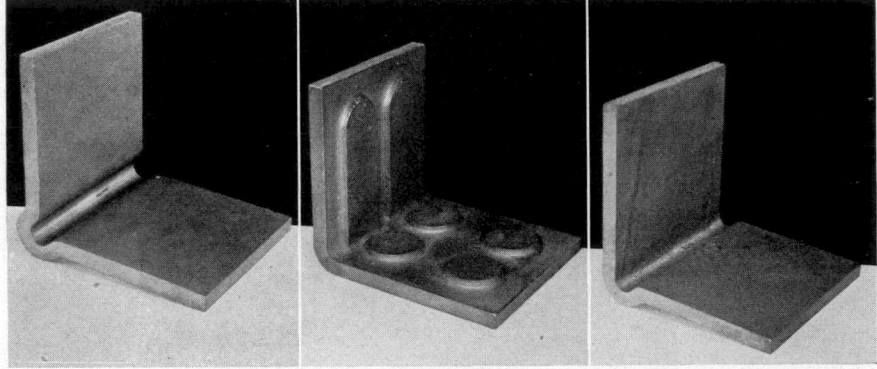

Fig. 30.

3. Figure 30 shows three ways of designing a casting with mounting surfaces at 90 degrees to each other, yet without the dangerous sharp inside corner that might be expected. If the corner is "relieved" in one of these ways, the danger of a crack or tear is removed. At the left, Fig. 30 shows a type of relieved corner frequently used. That at the right is in more general use because it permits green sand molding. In the center the use of raised mounting bosses is illustrated. This kind of design is suitable when the amount of surface contact required is not large. In this type of construction, it is usually desirable to add metal back of the bosses on one surface of the casting in order to avoid the need of cores.

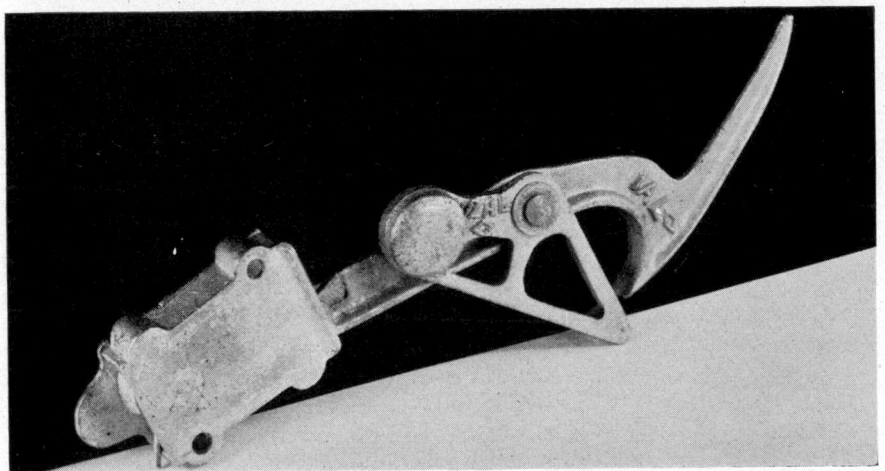

Fig. 31.

4. One way of utilizing the ductility of malleable iron is illustrated by the ladder bracket shown in Fig. 31. Instead of using a rivet to act as pivot for the pawl member, the designer has cast a boss on the hooked arm. This is peened over a washer, becoming a successful and inexpensive pivot.

Fig. 32.

5. The same ladder bracket, turned over, appears in Fig. 32, showing how the ductility of malleable iron may be used for another cost-saving purpose. Here lugs cast on the main frame are crimped over the rim of the plate covering the case which holds the bracket springs, providing a dependable closure and saving the cost of riveting.

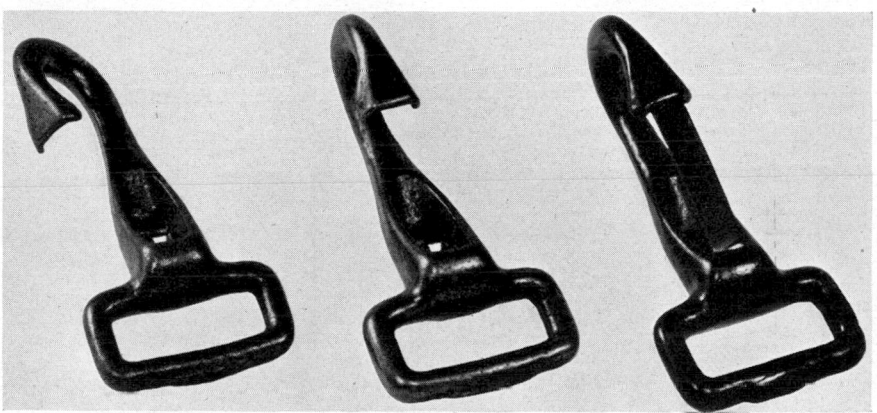

Fig. 33.

6. Figure 33 shows a further elaboration of the idea. For simplicity and thrift in making some devices, it is sometimes practical to design the piece for the most direct work in casting and to bring it into final shape by a subsequent forming operation. The harness snaps in Fig. 33 tell the story. "As cast," the loop of the snap is at an angle so that no core is required; maximum production and minimum cost are thus secured. In the forming operation, which is of course done cold, the loop is brought into its proper position with respect to the rest of the snap.

Fig. 34.

7. Conversion to malleable iron to save weight and gain strength is illustrated by the solid cast iron washer and the "designed" malleable iron washer shown in Fig. 34. Of the great number of conversion items available, this one is selected because of its simplicity.

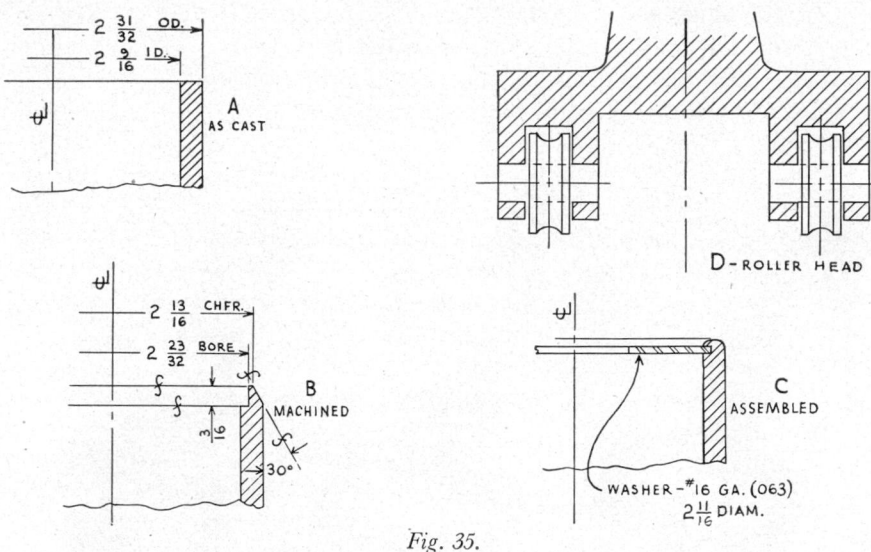

Fig. 35.

8. The sketches in Fig. 35 present another utilization of the ductility of malleable iron, this time in a rolling or spinning operation used in the manufacture of jacks. The jack body is cast cylindrical as shown at *A*, and is then counterbored and chamfered on the outside as shown at *B*. A washer is inserted in the counter bore, and to lock it in place as at *C* the malleable iron is rolled over by a roller head, *D*.

9. A punch press is used in the crimping operation shown in Fig. 36. *A* is the body of a jack, *B* the base. Neither part is machined, the two rough castings being assembled as shown at *C* by means of a crimping head *D* attached to the ram of the punch press. This way of assembling the units utilizes

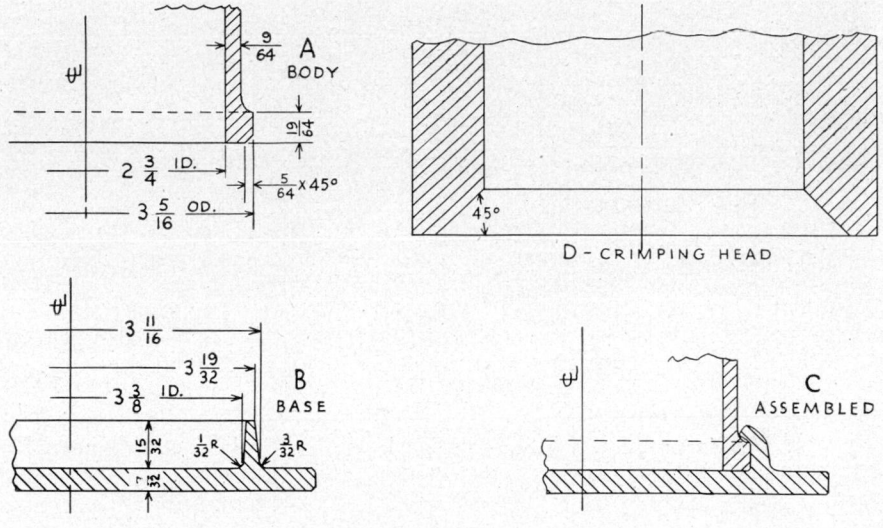

Fig. 36.

the ductility characteristic of American malleable iron. It is an inexpensive and thoroughly satisfactory method.

10. Staking to hold a roller in place in a pocket is permitted by the ductility of malleable iron, as the sketches of Fig. 37 show. As will be noted in Assembly E, the metal is swaged to stake the small keeper bar permanently in place. The staking tool is used in a punch press, and its working parts are ground at an angle of 15 degrees. For small production lots, this staking operation is often performed by hand, in which case it is found unnecessary to shape the face of the staking tool at an angle. Obviously, the use of this process of assembly should be confined to relatively small elements.

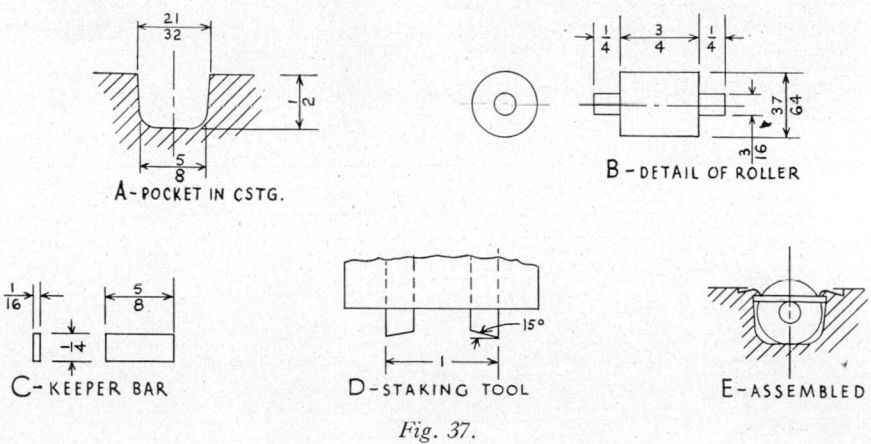

Fig. 37.

Fig. 38.

11. Under proper conditions, holes in malleable iron castings can be punched instead of drilled, as is illustrated in Fig. 38. The diameter of the hole should exceed its depth, and of course as in other materials, the holes should not be located too close to the edge of the piece.

Fig. 39.

12. Casting a chucking extension on a piece is especially helpful when the piece is of such shape as to be difficult to hold during machining, or when the entire surface must be machined. Often the provision of such an extension as is shown in Fig. 39 permits all important machining to be done from one chucking and thus assures maximum accuracy. A cutoff is the final operation.

Fig. 40.

13. The piece shown in Fig. 40 is to be machined all over. The narrow flat cast on the outside diameter permits it to be held firmly during machining. Chucked in this manner with its nose resting in a ring in the chuck, the piece can be easily machined, including threading at the cylindrical end, and can be finished at the conical end in a subsequent operation.

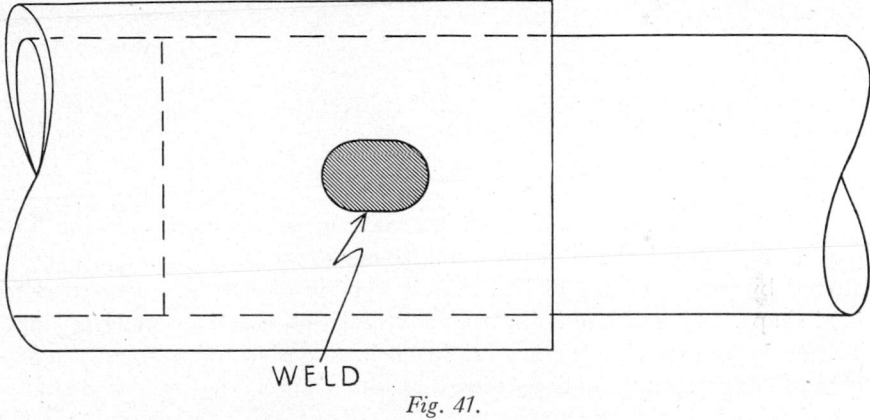

WELD

Fig. 41.

14. Welding is used in Fig. 41 to fasten a malleable iron casting to a steel rod or tube. The oval-shaped opening in the casting permits a button of weld metal to be deposited on the steel rod, locking the casting in place whether or not there is a complete bond between the malleable iron and the weld.

15. Collars welded to a U-shaped piece of steel bar stock are used in Fig. 42 (page 106) to hold the loop in place in holes cored in a malleable base plate. This scheme combines in a successful assembly two pieces well suited to the materials from which they are made. The malleable base plate is plain, simple, easy, and cheap to make. The loop is steel bar stock sheared to length and bent to shape. Coring the holes in the casting is economical. The collars of weld metal rigidly hold the loop in position, one being on each side

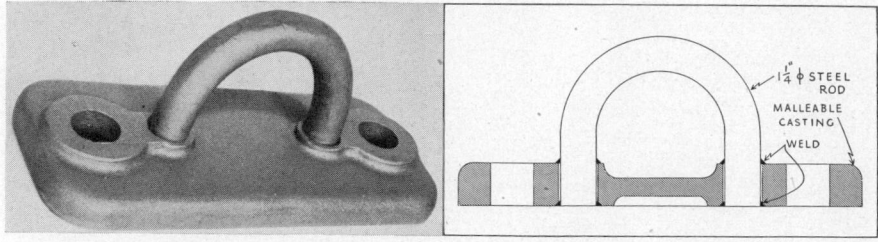

Fig. 42.

of the malleable plate. Whether there is a slight bond between the casting and the weld material is unimportant.

Fig. 43.

16. In some cases it is desirable to make malleable castings in the simplest form, which because of the ductility of the metal can subsequently be altered by processing the piece through forming dies to secure the desired final shape. This practice is illustrated by Fig. 43, showing conveyor links. The conveyor extension is cast straight for inexpensive and simple manufacture and then is put through forming dies which curve it to the desired shape.

X

PATTERN DESIGN

SINCE the process of casting has as its object the production of metal replicas of an original design, the pattern, or model, which shapes the mold cavity in accordance with that design is of primary importance. Too often, purchasers do not realize that the cost and the efficiency of castings are vitally dependent upon the factors in pattern design which this chapter will discuss. If good castings are to be produced, the foundry must be furnished with adequate pattern equipment that meets its requirements. The accuracy, the appearance, and the ultimate cost of castings — as affected, for example, by freedom from rejections after machining, — depend largely upon the type and quality of the patterns and upon their arrangement to facilitate production of castings true to size and free from defects. Foundryman and customer therefore share equally in their dependence upon pattern equipment and will benefit equally if careful analysis of foundry and production problems is made at the time new pattern equipment is being considered. The design and shape of the casting, the size of the order, and the production methods of the foundry must all be taken into account in such analysis, for they determine the type of pattern equipment best suited for the production requirements of each casting.

In the planning of pattern equipment, the customer's principal concern is that the pattern be a precise model, so that the castings made in molds formed from it shall be accurate in dimension and sound in section. The foundryman's concern is the same. His is expressed, however, not only in terms of the pattern's adherence to the engineering design, but also in terms of the pattern's efficiency and usefulness as a working foundry tool. The customer looks to dimensions and contour; the foundryman looks to these and in addition to gating, parting, and draft. These three foundry problems are of vital interest to the customer as well, because they affect the type of pattern equipment to be chosen.

A number-one requirement in casting is to assure that a full supply of molten metal will properly reach all parts of the mold cavity. This requirement poses the first foundry problem — the provision of suitable gating. A gate is a combination of a channel and elevated reservoir spaces to conduct metal from the pouring hole into the casting cavity. Gates may be cut by hand or may be formed by an addition to the pattern itself. The single loose pattern so-called, which is the simplest ungated model of the piece to be cast, does not efficiently solve the problem of supply of molten metal, because when such patterns are used, the gate must be cut in the sand by hand, a slow process. When more than a very few castings are to be made from such a pattern, the sensible answer is to attach a gate to the pattern. Thus the mold cavity and gates are reproduced in one molding operation, and more uniform results are obtained than with hand cutting of gates. Depending upon the size of the casting, duplicate patterns may be attached to one gating structure, so that the ramming up of a single mold will provide for the production of a number of identical castings. These duplicate patterns are called "gated patterns."

Whenever a number of patterns are attached to a gate, they should be properly spaced and arranged to permit sufficient molding sand to separate the individual pieces and to provide adequate but economical wall strength in the mold. In addition, arrangement should permit proper gating and feeding of the individual patterns.

A mold is formed by the ramming of a plastic material such as molding sand firmly about a pattern. The pattern must then be withdrawn from the rammed sand without tearing the mold, and here the second problem arises, for the pattern obviously must be of such construction that this operation is possible. The majority of patterns require merely a two-part mold, the two halves of which meet at what is known as the parting line of the pattern. The simplest parting line is obtained when the halves of the mold meet in a flat or plane surface cutting horizontally through the pattern at its largest dimension. For example, on a sphere such a parting line would be at the "equator." In a two-part mold of the sphere, with the parting line thus located, the pattern obviously can easily be withdrawn without tearing any part of the mold.

The largest dimensions of some castings, however, often are not in a single plane, so that the parting surfaces are irregular in profile. The simple two-part mold nevertheless can often be used in the production of such castings. When projecting flanges or ribs or similar obstructions to molding which are not on the parting line further complicate the parting profile, the foundry frequently is forced to resort to the use of cores or of three-part flasks. These tend to increase the cost of producing the castings. Simplification of parting line design thus directly affects not only the cost of pattern equipment but also the cost of molding, and should be given the utmost consideration.

Removing or drawing a pattern from the sand still may offer some difficulty even though the pattern has been so designed that a satisfactory parting line is obtained. Pattern draft — the tapering of those parts of the pattern which will be in a position vertical to the parting line as the pattern is lifted from the mold — to some extent solves this third problem. The molding sand tends to adhere to the pattern, however, and resists its being readily withdrawn from the mold. A hand rapping operation jars the pattern slightly and loosens it from the adhesion of the sand, so that when the two halves of the mold are separated the pattern can be drawn easily without tearing the mold. The direction and force of the blows of the rapping bar must be carefully judged; they must free the pattern but not distort the mold. On patterns which are rigged for machine molding, vibrating takes the place of hand rapping. A vibrator, or miniature air hammer, is attached to the plate or vibrator frame on which the pattern is mounted, and its blows produce a gentle uniform vibration of the pattern, thus freeing it from the grip of the sand. This method is most satisfactory as it eliminates the human element in rapping and drawing the pattern, so that the casting is held nearer the pattern size.

Which of the various types of pattern equipment will be used for a particular job should be determined by consultation between the customer and the foundry. With full information as to present and future requirements of a fixed design, the foundry can recommend the type of pattern equipment which will not only meet its production requirements, but at the same time insure the lowest cost of castings and pattern equipment to the customer. In evaluating the various types, however, the customer does well to remember that with pattern equipment as with many other tools, a somewhat larger first cost is often more than justified by the gains in economy and quality which it produces.

PATTERN EQUIPMENT

The types of pattern equipment in general use in malleable iron foundries are discussed here in the order of their general effectiveness in overcoming the problems which have been outlined.

1. *Metal match plates*. A metal match plate is manufactured by making a mold of the master pattern and then separating the cope and drag halves of this mold by a space of usually three-eighths inch. When the pattern metal (generally aluminum) is poured into the mold, a plate is obtained which has

Fig. 1. Metal match plates; left, multiple piece pattern; right, single piece pattern.

Fig. 2. At left, wood patterns mounted on wood; at right, metal patterns mounted on metal plate.

the cope impressions of the pattern on the top portion of the plate and the drag impressions on the bottom. Gates and risers may be cast integral with the plate or attached after the plate has been poured. The production molds for malleable castings are made by assembling cope and drag with the pattern plate between, filling the drag half with sand, affixing a bottom board, turning the mold over, then filling the cope half with sand, squeezing or ramming the mold, vibrating the plate, withdrawing the cope, then the plate as it is vibrated, and reassembling the cope and drag halves of the mold. Plate pattern molding requires less dexterity on the part of the molder and is relatively speedy, so that it contributes to increased production while maintaining uniformity and accuracy. For large production quantities, this type of equipment, which is shown in Fig. 1, will invariably be found to justify its higher initial cost.

2. *Mounted wood or metal patterns.* A variation of the cast metal match plate is possible with some patterns of simple design and flat parting. A pattern of this kind can be mounted on a metal plate or for smaller production on wood or plastic, thus becoming a simplified form of plate pattern. This type of equipment, illustrated in Fig. 2, is generally lower in cost than are match plates. When the entire pattern is of a shape which permits it to be mounted on one face of the plate or board, and is molded in one half of the mold, it is known as a "flatback."

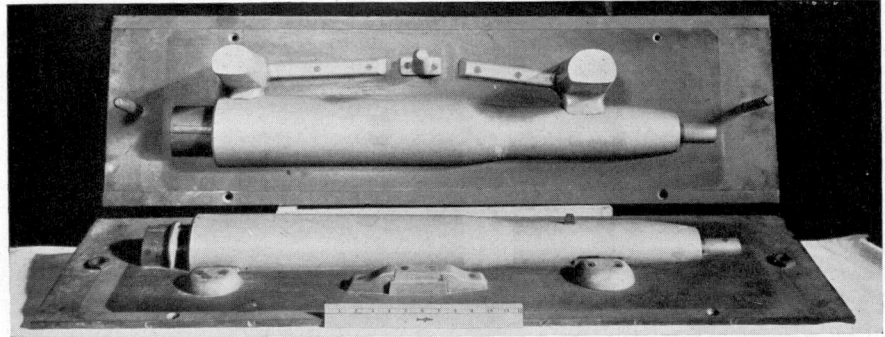

Fig. 3. Metal cope and drag patterns, the drag pattern in the foreground.

Fig. 4. Wood cope and drag patterns, the drag pattern in the foreground.

3. *Cope and drag patterns* (*wood or metal*). For castings where the complete mold is too heavy to be handled by a single molder, cope and drag patterns of wood or metal shown in Figs. 3 and 4 are generally used. They are essentially the cope and drag halves of the pattern cast or mounted on separate plates or boards. Such equipment allows one molder, or a gang, to work on the cope half of the pattern, while another molder or gang is preparing the drag. When the castings to be poured are of large size, this distribution of work during the molding process naturally results in increased production. When the castings are to be made by machine molding in large quantities, metal patterns are to be preferred, but for small production runs wood construction is satisfactory.

4. *Gated patterns in vibrator frames.* Relatively light gated patterns may be centered by strips of metal in light metal frames to which vibrators are attached to facilitate withdrawal from the sand as is done with plate pattern equipment. The assembly resembles a match plate minus the metal between the pattern and the rim of the plate. In molding with this type of equipment, it is customary to use a clay or composition match, which acts as the cope half of a match plate. The clay or composition match is a shallow open auxiliary half-mold in which the pattern is sunk as far as the parting line, much as occurs with the follow-boards mentioned in the next paragraph.

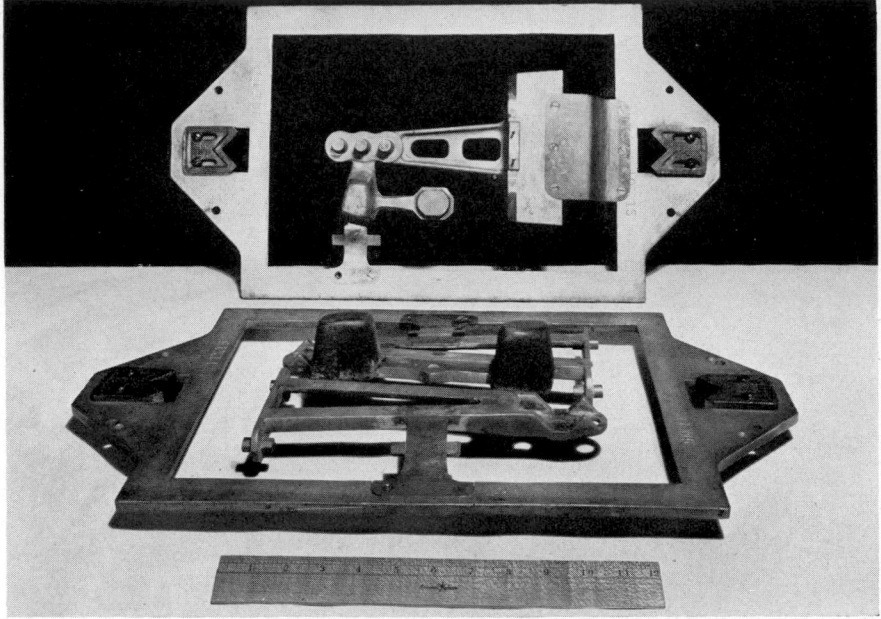

Fig. 5. Two types of gated patterns mounted in vibrator frames.

Vibrator-frame mounting of gated patterns, illustrated in Fig. 5, is used in machine molding.

5. *Gated patterns.* Illustrated in Fig. 6, gated patterns are made of wood or metal. Those of wood are usually employed for production up to 100 molds. Some types of castings, however, because of their particular design, can be produced in large quantities more satisfactorily from gated patterns than from match plate equipment. Wood patterns warp from moisture and also are readily damaged in handling and should not be considered for production of large orders. For large runs, therefore, metal gated patterns are used with

Fig. 6. Gated patterns of wood, left, and of metal, right.

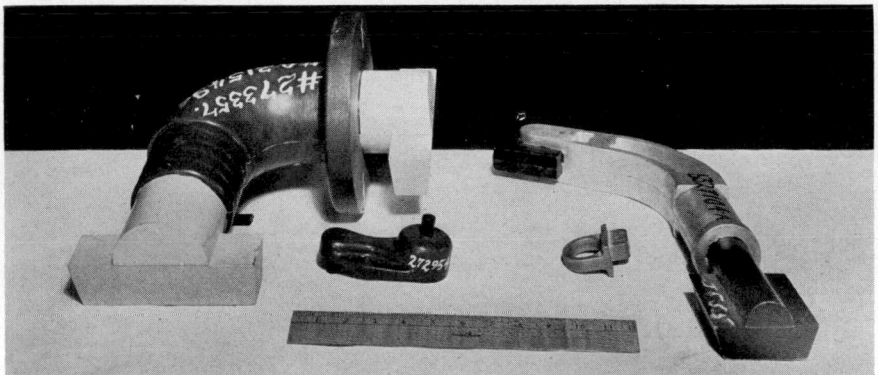

Fig. 7. Single loose wood and metal patterns.

follow-boards or with clay or composition matches, in order to shorten the time needed for making a mold. The follow-board is a wood board into which a recess matching the pattern has been routed or carved, so that the pattern lies in it as deep as the parting line. Either device serves as a temporary mount for the pattern, and provides a parting for the mold. For short runs, a green sand temporary match may be used. To produce castings from gated patterns, whether of wood or metal, usually requires a skilled molder even when follow-boards and matches are used, and the rate of production generally is lower than it is with match plates or mounted patterns, with a resulting higher cost.

6. *Single loose patterns.* This type of pattern equipment, shown in Fig. 7, may be of wood or metal. It is the least expensive type of pattern that can be employed, but it is satisfactory only for small orders running generally from one to ten pieces. When single loose patterns are used, it is necessary for the molder to cut the gates and risers in the sand molds by hand, using a "slick," or gate-cutter, with a resulting low production rate and high cost. Hand cutting of gates and feeders also makes it difficult to obtain uniform results. Hence this type of pattern equipment is to be recommended only for experimental lots of castings or for very small orders where the cost of superior pattern equipment is not warranted.

CORES AND CORE BOXES

Cores are of two types, green sand and baked sand. The first type, less frequently used, requires support by a baked sand half or an arbor. Whenever possible, those of the second type are so designed that they have an adequate supporting surface to keep them in shape during the baking process. The shape of some cores, however, necessitates the use of a support known as a core drier, which acts to prevent distortion of the core during baking. Foundries frequently use sand core driers for small orders, but on large production

Fig. 8. Core box equipment: left to right, wood, metal-faced wood, and metal core boxes.

runs metal core driers are often necessary. They are an item of pattern equipment which the customer furnishes, and are illustrated in Fig. 9.

Core box equipment may be of wood, of wood faced with metal, or of metal, as illustrated in Fig. 8. Particularly on small castings, core boxes are often constructed to produce a number of cores in one operation, and are known as gang or multihole boxes. For large quantity production, cores may be originally formed by core-blowing machines, requiring special core-box construction. Special construction is also generally required for boxes from which green-sand cores are to be made. The type of construction should be recommended by the foundry. In making cores, the principle of draft should be applied as in molding, to permit withdrawal of the box from the core.

PATTERN MARKINGS

Wood patterns which the customer furnishes to a foundry should be adequately marked with the standard colors used for identifying wood patterns and core boxes by the foundry when it makes its own. The standard colors, shown in Fig. 10, are: (1) Black: surfaces to be left unfinished. (2) Red: surfaces to be machined. (3) Red stripes on yellow background: seats of and for loose pieces. (4) Yellow: core prints and seats for loose prints. (5) Diagonal black stripes on yellow background: stop-offs.

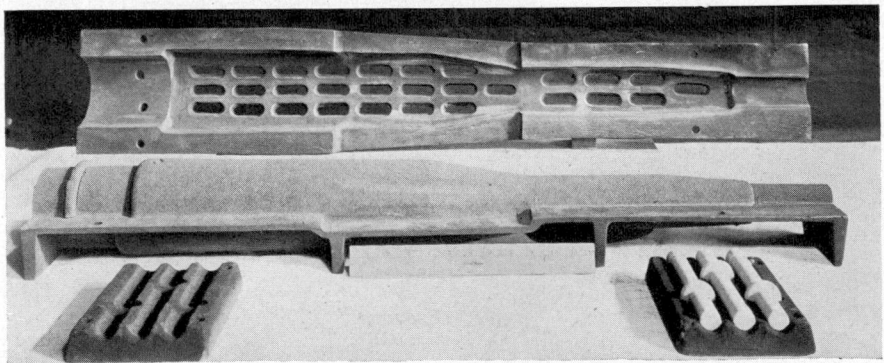

Fig. 9. Core driers: small sand driers in foreground; large metal driers at rear.

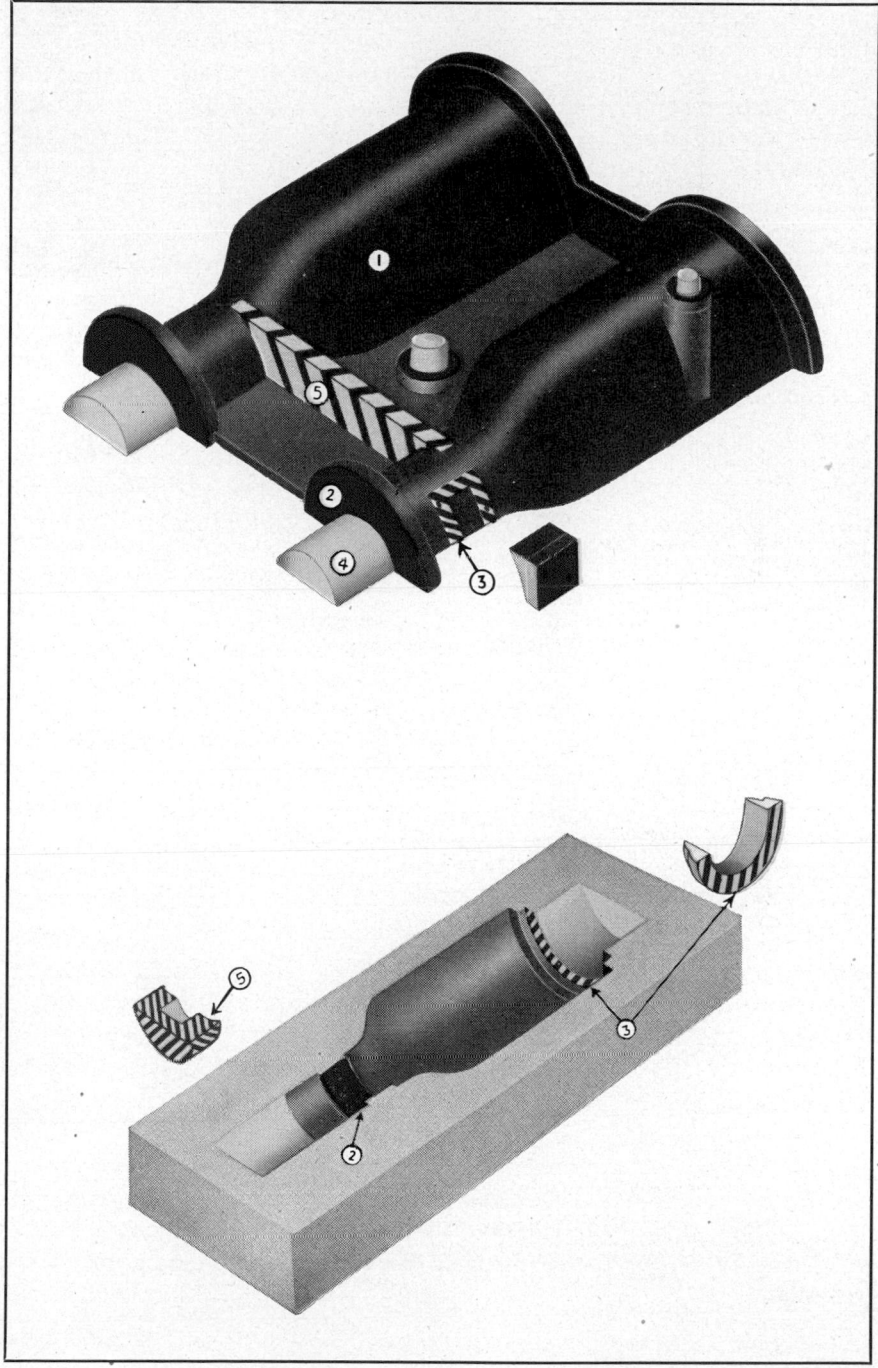

Fig. 10. Standard colors for identifying wood patterns and core boxes.

The majority of casting producers maintain their own pattern shops, and whenever new pattern equipment is required it is advisable that the order for the pattern equipment be placed with the foundry which is to make the castings. Pattern equipment then will fit the particular needs of the producing foundry, which thus can more readily assume responsibility not only for the dependability of the patterns but also for the accuracy and soundness of the castings to be produced from them.

Practically all foundries prefer to gate patterns which they are to use, because by so doing they are able to allow for their own particular practices. Generally, the foundry makes sample castings from the master or loose pattern in order to determine the size of the gate connections and feeders necessary to insure satisfactory castings. The pattern equipment is then gated in accordance with these findings.

However, if a customer intends furnishing his own pattern equipment, he should consult the foundry regarding type of equipment, shrinkage allowance, finish allowance, size tolerances, arrangements for required draft of pattern, position of locating points for machining operations, parting line, the method of molding, and in the case of machine molding pattern equipment, the size of flasks and plates and layout for the exact location of patterns on the boards or plates. If for some reason the gating is to be done by other than the foundry, the foundry's directions as to layout are especially important; they should specify the exact size of feeders and risers and the arrangement of gating, together with the spacing of patterns.

The allowances for machining should be correct, neither wastefully excessive nor stingily insufficient. During machining operations, tolerances are naturally required; the foundry likewise is allowed size tolerances. With experience, correct finish allowances are established, assuring that castings are cleaned up during machining. Finish allowance is discussed in greater detail in Chapter IX.

Shrinkage allowance necessarily varies somewhat with the length, size, and type of casting. The malleable iron industry generally uses a shrinkage allowance of one-eighth inch per foot, which is slightly varied in some cases, the variation being imperceptible in small castings. Some castings having intricate construction and others having flanges or projections are likely to require special treatment as far as shrinkage allowance is concerned. Since shrinkage allowance and the size of gates and risers necessary to produce sound castings vary with different metals, it is desirable that the foundry be consulted when patterns constructed for the requirements of another metal are to be adapted for the production of malleable iron castings. Often, minor modification is found to be sufficient for the conversion from other metals to malleable.

XI

MACHINING PRACTICE

T HE machining by which castings and forgings are fabricated into finished
machine parts is a critical stage in manufacturing, not merely because it
is often the determining factor between profit and loss but because efficiency
in the use of materials depends upon it. Machining procedures must be guided
first of all by the inherent characteristics of the material to be worked. Although this volume is principally concerned with American malleable iron,
the present chapter includes a fair share of practical information dealing
with the mechanical, chemical, and engineering properties of other metals.
This additional discussion plus one regarding cutting fluids is presented both
to aid in the appraisal of American malleable iron as an engineering material
and, it is hoped, to make this volume more useful to engineers and production
men.

Because of the many variable conditions affecting the speeds and feeds at
which metals are machined, this chapter is divided into three principal sections as follows:

1. Machinability of Metals.
2. Speeds and Feeds for Machining.
3. Machinability Tables and Cutting Fluids.

The science of the machining of metals has undergone many changes in
technique during the past fifty years. Prior to the 1890's, the common cutting
medium for tools and drills was called carbon steel. During the 1890's, the
so-called high speed steels were introduced, and the science of cutting metals
was revolutionized, in that much higher speeds could be obtained than with
the carbon steels. In the 1920's, carbide-tipped cutters gained prominence in
the machining of cast iron; further refinements of these tools have become
widely accepted for many general as well as special applications for all the
metals. Carbide-tipped cutters fall into three general classifications as follows: (1) Tungsten carbides for machining cast iron; (2) Tungsten carbides
and tantalum carbides for machining malleable iron; (3) Tantalum and

titanium carbides for machining steels. These are broken down into many special grades for various applications. Carbon steel tools are still made and used for certain applications but may be disregarded when machining from a production standpoint is being considered. The relative values of the three cutting mediums in terms of cutting speed are roughly as follows:

1. Carbon steel: 25–30 feet per minute when machining cast iron.

2. High speed steel: 75–80 feet per minute when machining cast iron.

3. Carbide-tipped cutters: 150–300 feet per minute when machining cast iron.

Cast iron is used here to bring out the comparative value of the three types of cutters because it is the customary base in shop practice.

MACHINABILITY OF METALS

The term machinability generally refers to how well a piece of material can be fabricated and at what speed this machining can be accomplished at some selected rate of feed for each passage of the tool. Further factors in judging the machinability of a metal are the desired tool life between grindings, conformity to size tolerances as specified on the blueprint for the part in question, and the acceptable finish. These considerations may be reduced to:

> Speed in surface feet per minute;
> Feed in thousandths of an inch per revolution;
> Desired tool life, which is the period between grindings;
> Size tolerances for the part;
> Surface finish requirements for the part.

If a metal can be cut at a higher speed and heavier feed than some other metal, and at the same time can satisfy the requirements of tool life, size tolerance, and surface finish, it can clearly be seen as of greater machinability.

Frederick Taylor in his classic experiments specialized in the study of single point cutting tools and aimed at one and one-half hours as the desired tool life between grindings. Since Mr. Taylor's developments, the tool life which is desired and sought for varies widely from one type of machine to another. In many cases it is most important to obtain maximum time between grindings because of the cost of grinding and resetting the tools. An example of this is the multiple-spindle automatic screw machine which, when fabricating a part in but a few seconds of cutting time, may require an hour or more for grinding one tool and resetting that and the other tools which must be synchronized. In some cases, the most economical arrangement is to provide for grinding and resetting tools for automatics but once for each shift, which represents an average gross tool life of approximately six and one-half hours. This is made possible and advisable by selecting more costly cutting tools, by continuous flooding with the cutting fluid, and by employing the machine's automatic features which permit the selection of the most advantageous feeds and speeds. In other cases, best economy may result when the tool life is as short as twenty minutes. An example of this is the turret lathe which employs several tools but which may require the use of one of these for only a small fraction of the time the other tools are cutting. In this case, tool life may well be sacrificed for the one tool, for the sake of greater production, through employing for it most severe speeds and feeds.

As a general rule, when machining a specific steel, which may be treated to have varying hardnesses, the tool life is inversely proportional to the hardness of the steel being machined. If the Brinell hardness of a given steel is doubled, the tool life will be cut in half.

In addition to the factors previously outlined, the cutting lubricant used and the angle of contact between the cutting tool and the workpiece also contribute to machinability. Cutting lubricants are discussed later in this chapter with recommendations for their application. Recommended rake angles for grinding single point tools are shown in Table 7, page 138. The back rake angle, which largely determines the friction between the tool and the chip, is illustrated in Fig. 1.

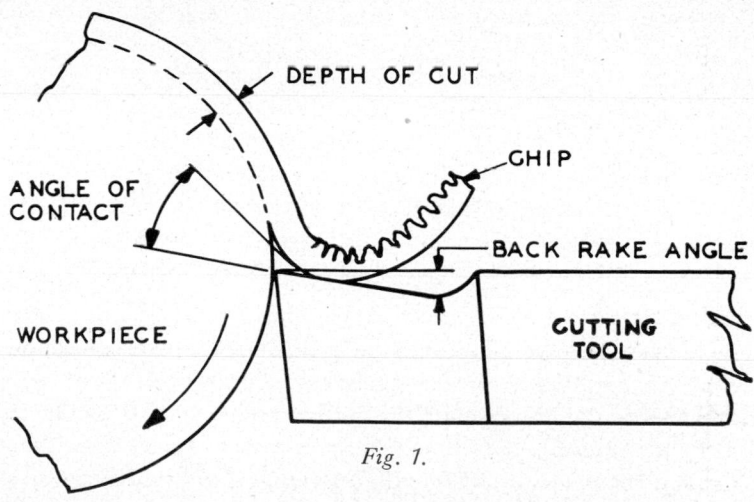

Fig. 1.

It will be seen from the diagram that the chip breaks off ahead of the point of the cutting tool, coming in contact with the top face. The friction caused by the contact of the chip with the top face of the tool, plus the high temperature generated by the deformation of the metal, creates intense heat on the tool. Increasing the angle of contact increases the pressure, and decreasing it decreases both the pressure and the deformation. Since the angle of contact is largely governed by the back rake angle, it can be seen that the back rake angle affects machinability. It must be remembered that the back rake angle pertains to the tool only. But the angle of contact is determined by the relationship established between the piece being machined and the cutting tool. This angle of contact may vary from the back rake angle on all machining operations, if the tool is improperly tilted in its holder. In addition, when cutting on a periphery, as in turning or boring, setting the tool in differing positions in relation to the centerline of the workpiece also alters the angle of contact.

CUTTING CHARACTERISTICS

As machinability is relative, some generally known material must be set up as a standard and considered as one hundred per cent machinable. A rating above 100 per cent represents a more easily machinable material than the standard and those below, less machinable materials.

The A.I.S.I. (American Iron and Steel Institute) B1112 steel, which is equivalent to the S.A.E. (Society of Automotive Engineers) 1112, has been selected for this standard, as is explained on page 141. It is commonly known as free cutting Bessemer screw stock. It is suitable as a standard because, in the average plant, machinability problems involve this steel as well as other types, malleable iron, gray iron, cast steel, and bronze, aluminum, and other nonferrous materials.

When considering the various types of steels, it should be recognized that the two chemical elements, sulphur and phosphorus, which contribute to higher machinability, also tend to weaken the steels. This explains the reason for not including these elements in all steels in quantities sufficient to make them highly machinable. It is necessary to sacrifice machinability in some applications in order to gain strength and toughness. It is considered that the sulphur in steel, which appears as manganese sulphide, tends to lubricate the tool, and also permits the chip to break more easily. Phosphorus causes hot embrittlement; so if the chip is hot it breaks off more easily.

Malleable Iron

The machinability of malleable iron with its high ductility is found to be relatively high because of the free carbon in the form of graphite, which serves as a substantial lubricant on the cutting point of the tool. The characteristics of the chip formation, that is, the tendency to break up without creating undue pressure on the top face of the tool, also serves to avoid the generation of high heat, with a consequent lengthening of tool life. In the pearlitic malleables the carbon is found in a free state to a lesser degree, making these metals slightly lower in machinability than the standard malleable irons.

Cast Iron

The existence of free carbon in the form of graphite tends to keep the machinability high in cast iron as well as in malleable iron. However, cast iron's content of iron carbide lessens its machinability; the addition of certain alloys such as nickel and chromium will tend to decrease it.

Steels

In considering and applying the various steels, particularly the alloyed ones, it is interesting to note the effect of the various elements which are inherently present and those added for desired effects. Plain steels are essentially iron and carbon, with small amounts of silicon, manganese, phosphorus, and sulphur inherently present. Carbon is the essential hardening agent and more is added to make the steel more hardenable.

However, in steels, with a few exceptions, only the amount of carbon that will remain in combination as a carbide of iron is generally added, and it does not appear as free carbon in the graphitic form. As previously noted, phosphorus and sulphur tend to make steels more machinable but also weaken the metal.

Silicon, tungsten, manganese, nickel, chromium, vanadium, and molybdenum are the elements generally added in varying proportions and combinations to give strength, toughness, and hardenability. The effect of some strengthening alloys is to increase the difficulty in machining.

PLAIN CARBON STEELS

Low carbon content, which usually typifies soft structure, does not necessarily result in the best machinability. The plain, low carbon steels, including the 1010 and 1015 grades, involve many machining problems. They may be soft and mushy and are liable to tear badly in machining. This condition can be corrected, at times, by a change in the tool grind, although never completely eliminated. Such types of steels are usually machined with lighter feeds per revolution.

The 1020 and up to 1030 grades present the best machining qualities of the plain carbon steels. The higher carbon steels in the 1045 and 1050 grades again become more difficult to machine.

ALLOY STEELS

Among the alloy steels, there is the nickel series, for example the 2300, containing 3.5 per cent nickel and, except for carbon, no other elements considered as effective alloys. There is little difference in machining between the 2315 and 2330 grades, as may be noted in Table 10. The carbon content has had little effect on the machinability of these grades as they both compare in machining character with the plain carbon 1020 series. Increased carbon shows a marked effect between the 1015 and 1030 plain carbon grades. However, as the 2300 series is compounded to contain 0.45 per cent carbon, severe machining characteristics develop. All steels of this type with 0.30 per cent carbon or more should be thoroughly annealed in order to present a better machining character.

When the steels with two or three included alloys are reached, further characteristics develop. For example, in the nickel-chromium steels, the 3100 series, the additional alloy here (chromium) makes them approximately 5 per cent less machinable than the 2300 plain nickel alloy steels, especially in the unannealed condition.

A.I.S.I. AND S.A.E. STEEL SPECIFICATIONS

As both S.A.E. and A.I.S.I. steel specifications are now in use, it frequently becomes necessary to interpret one in terms of the other. Starting on page 331, details of the respective systems and their relationships, including exact chemical compositions, are given.

MACHINABILITY HARDNESS

It has been generally accepted that the limiting value of hardness, for normal machinability, is of the order of 355 Brinell, although many metals are now being machined in mass production at hardnesses of 400 or more. The introduction of carbide-tipped cutting tools has made this practical.

RELATIVE SEVERITY OF MACHINING OPERATIONS

Some machining operations are more severe than others. A classification has been given to machining operations in Table 11 (page 149), arranging them in the order of their severity. This classification becomes a part of the conditions for recommendations for cutting fluids, also given in Table 11.

CRITICAL POINTS IN MACHINING

The many variable factors in machining make it difficult to lay down hard and fast rules which represent the most favorable opportunities in the majority of cases. It will be found that the ultimate for both speed and feed is often above the recommended range. This is due in some cases to what might be called "critical points." These criticals arise from such causes as: backlash, badly worn ways, or machine construction so light as to permit injurious periods of vibration at various combinations of speeds and feeds within normal working ranges. The operator of experience has probably discovered that some machines will labor, or "chatter," at a certain speed or feed, but will operate easily at higher rates when this critical has been passed. Experience has shown that increasing the speeds, especially with carbide-tipped tools, may result in longer tool life and smoother operation.

SPEEDS AND FEEDS

Selection of the right speed and feed is one of the most difficult problems confronting the foreman, the time-study man, or the machinist. Beset on the one hand by the pressure of getting the job out in the allowed time and meeting competitive costs, he is faced on the other with "burned" or broken tools, bent arbors, and strained machine tools as the dire consequences of too much feed or speed.

He knows that a world record has been made of drilling cast iron at the rate of 142 cubic inches a minute with a $1\frac{1}{4}$ inch diameter drill. He knows, too, that innumerable tables will give him from .001 to .020 feed per tooth on the milling cutter and from .001 to .080 feed on the tool bit. This is, in a manner of speaking, like asking him to take a number from one to ten; highly technical treatises are little help to him. In the final analysis, he will make the selection of feeds and speeds on a practical basis, but possibly only after expensive experience, which the tables in this chapter are designed to prevent.

The practical choices which he makes from day to day are shop applications of the 12 basic principles which Frederick W. Taylor laid down as governing the machining of metals.* Little has been added to them in the years since except a better understanding of the physical changes which take place at the point of the tool. Taylor's principles stand. If the shop man has them in mind as he considers tables and suggested speeds, so much the better. Taylor held that machining depends upon:

1. The quality of the metal which is to be cut; that is, its hardness or other qualities which affect the cutting speed.

2. The chemical composition of the steel from which the tool is made, and the heat-treatment of the tool.

3. The thickness of the shaving, or chip, which is to be removed by the tool.

4. The shape or contour of the cutting edge of the tool.

5. Whether a copious stream of water or other cooling medium is used on the tool.

6. The depth of the cut.

7. The duration of the cut; that is, the time which a tool must last under pressure of the shaving without being reground.

8. The lip and clearance angles of the tool.

9. The elasticity of the work and of the tool on account of producing chatter.

10. The diameter of the workpiece which is being cut.

11. The pressure of the chip or shaving upon the cutting surface of the tool.

12. The pulling power and the speed and feed changes of the machine.

In discussing the machining of metals in the light of these principles, it is well to consider each machine as a special unit rather than to treat machining as a whole. This segregation is the first step toward definition. The following discussion, therefore, will consider machining on drilling machines, milling machines, and lathes.

DRILLS

The shop man's first rule in drilling is "Line it up; clamp it down." The more emphasis is placed on these two factors, the better feeds and speeds can be applied in drilling.

ALIGNMENT

The setup should be very carefully checked before drilling is started. Misalignment contributes perhaps more to inefficiency in drilling operations than does any other factor. Slight misalignment in the relationship of the

* Frederick W. Taylor, *The Principles of Scientific Management*, New York, Harper and Brothers, 1915, pp. 107 ff. Used by permission.

drill to the drill bushing will produce undue wear on the margin of the drill and cause the drill to labor where it should be cutting easily.

The over-all cost of any machined cast piece is represented by the combination of the casting cost and the machining cost. Cored holes may decrease the cost of the casting as a piece because of the saving in metal as a result of the coring. This saving may, however, be lost in the machining operation, for example because of the tendency of the drill to follow the cored hole, with or without the use of jigs. This tendency is greatest in drilling when the misalignment is severe, but even with boring tools it will occasionally be found necessary to take additional cuts in order to produce a straight hole. In design, therefore, planning for machining should be taken into consideration. For drilling holes through relatively thin sections, the position accuracy of the holes is promoted by jig-drilling from the solid. On the other hand, lever arms, for example, are often drilled from a cored hole because the design favors coring in order to permit the casting to solidify properly at the hub after pouring. Hence, though machine shops often are asked to drill cored holes in castings without the choice of machining either from the cored hole, or from the solid, they should be given the option whenever possible. The designer thus may safeguard himself against false economy.

As even with sturdy jigs occasional misalignment of a cored hole in the casting will cause misalignment of the drill, extra finish allowance should be provided in the cored hole. In working with cored holes, it is good practice to put greater emphasis on feed and less on speed.

Breakage of smaller drills is occasionally found to be excessively high at the moment the drill point breaks through the far side of the work. High speeds will tend to eliminate this danger. Backlash should be watched, for it is often the cause of the drill's snapping when the break-through point is reached.

In general, high speed and light feed are recommended for the drilling of most materials. Experience will show, however, that this should not be taken as an infallible rule.

As a visual test of whether a drill is properly ground, one of the best is comparing the chips from both flutes of the drill. If they are of nearly the same form and size, the drill may be judged as correctly ground. If not, it has not been properly ground. Sharpness is another matter and it goes without saying that a sharp tool is necessary to good performance; but sharpness alone is not enough. The drill is one of the most difficult tools in the machine shop to grind properly by hand. Though nine out of ten shop people will claim to be experts at hand-grinding drills, it is good management to grind drills on a drill grinder whenever possible. A number of excellent discussions on the proper care and operation of drills are published and distributed without charge by various manufacturers of drills.

Following is a list of the troubles encountered at times in drilling operations and also a check list to help in their solution. While this check list refers to drills, the principles on which it is based generally are found to apply to most machine tools.

DRILL TROUBLE CHECK CHART

When:	Check For:
Drill breaks	Rigidity
	Too low speed
	Too high speed
	Dullness of tool
	Too little lip clearance
Outer corners of cutting edges break down	Too much speed Poor lubrication
Lips or cutting edges chip	Too much feed Too much lip clearance
Chipping or checking occurs on a high speed drill	Too much feed Too rapid heating and cooling of tool while working or grinding
Chips change in nature during drilling	Change in condition of drill, as dulling, chipping, etc.
Hole drills out too large	Unequal angle or length of the cutting edges Loose spindles
One lip only is cutting	Unequal angle or length of the cutting lips
Drill splits up center	Too much feed Too little lip clearance
Hole drills out rough	Dullness of tool Poorly ground tool Poor lubrication Wrong lubricant Too much feed Improper setup

DEEP HOLE DRILLING

The rate of feeding drills is regulated entirely by the diameter of the drill. For example, on a one-eighth inch drill a feed of .004 inch per revolution is proportionally correct, but when a three-eighths inch diameter drill is used, it is possible to push this drill much faster to a feed of from .008 inch to .010 inch. This is because of the relatively greater strength of the larger drill. As the holes being drilled become deeper in relation to the diameter of the drill, the operation becomes more difficult. In some difficult ones it is possible to use a so-called "oil hole" drill which has an oil passage, feeding lubricant directly to the cutting edge, regardless of chips in the hole. Through the use of these it is possible to extend the length of the cut four to five times the diameter of the drill. Oil hole drills are not usually available in the smaller sizes, and are confined to as few jobs as possible, because of their cost. The five-eighths inch size is generally the smallest available. They are commonly used on automatic screw machines. Drilling generally employs a surface cutting speed lower than one used for turning. It is good practice to reduce both the speed and feed when drilling holes with a depth several times the diameter of the drill, because of:

1. Clogging of chips in the drill flutes.
2. Inability of the coolant to reach the cutting lips through the clogged flutes.

It is desirable to back the drill out at regular intervals in deep hole drilling, to help clear the chips. There is no hard and fast rule for this, since the depth of the hole in relation to its diameter, the amount of chips to be cleared, and the number of cutting lips all influence the amount of coolant reaching the cutting lips. A rough rule of thumb is to back the drill out once for each drill diameter of depth. Table 3, page 129, showing this reduction in speed and feed, may be used as a guide.

Reaming or Finish Boring

After holes have been drilled or bored, finishing to close tolerances can be done by either a reaming or a finish-boring operation. It should be kept in mind that a reamer is a balanced tool, in that it cuts on both sides. Also, cutting edges which are adjustable to balance and size may be inserted on a boring bar to accomplish the same result as reaming. This boring tool may offer the advantage of quickly finishing the piece with the size tolerances and surface condition required, at high speed and relatively heavy feed, since the balanced effect of the cutting edges tends to avoid inaccuracies that might result from spring in the boring bar or tool holder. They are commonly used on horizontal boring machines. Another method of finishing holes to close tolerances is to use carbide-tipped tools with either single or multiple cutting edges, employing very light feeds but very high speeds to do the job quickly. Holes may be finished to close tolerances by grinding or honing after drilling or rough boring. This method is more applicable in finishing holes in steel which has been hardened after the drilling or rough boring. Hardening heat-treatment may cause distortions and also may injure finished surfaces; grinding or honing frequently offers the best method of making the corrections.

Recommended feeds and speeds for reaming are not presented in the tables that follow, since they may be determined directly from the various tables of recommended drilling practice. In general, *speeds in reaming* should be two-thirds to three-fourths the speed listed for drills of similar size. Choice should be on the lower side, since a reamer can be quickly ruined by speeds even only slightly too high. *Feeds in reaming* should be two to three times the feed listed for drills of the same diameter. A coarse feed will tend to produce revolution marks and rough walls. Too fine a feed makes the reamer idle in the cut and subjects it to undue wear in proportion to the amount of work produced. An important exception to this general rule is cast iron. It is good practice in reaming cast iron to use hand feed and push the reamer through rapidly.

Tapping

Most taps are broken by insufficient speed. It is highly important that the tap be given enough momentum to carry it through the terrific job it has to do. Caution must be observed in bottom tapping, however, that the speed is not so high as to give the operator insufficient time to reverse the tap before it strikes the bottom. If a mechanical tapper is used, this evil will be eliminated, since the tapper will trip and reverse itself as it bottoms in the hole.

Taps should be operated at the highest speed permitted by equipment, lubrication, and type of work, for high speed not only increases production, but gives longer tap life and more accurate threads. A good practical rule for the speed of taps is to run them at the same speed as the tap drill. The tap will, however, often give excellent results at still higher speeds. In general, the speed recommended for taps may be resolved into the following, with the

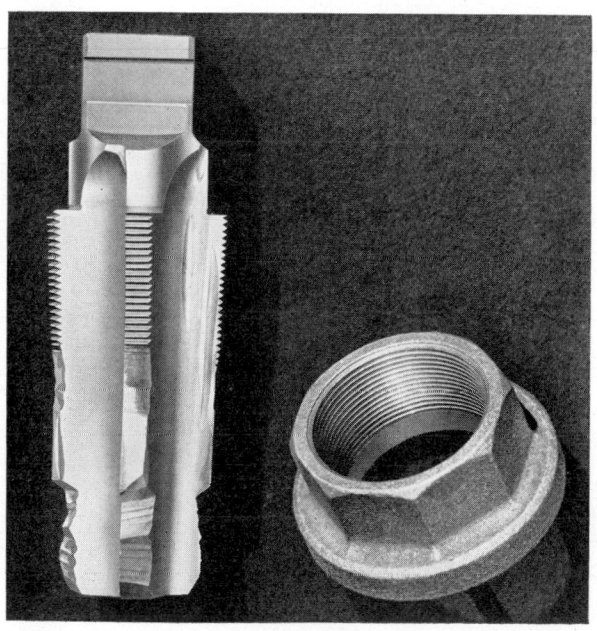

This tap produced 160,000 malleable iron ring nuts at a cutting speed of 120 feet per minute.

first figure shown as the safe starting speed and the second figure the possible, but not necessarily the maximum, speed obtainable:

Malleable and cast iron............	90 to 150 feet per minute
Low carbon steels.................	80 to 100 feet per minute
High carbon steels.................	40 to 75 feet per minute
Alloy and stainless steels............	40 to 75 feet per minute
Free-cutting yellow brass............	150 to 250 feet per minute
Leaded commercial bronzes.........	150 to 250 feet per minute
Extruded architectural bronzes.......	150 to 250 feet per minute
Yellow or red brass................	60 to 150 feet per minute
Naval brass......................	60 to 150 feet per minute
Tobin bronzes....................	60 to 150 feet per minute
Leaded phosphorous bronzes........	60 to 150 feet per minute
Everdur.........................	60 to 150 feet per minute
Manganese bronzes................	60 to 150 feet per minute
Phosphorous bronzes..............	30 to 60 feet per minute
Nickel silver.....................	30 to 60 feet per minute

TABLE 1. CUTTING SPEEDS FOR DRILLING VARIOUS MATERIALS

Material Being Machined	Cutting Speed in Feet per Minute With High Speed Steel Drills
Standard Malleable Iron............................	70–90
Pearlitic Malleable Iron — Brinell 180–200..............	60–80
Pearlitic Malleable Iron — Brinell 200–240..............	50–70
Cast Iron, Soft — Brinell 160–193	80–100
Semi-Steel Cast Iron — Brinell 193–220..................	70–90
Cast Iron, Hard — Brinell 220–240.....................	60–80
Steel — Class I * — See Table 10......................	90–110
Steel — Class II — See Table 10......................	80–100
Steel — Class III — See Table 10......................	60–80
Steel — Class IV — See Table 10......................	50–65
Steel Castings — to 0.20 per cent carbon................	70–80
Steel Castings — high carbon annealed..................	65–75
Steel Castings — 3½ per cent nickel — 0.30 per cent carbon annealed.....................................	60–70
Drop Forgings, 0.15 to 0.25 per cent carbon.............	60–70
Drop Forgings, high carbon annealed...................	50–60
Drop Forgings, alloy................................	50–60
Stainless Steel — Allegheny No. 33 — Type 410...........	50–60
Tool Steel well annealed.............................	50–60
Brass, soft yellow..................................	200–275
Bronze (Tobin-Everdur etc.).........................	90–110
Bronze (Manganese Bronze, Vanadium Bronze)...........	55–75
Aluminum...	600–900

* For definition of these Classes of Steel, see Table 10, page 143.

TABLE 2. FEEDS FOR DRILLING VARIOUS MATERIALS, USING HIGH SPEED STEEL DRILLS

Minimum feeds for two lip drills in inches per revolution. For core drills, add one-half of the given feed for each additional lip. The feeds for the various metals are about the same for very small drills; for the large diameters the general relationships are that malleable iron may be fed about 25 per cent heavier than steel and 20 per cent less than cast iron.

Drill Diam., Inches:	$\frac{1}{16}$	$\frac{3}{32}$	$\frac{1}{8}$	$\frac{5}{32}$	$\frac{3}{16}$	$\frac{7}{32}$	$\frac{1}{4}$	$\frac{9}{32}$
				Feeds per Revolution in Inches				
Malleable Iron	.003	.0035	.0045	.005	.0058	.0065	.0075	.008
Cast Iron	.003	.0035	.0045	.005	.006	.007	.008	.009
Steel	.003	.0035	.004	.0045	.005	.0055	.006	.0065

Drill Diam., Inches:	$\frac{5}{16}$	$\frac{11}{32}$	$\frac{3}{8}$	$\frac{13}{32}$	$\frac{7}{16}$	$\frac{15}{32}$	$\frac{1}{2}$	$\frac{9}{16}$
				Feeds per Revolution in Inches				
Malleable Iron	.009	.0095	.010	.0105	.011	.012	.0125	.013
Cast Iron	.009	.010	.011	.011	.012	.013	.013	.014
Steel	.007	.0075	.008	.0085	.009	.0095	.010	.0105

Drill Diam., Inches:	$\frac{5}{8}$	$\frac{11}{16}$	$\frac{3}{4}$	$\frac{13}{16}$	$\frac{7}{8}$	$\frac{15}{16}$	1	$1\frac{1}{8}$
				Feeds per Revolution in Inches				
Malleable Iron	.014	.0145	.015	.016	.016	.017	.0175	.019
Cast Iron	.015	.015	.016	.017	.017	.018	.019	.020
Steel	.011	.0115	.012	.0125	.013	.0135	.014	.015

Drill Diam., Inches:	$1\frac{1}{4}$	$1\frac{3}{8}$	$1\frac{1}{2}$	$1\frac{5}{8}$	$1\frac{3}{4}$	$1\frac{7}{8}$	2
			Feeds per Revolution in Inches				
Malleable Iron	.020	.020	.020	.020	.020	.020	.020
Cast Iron	.021	.021	.021	.021	.021	.021	.021
Steel	.016	.016	.016	.016	.016	.016	.016

TABLE 3. DEEP HOLE DRILLING

Speed and Feed Reduction for Deep Hole Drilling. (This is general and not to be used literally for small diameter drills.)

Depth of Hole	Reduction Below Standard Drilling in Per Cent	
	Speed	Feed
3 times drill diameter	10 per cent	10 per cent
4 times drill diameter	20	10
5 times drill diameter	30	20
6 to 8 times drill diameter	40	20

MILLING

Following are the factors which will make it possible to obtain the feeds per tooth which authorities recommend for milling machines:

1. *Arbors.* Few milling arbors which have been in the production line for even a few days are still straight and true. And as a snowball rolling down hill gains size as it travels, a bent arbor becomes less true as it is used. In order that the machine may produce its best results, the following points in the care and use of arbors should be observed:

    a. The cutter should never be allowed to strike the workpiece at rapid travel.

b. The arbor must not rub or strike the fixture.

c. Bushings and collars should be cleaned before being assembled on the arbor.

d. The arbor nut should be tightened only when the over-arm support is in place.

e. Arbors should be kept suspended when not in use. An arbor under the work bench is decidedly out of place.

f. Cutters should be carefully ground on true mandrels, so that they will work in true relationship to the arbor.

The fifth (e) of the factors listed above is decidedly important. More failures in milling are caused by abuses in the care of arbors than by lack of capacity of the arbor or the machine to do the job. It must be remembered that the milling cutter, if properly ground, is round and true in relationship to the hole. When it is placed on a bent or sprung arbor, it is made to do with only two or three teeth the work that should be done by 10 or 12.

2. *Efficiency or Capacity of the Machine.* It is idle to expect an old and worn machine to accomplish the results which should be expected of a new machine or of one in first-class condition. In order that feeds from the higher range of recommendations may be used, it is well to guard against the following:

a. Backlash in the gears.

b. Badly worn ways.

c. Loose gibs.

d. Worn spindle bearings.

It should be remembered that any one of these factors will tend to create the others and that each will contribute to poor production.

3. *Setup of the Workpiece.* Jigs and fixtures should be massive and rigid. Clamps should be provided to hold the piece without vibration. Place clamps and supports as close to the cut as possible. Back stops, or "kickers," to prevent any slight slippage of the fixture, should be available.

4. *Setup of the Machine.* Full use should be made of the accessories provided by the manufacturers of milling machines.

a. The cutter should be kept as close to the nose of the spindle as possible.

b. The over-arm support should be set as near to the cutter as possible. If the cut is heavy and the cutter cannot be kept close to the spindle nose, an over-arm support should be used on each side of the cutter.

c. The braces for the over-arm support should be used whenever possible.

5. *The Nature of the Workpiece.* The material of the workpiece will be discussed later. The shape of it is highly important in determination of feeds. A heavy, rigid workpiece can be machined with higher feed than a workpiece with long or thin sections, which sections tend to vibrate, so that the workpiece must be supported at these points.

6. *Cutters*. A cutter with too few teeth is to be preferred to one with too many. Too many teeth will tend to drag in the work and create friction. This trouble is particularly true for carbide milling cutters which, though the question is somewhat controversial, are generally designed with fewer teeth than are conventional cutters.

Everything about the workpiece, the machine, the setup, and the fixture should be as rigid as possible for best results in milling. It is advantageous to emphasize feed in milling, with the speeds on the conservative side, and within the ranges shown in Table 5.

7. *Depth of Cut*. In the machining of hot rolled steel bars and of castings — such as malleable iron, cast iron, and cast steel — it is advisable to give the tool or cutter sufficient depth of cut to get below the outside surface. Even where only a true-up cut is desired, it is not good practice to force the tool to work on the immediate surface since the cutter may be working against occasional bits of sand, scale, etc., which would break down the cutting edges more rapidly than when the cutter is working in a deeper or normal cut.

8. *Cutter Materials*. In Tables 4 and 5, pages 133 and 134, speeds and feeds recommendations are limited to the use of high speed steel cutters. Cutters with carbide-tipped cutting edges are gradually coming into the picture as suitable machines and practices are developed and put into use. Up-to-date machine shop practice dictates employing them for many applications, and the alert shop man will avail himself of the many opportunities afforded for their study and use. The following factors will be helpful when carbide-tipped cutters are being used:

a. The milling machine should be in very good condition.

b. The power capacity should be sufficient to avoid stalling in the cut.

c. Fly-wheels on the arbor, or, better still, built into the machine, are recommended.

d. The orthodox grinding practices with regard to rake and lead angles for high speed steel cutters are usually found to be unsatisfactory for carbide-tipped cutters. Many applications require a negative, rather than a positive lead and rake angle.

e. The number of teeth in the cutter is usually well below the requirements for high speed steel cutters. Cutters with as few as two or three teeth are being successfully used for face milling.

f. Extremely high cutting speeds may be used. These may vary from five to ten times the speed recommended for high speed steel cutters on a given material.

g. As a rule, lighter feeds per tooth are recommended for carbide-tipped cutters than are used for high speed steel. This is not a sovereign rule, however, since the smaller number of teeth will often permit the use of relatively high chip loads.

h. Each application for carbide-tipped cutters should be studied as an individual case and treated on its own merits.

9. *Measure of Production.* Production possibilities may be visualized more clearly by keeping in mind that *milling speed* involves two separate and distinct elements — the surface speed of the rotating cutter and the rate of feed at which the workpiece travels past the cutter. Each of these speeds is controlled by a separate train of gears unrelated to each other, but both must be established by the operator. Consideration of both is necessary to establish the feed per tooth (also commonly called the chip per tooth, although strictly this chip involves, in addition, the depth and surface of the cut). This chip multiplied by the number of teeth that will cut into the piece per minute, represents the major measure of production; the depth and face of cut are the remaining factors.

The depth and face of cut usually control the selection of the type and size of cutter, and in most cases the selection is correct. When the feed or chip per tooth is also correct, it generally follows that favorable production is being secured for any given cutter run at the right speed.

The average operator instinctively checks the cutter's surface speed and sets some travel feed, but does not always check the feed per tooth. This is apparently due to the fact that milling cutters have multiple rather than single cutting edges, and that it is somewhat difficult to calculate the feed per tooth. The chart on page 135 presents a simple way of determining this feed or chip.

The following is an example of where an operator did not secure the most favorable production:

Type of Cutter. . . . .   6 inch-diameter side mill
Number of Teeth in Cutter.   20
Depth of Cut — or Thickness of Slab
    Removed. . . . . $3/16$ inch
Cutter Spindle Speed. . . . . $44\frac{1}{2}$ revolutions per minute for cutting speed of 70 feet per minute (See Tables 4 and 9)
Travel or Feed of Piece past Cutter.   3 inches per minute

In the above selection the cutting speed was reasonable and the feed of the table may have seemed logical on the basis of previous experience with a

Milling a 1 x 1½ inch slot in C1020 steel.

somewhat similar piece. But it is possible that in this previous experience a 10-tooth cutter may have been properly used and excellent production secured. In this example, however, had the operator carefully checked all his selections, he would have found that the chip per tooth on the 20-tooth cutter was only about .0035 inch or just one-half the reasonable figure shown in Table 5. Consequently, to secure the correct feed per tooth — .007 inch — when using the 20-tooth cutter, the table travel feed has to be about six inches per minute instead of three.

In addition to the chart on page 135, the formula for figuring the feed per tooth is shown in Table 8, page 139.

TABLE 4. CUTTING SPEEDS FOR MILLING VARIOUS MATERIALS

Material Being Machined	Cutting Speed (F. P. M.) With High Speed Steel Cutters	
	Rough	Finish
Standard Malleable Iron	70–80	100–120
Pearlitic Malleable Iron — Brinell 180–200	60–75	90–100
Pearlitic Malleable Iron — Brinell 200–240	55–65	80–90
Cast Iron, Soft — Brinell under 160–193	70–80	100–120
Semi-Steel Cast Iron — Brinell 193–220	60–75	90–100
Cast Iron, Hard — Brinell 220–240	55–65	80–90
Steel — Class I * — See Table 10	90–100	100–120
Steel — Class II — See Table 10	80–90	90–100
Steel — Class III — See Table 10	60–70	70–80
Steel — Class IV — See Table 10	50–55	60–65
Steel Castings — to 0.20 per cent carbon	50–60	60–70
Steel Castings — high carbon annealed	40–50	50–65
Steel Castings — 3½ per cent nickel — 0.30 per cent carbon annealed	40–50	50–60
Drop Forgings, 0.15 to 0.25 per cent carbon	45–55	55–65
Drop Forgings, high carbon annealed	50–60	60–70
Drop Forgings, alloy	50–60	60–70
Stainless Steel — Allegheny No. 33 — Type 410	50–60	60–70
Tool Steel well annealed	50–60	60–70
Brass, soft yellow	200–250	300–500
Bronze (Tobin-Everdur, etc.)	80–100	150–200
Bronze (Manganese Bronze, Vanadium Bronze)	40–60	80–100
Aluminum	600–800	800–1000

* For definition of these classes of steel, see Table 10, page 143.

In arriving at the proper feed to use on a given milling cutter for various materials, Table 5 should be consulted, and the following guides should be borne in mind:

Malleable Iron. It is good practice to lean toward the higher feeds per tooth.

Gray Iron. The higher feeds per tooth should, as a general rule, be used.

Steel. Feeds toward the middle of the range recommended in Table 5 should be employed.

Cast Steel. Feeds should be selected from the lower part to the middle of the range, for annealed cast steel, and from the lower part of the range for heat-treated and alloy cast steels.

TABLE 5. FEEDS FOR MILLING

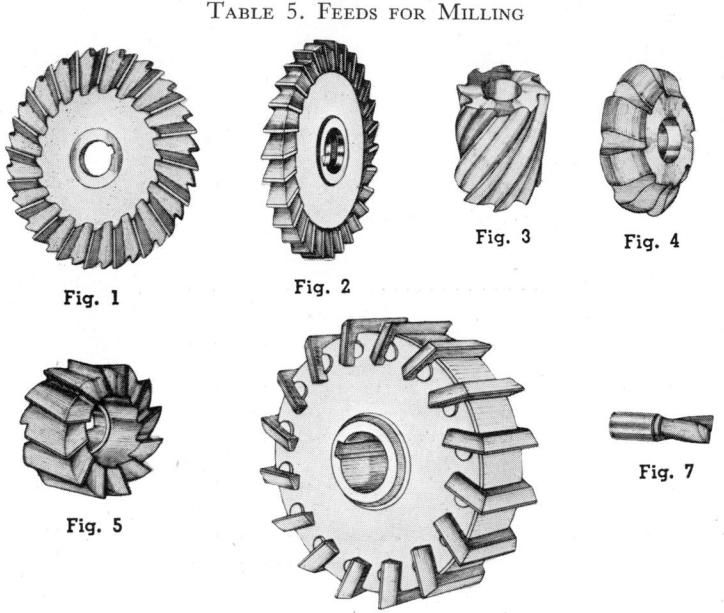

Fig. 1   Fig. 2   Fig. 3   Fig. 4

Fig. 5   Fig. 6   Fig. 7

Using High-Speed Steel Cutters, Figs. 1–6.

Fig. No.	Nature of Cut — Cutter	Rough Cuts to $\frac{3}{16}$ Inch Depth	Coarse Finishing Cuts to $\frac{1}{16}$ Inch Depth	Finishing Cuts to $\frac{1}{32}$ Inch Depth
		Feed (Chip) Per Tooth Per Revolution of Cutter in Inches		
1	Metal slitting saw with side chip clearance............	.001 to .003 all cuts		
2	Side milling cutter..........	.004 to .010	.006 to .012	.002 to .004
3	Plain helical mill...........	.006 to .012	.008 to .015	.002 to .005
4	Form cutter................	.004 to .010	.006 to .010	.002 to .004
5	Shell end mill — over 2 inches.	.006 to .010	.006 to .012	.002 to .006
6	Face mill — inserted tooth ...	.007 to .016	.010 to .020	.004 to .008

Using Two-lipped End Mill, Fig. 7

Cutter Diameter, Inches	$\frac{1}{4}$	$\frac{3}{8}$	$\frac{1}{2}$	$\frac{3}{4}$	1 to 2
Feed per Tooth, Inches	.0006 to .001	.001 to .0015	.0015 to .003	.002 to .004	.003 to .008

TABLE CHART 5A. FEEDS OR CHIPS PER TOOTH

Before a milling job is started, the cutter has been selected. Then the surface cutting speed is set for that particular cutter and the material to be machined. Table 9 translates the cutting speed into the R.P.M. of the cutter shaft or spindle. Recommended feeds and speeds are given in Tables 4 and 5.

To determine the table travel or the feed of the piece past the cutter which is necessary to obtain the desired chip per tooth:

    (a) Enter the chart on the line representing the spindle R.P.M. and stop where this line crosses the line for the number of teeth in the cutter.
    (b) Drop vertically on the chart from this point until the resulting vertical line crosses that line representing the desired chip per tooth.
    (c) Then proceed to the left and determine directly the necessary table feed in inches per minute.

In the chart below, the dotted lines describe the example given on page 132, under the subject "Measure of Production."

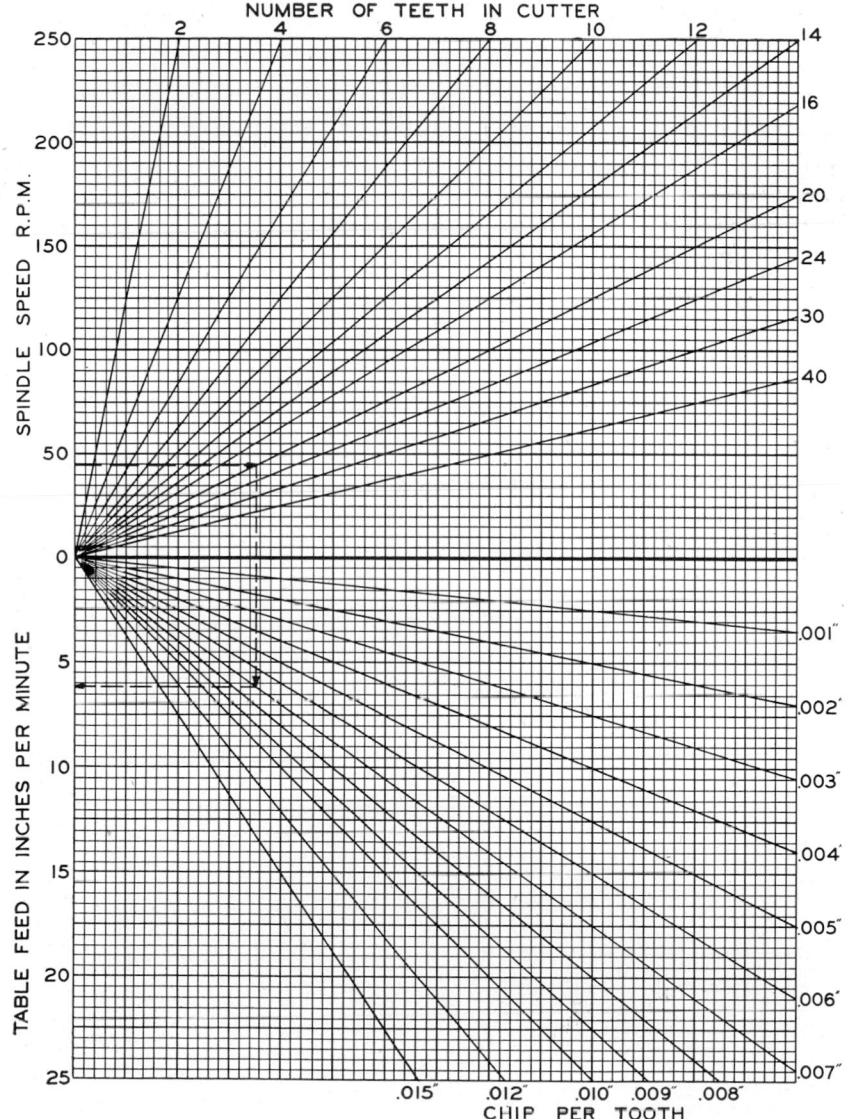

The three types of cut listed in Table 5 may be defined as follows:

Rough cuts are the initial cuts made for the purpose of removing material but not for sizing. A rough cut alone may be sufficient for clearance purposes.

Coarse finishing cuts are secondary cuts made for the purpose of obtaining a level surface but where roughness or coarseness to touch is not objectionable. Coarse finishing cuts are to be desired when the part is subsequently ground, since the grinding wheel will "bite in" on a coarse surface much better than on a smooth surface. This is true of other types of machine work as well as milled surfaces.

Finishing cuts are used when the quality of smoothness to touch as well as a level surface is desired. In general, finishing cuts are used when a rubbing motion will occur between the parts in the final assembly.

TURNING

The things which have been said about milling will, in general, apply also to lathe work. Since the design of the machine and the application of the cutter to the work are somewhat different, these additional factors must be considered:

1. Backlash in the gears, worn spindle bearings, misalignment in the chuck, loose and worn gibs are all conditions which will make it difficult to obtain the higher values in the feed and speed range given in Table 6.

2. Excessive overhang of the part in the chuck should be avoided.

3. Care must be exercised that the desire to obtain high feeds does not lead to the work's being gripped so tightly that it is distorted by the pressure of the chuck jaws, though tight chucking is, of course, desirable where possible.

4. A wobbling turret saddle will never permit the feeds that are possible with a machine that has been kept in good condition. The gibs must be kept tight and the ways in good condition.

5. Tool bits should be carefully ground with particular attention paid the rakes and clearances. Recommended grinding practice is shown in Table 7, page 138.

6. Tool bits should be honed. Five minutes of honing will save 30 minutes of regrinding.

7. Lathe centers should be true with the spindle and with each other.

Machining a malleable iron cover with carbide-tipped tools.

Carbide-tipped cutters have gained widespread recognition for use on turret and engine lathes. The following points should be carefully considered when applying them so as to gain the fullest advantage in their use:

a. The lathe should be in good condition.

b. The power capacity should be sufficient to avoid stalling in the cut.

c. The orthodox grinding practices with regard to side and back rake angles for high speed steel cutters are found to be unsatisfactory for carbide-tipped cutters. When the material is being cut intermittently, or when the machines are old, negative rakes should be used.

d. Extremely high cutting speeds may be used. These may vary from three to ten times the speed recommended for high speed steel cutters on a given material.

e. As a rule, lighter feeds are recommended for carbide-tipped cutters than are used for high speed steel.

TABLE 6. RECOMMENDED FEEDS AND SPEEDS FOR TURRET AND ENGINE LATHES

(All data are for continuous cutting with lubricant)

		Feed in Inches Per Revolution					
		High Speed Steel		Stellite "J" Metal		Cemented Carbides	
Type of Material	Depth of Cut in Inches	Up to $\frac{1}{32}$	$\frac{1}{32}$ to $\frac{3}{32}$	Up to $\frac{1}{32}$	$\frac{1}{32}$ to $\frac{3}{32}$	Up to $\frac{1}{64}$	$\frac{1}{64}$ to $\frac{1}{32}$
		Surface Speed in Feet Per Minute					
Malleable Iron	$\frac{1}{32}$ to $\frac{1}{8}$	120–160	90–120	170–250	140–170	220–500	175–350
	$\frac{1}{8}$ to $\frac{1}{2}$	90–120	55–90	140–170	110–140	175–400	175–300
Pearlitic Malleable	$\frac{1}{32}$ to $\frac{1}{8}$	110–140	80–110	150–220	130–160	200–400	150–300
	$\frac{1}{8}$ to $\frac{1}{2}$	80–110	50–85	120–155	100–130	150–350	150–250
Soft Cast Iron	$\frac{1}{32}$ to $\frac{1}{8}$	80–120	50–70	130–175	100–135	250–400	200–350
	$\frac{1}{8}$ to $\frac{1}{2}$	50–65	40–55	90–130	80–105	200–350	150–350
Semi-Steel	$\frac{1}{32}$ to $\frac{1}{8}$	75–115	45–60	120–150	90–125	200–400	200–350
	$\frac{1}{8}$ to $\frac{1}{2}$	50–65	35–50	85–120	65–110	175–300	175–250
Hard Cast Iron	$\frac{1}{32}$ to $\frac{1}{8}$	65–100	40–55	100–145	80–115	200–350	150–300
	$\frac{1}{8}$ to $\frac{1}{2}$	40–55	30–45	75–110	55–95	150–250	150–200
Steel Class I*	$\frac{1}{32}$ to $\frac{1}{8}$	70–175	50–120	110–275	80–200	340–690	300–625
	$\frac{1}{8}$ to $\frac{1}{2}$	40–120	30–90	70–185	50–130	220–550	200–460
Steel Class II	$\frac{1}{32}$ to $\frac{1}{8}$	60–110	40–75	90–165	70–120	280–420	240–375
	$\frac{1}{8}$ to $\frac{1}{2}$	35–70	20–55	50–110	40–75	180–330	170–275
Steel Classes III and IV	$\frac{1}{32}$ to $\frac{1}{8}$	35–80	25–60	50–130	40–100	170–330	150–310
	$\frac{1}{8}$ to $\frac{1}{2}$	20–55	15–40	30–90	20–65	110–275	100–220

* For definitions of these classes of steel, see Table 10, page 143.

NOTE: For continuous cuts without lubricant, decrease speeds 25 per cent. For intermittent cuts with lubricant, decrease speeds 15 per cent. For intermittent cuts without lubricant, decrease speeds 40 per cent. For light finishing cuts and fine feeds, speeds can be increased 50 to 100 per cent.

TABLE 7. PROPER RAKES AND CLEARANCES FOR TOOL BITS

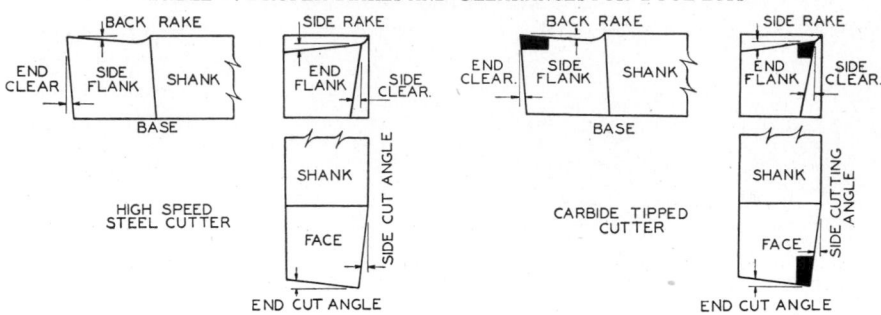

The following rakes and clearances are recommended for average conditions. Special production setups may require some variations:

Rakes and Clearances in Degrees

| | High Speed Steel Cutters | | | | Carbide-Tipped Cutters | | | |
	Back Rake	Side Rake	Side Clearance	Front Clearance	Back Rake	Side Rake	Side Clearance	Front Clearance
Irons								
Standard Malleable Iron	3	3	6	6	0	0–2	4–6	4–6
Pearlitic Malleable Iron	6	6	6	6	0	0–2	4–6	4–6
Cast Iron, Soft — Brinell 160–193	3	3	6	6	0	0–2	4–6	4–6
Cast Iron, Medium — Brinell 200–220	2–3	2–3	6	6	0	0–2	4–6	4–6
Cast Iron, Hard — Brinell 220–240	2	2	6	6	0	0–2	4–6	4–6
Steels								
Screw Stock, SAE 1112, 1118 AISI B1112, C1118	15	20	6	6	0	3	6	6
Plain Carbon, SAE 1020, 1035 AISI C1020, C1035	15	15	6	6	0	3	6	6
High Carbon, SAE 1095 AISI C1095	5	10	6	6	0	3	6	6
Nickel Alloy, SAE 2317, 2330 AISI A2317, A2330	15	15	6	6	0	3	6	6
Nickel Chromium, SAE 3140, 3240 AISI A3140, A3240	8–10	12	6	6	0	3	6	6
Chrome Molybdenum, SAE 4140 AISI A4140	10	12	6	6	0	3	6	6
Nickel Molybdenum, SAE 4615 AISI A4615	15	15	6	6	0	3	6	6
Chrome Vanadium, SAE 6150 AISI E6150	8	12	6	6	0	3	6	6
Nonferrous								
Aluminum	8	18	6	6	25	15	8–10	8–10
Brass	2	2	6	6	0	4	6	6
Bronze	6	5	6	6	0	4	6	6
Copper	10	25	6	6	4	20	8–10	8–10

For carbide-tipped tools, keep back rake angle as small as possible for greatest strength. Use negative rakes for older machines.

Most of the abuses in the handling and operation of machine tools are traceable to the operator and the training he has had. The shop supervisor of today is confronted with an almost total lack of highly trained machinists of the old school, who were well versed in the care of the machine. Much time has been spent in training people to operate, and very little in training them to care for their equipment. If the operator understands that his own success or failure depends largely upon the care he gives the equipment entrusted to his use, the shop supervisor will find his job of getting the right feeds and speeds much easier.

Tables 8 and 9 which follow show the speed and feed calculations and a quick reference for the revolutions required to obtain a given surface speed.

TABLE 8. SPEED AND FEED CALCULATIONS
For Turning Tools, Milling Cutters, and Other Rotating Tools

To Find	Having	Formula
Revolutions per Minute = R.P.M.	Cutting Speed in Feet per Minute = C.S., and Diameter of Tool in Inches (or Diameter of Piece Being Turned) = D	$R.P.M. = \dfrac{C.S. \times 12}{D \times 3.1416}$
Cutting (surface cutting) Speed in Feet per Minute = C.S.	Diameter of Tool in Inches (or Diameter of Piece Being Turned = D, and Revolutions per Minute = R.P.M.	$C.S. = \dfrac{D \times 3.1416 \times R.P.M.}{12}$
Feed per Minute in Inches = Fd.M.	Feed per Revolution in Inches = Fd.R., and Revolutions per Minute = R.P.M.	$Fd.M. = Fd.R. \times R.P.M.$
Feed per Revolution in Inches = Fd.R.	Feed per Minute in Inches = Fd.M., and Revolutions per Minute = R.P.M.	$Fd.R. = \dfrac{Fd.M.}{R.P.M.}$
Feed per Tooth = Fd.T.	Number of Teeth in Tool = T, and Feed per Revolution in Inches = Fd.R.	$Fd.T. = \dfrac{Fd.R.}{T}$
Feed per Tooth = Fd.T.	Number of Teeth in Tool = T, Feed in Inches per Minute = Fd.M., and Speed in Revolutions per Minute = R.P.M.	$Fd.T. = \dfrac{Fd.M.}{T \times R.P.M.}$
Number of Cutting Teeth per Minute = T.M.	Number of Teeth in Tool = T, and Revolutions per Minute = R.P.M.	$T.M. = T \times R.P.M.$

TABLE 9. CUTTING SPEEDS

For Drills, Reamers, Milling Cutters, Turning Tools, and Taps

Cutting Speed, Feet per Minute

Revolutions per Minute

Expressed to nearest single R.P.M. below 1000, and to nearest 10 above 1000.

Higher or intermediate speeds are easily found by multiplication or division. For 150 feet, use the 50 column and multiply by 3. For 25 feet, use the 50 column and divide by 2.

Diameter of Moving Cutter or Piece, Inches	30	40	50	60	70	80	90	100	120	140	200
$\frac{1}{16}$	1830	2440	3060	3670	4280	4890	5500	6110	7330	8560	
$\frac{3}{32}$	1220	1630	2040	2440	2850	3260	3670	4070	4890	5700	8150
$\frac{1}{8}$	917	1220	1530	1830	2140	2440	2750	3060	3670	4280	6110
$\frac{5}{32}$	733	978	1220	1470	1710	1960	2200	2440	2930	3420	4890
$\frac{3}{16}$	611	815	1020	1220	1430	1630	1830	2040	2440	2850	4070
$\frac{7}{32}$	524	698	873	1050	1220	1400	1570	1750	2100	2440	3490
$\frac{1}{4}$	458	611	764	917	1070	1220	1380	1530	1830	2140	3060
$\frac{5}{16}$	367	489	611	733	856	978	1100	1220	1470	1710	2440
$\frac{3}{8}$	306	408	509	611	713	815	916	1020	1220	1430	2040
$\frac{13}{32}$	282	376	470	564	658	752	846	940	1130	1320	1880
$\frac{7}{16}$	262	349	437	524	611	699	786	874	1050	1220	1750
$\frac{1}{2}$	229	306	382	459	535	611	688	764	917	1070	1530
$\frac{9}{16}$	204	272	340	407	475	543	611	679	813	951	1360
$\frac{5}{8}$	184	245	306	367	428	489	552	612	736	857	1220
$1\frac{1}{16}$	167	222	273	333	389	444	500	555	666	770	1110
$\frac{3}{4}$	153	203	254	306	357	408	458	508	610	711	1020
$1\frac{3}{16}$	142	190	237	284	332	379	427	474	569	664	948
$\frac{7}{8}$	131	175	219	262	306	349	392	438	526	613	876
$1\frac{5}{16}$	122	163	204	244	285	326	366	407	488	570	814
1	115	153	191	229	267	306	344	382	458	535	764
$1\frac{1}{8}$	102	136	170	204	238	272	306	340	408	476	680
$1\frac{1}{4}$	92	123	153	183	214	245	274	306	367	428	612
$1\frac{3}{8}$	83	111	139	167	195	222	250	278	334	389	556
$1\frac{1}{2}$	76	102	127	153	178	204	230	254	305	356	508
$1\frac{5}{8}$	71	94	117	141	165	188	212	234	281	328	468
$1\frac{3}{4}$	66	87	109	131	153	175	196	218	262	305	436
2	57	76	96	115	134	153	172	191	229	267	382
$2\frac{1}{4}$	51	68	86	102	119	136	153	170	204	238	340
$2\frac{1}{2}$	46	61	76	92	107	122	138	153	184	213	306
$2\frac{3}{4}$	42	56	70	83	97	111	125	139	167	195	278
3	38	51	64	76	89	102	114	127	152	178	254
$3\frac{1}{2}$	33	44	55	66	76	87	98	109	131	153	218
4	29	38	48	57	67	76	86	96	115	134	191
$4\frac{1}{2}$	25	34	42	51	59	68	76	85	102	119	170
5	23	31	38	46	54	61	69	76	92	107	153
$5\frac{1}{2}$	21	28	35	42	49	56	63	69	83	97	139
6	19	26	32	38	45	51	57	64	76	89	127
7	16	22	27	33	38	44	49	55	66	76	109
8	14	19	24	29	33	38	43	48	57	67	96
9	13	17	21	25	30	34	38	42	51	59	85
10	12	15	19	23	27	31	35	38	46	54	77
12	10	13	16	19	22	25	29	32	38	44	63

RELATIVE MACHINABILITY

This section utilizes generally accepted machinability ratings for various materials, originally investigated by steel makers and large volume machiners. For the purposes of this book, the following discussion extends certain parts of published material by including, in addition, other steels designated by the American Iron and Steel Institute (A.I.S.I.) to be close or approximate substitutes for those originally listed by being comparable in chemistry and physical properties. The corresponding S.A.E. (Society of Automotive Engineers, Inc.) numbers are shown where applicable. As the differences in composition ranges between the A.I.S.I. steels are less than those of the S.A.E., a single S.A.E. number is apt to include several A.I.S.I. specifications.

For both A.I.S.I. and S.A.E. systems, numerals are used to indicate chemical composition. However, for A.I.S.I. steels, capital letter prefixes identify the process of manufacture for the steel considered standard. Further, A.I.S.I. employs lower case letters as suffixes to indicate special requirements affecting quality; these latter are explained on page 332, in the section of this book presenting greater details of the respective systems, including exact chemical compositions.

Prefixes before A.I.S.I. steel numbers are used as follows:

A designates basic open hearth alloy steels.
B denotes acid Bessemer carbon steels.
C denotes basic open hearth carbon steels.
CB denotes either acid Bessemer or basic open hearth carbon steels, at the option of the manufacturer.
D denotes acid open hearth carbon steels.
E designates electric furnace alloy steels.

MACHINABILITY RATINGS

The rating of machinability is on a relative and not an absolute basis. While speeds and feeds of cutting the metal are among the most important considerations, the tool life, or period in use before the tool must be reground, is also a strong influence in establishing a rating. Likewise, the metal's relative capabilities to be readily finished with good surfaces and closely to size affect each rating.

The metal selected as a standard and so given a 100 per cent rating is the A.I.S.I. steel B1112 cold rolled or cold drawn Bessemer screw stock. As 180 feet per minute is currently a usual cutting speed for this steel in automatic screw machines, then when defining its machining characteristics the speed is held at this figure, but the feed is varied to attain normal tool life and surface finish, using a suitable cutting fluid. When other metals are being tested, the feeds and speeds are varied to attain comparable tool life and finish results, and the rating assigned fairly expresses the ratio of the speed at which the steel in question may be machined when compared with the standard. It should be noted that the machinability ratings of the other rolled steels listed are also based on their being in a cold rolled or cold drawn condition, and further that if they have been heat-treated or processed in any other way they will have different ratings.

Machinability of Hot and Cold Rolled Steels

Because of the favorable price differential many users prefer hot rolled steels for numerous purposes. The effect of hot rolling may be expressed briefly as follows:

1. In steels containing up to 0.30 per cent carbon, cold rolled or cold drawn bars have better machinability than hot rolled bars.

2. In steels containing from 0.30 to 0.40 per cent carbon, there is little difference in machinability between cold rolled and hot rolled bars.

3. In steels containing over 0.40 per cent carbon, the hot rolled material has superior machinability over the cold rolled or cold drawn. It is recommended that plain carbon steels with over 0.40 per cent carbon and alloy steels over 0.30 per cent carbon be annealed for machining.

Machinability of Open Hearth and Electric Steels

A question may arise whether two steels of like chemical composition will have different machinability if one has been made by the open hearth and the other by electric furnace practice. The two manufacturing practices are not considered to cause different machining characteristics, as there is no apparent difference between the grain structures under similar conditions of analysis, furnace bottoms (acid or basic), and subsequent treatment.

Machining a hot rolled C1019 bar, 1⅝ inches in diameter, in a turret lathe.

TABLE 10. MACHINABILITY RATINGS

Machinability ratings are arranged in this table in four classes or groups for malleable irons, other irons, and steels, plus two classes for nonferrous alloys. The percentage values given express relative machinability, the higher values indicating the more easily machined materials. This grouping simplifies the use of the table of recommendations for applying cutting fluids to various machining processes, Table 11.

It should be noted that comparisons are for bar steels only. The table numbers in **bold** face type are the A.I.S.I. steels whose ranges are closely equivalent or represent a more narrow range within the S.A.E. specification also indicated by **bold** face type. The other A.I.S.I. listings in light face type may be considered as substitutes, comparable in chemical and physical properties, though certain of their element ranges are slightly over or under the S.A.E. specification limits. When no S.A.E. equivalent is given, there is no comparable analysis.

The range of hardness values for each of the listed ferrous materials indicates a desirable range for normal machinability and, in general, describes usual commercial practice in filling purchase orders.

In this table, the following references are used:

   *   denotes steel in mill annealed condition.
  (b)   denotes acid Bessemer carbon steel.
  (c)   denotes spheroidize annealed by mill.
  (d)   denotes A.I.S.I. type No. 303; 18–8 of free machining type.

Material	Machinability Rating in Per Cent	Normal Machinability Brinell Hardness	Closely or Approximately Comparable A.I.S.I. Spec. No.	Comparable 1943 S.A.E. Spec. No.
Class I — Ferrous, Ratings 70 Per Cent Plus				
Irons †				
Standard Malleable Iron.	120 Per Cent	110–145		
Pearlitic Malleable Iron..	90	180–200		
Pearlitic Malleable Iron..	80	200–240		
Stainless Iron (b)........	70	163–207		
Steels				
Cast Steel — 0.35 Per Cent Carbon..............	70	170–212		
A.I.S.I. Steels				
C1016.................	70	137–174	C1018, **C1019**	**1016**
C1022................	70	159–192	C1016, **C1019**	**1022**
C1110.................	85	137–166	C1109, C1113, C1120	
B1111................	95	179–229	B1112	**1111**
B1112.................	100	179–229	B1113	**1112**
B1113.................	135	179–229	B1112	**1113**
C1115................	85	143–179	**C1116**, C1121	**1115**
C1117................	85	143–179	**C1112**	**1117**
C1118...............⚬	80	143–179	C1122	**1118**
C1120.................	80	143–179	C1109, C1110, C1113	
C1132................	75	187–229	C1137	**1132**
C1137................	70	187–229	C1132	**1137**

† These values established by the Handbook Committee and approved by Professor O. W. Boston.

(Table 10 continues on following pages)

Table 10. (Continued)

Material	Machinability Rating in Per Cent	Normal Machinability Brinell Hardness	Closely or Approximately Comparable A.I.S.I. Spec. No.	Comparable 1943 S.A.E. Spec. No.
A.I.S.I. Steels				
A4023...............	70	156–207	A4024, A4027, A4032, A4037, A4047, A4063, A4065	**4023**
A4027*...............	70	166–212		**4027**
A4119...............	70	170–217	A4120	**4119**

Class II — Ferrous, Ratings 50 Per Cent to 65 Per Cent

Material	Machinability Rating in Per Cent	Normal Machinability Brinell Hardness	Closely or Approximately Comparable A.I.S.I. Spec. No.	Comparable 1943 S.A.E. Spec. No.
A.I.S.I. Steels				
C1020...............	65 Per Cent	137–174	C1014, C1015, **C1017,** CB1017, **C1021, C1023**	**1020**
C1030...............	65	170–212	C1029, CB1032, C1033, C1035	**1030**
C1035...............	65	174–217	C1030, CB1032, **C1033,** C1038, C1040	**1035**
C1040*...............	60	179–229	C1035, **C1038,** C1042, C1043	**1040**
C1045*...............	60	179–229	C1040, **C1042,** C1043, C1046, C1050	**1045**
C1141...............	65	183–241		1141
A2317...............	55	174–217		**2317**
A3045*...............	60	179–229		
A3120...............	60	163–207	**A3115**	3120
A3130*.............	55	179–217		**3130**
A3140*.............	55	187–229	A3135	**3140**
A3145*.............	50	187–235	A3140, **A3141**	**3145**
A4032*.............	65	170–229	A4023, A4024	4032
A4037*.............	65	170–229	A4027, A4037, A4047, A4063, A4065	4037
A4042*.............	60	183–235		4042
A4047*.............	55	183–235	See A4037	4047
A4130*.............	65	187–229	**E4132,** A4134	**4130**
A4137*.............	60	187–229		4137
A4145*.............	55	187–229		4145
A4150*.............	50	187–235		**4150**
A4320*.............	60	187–235	A4317	**4320**
A4615.............	65	174–217	**E4617,** A4620, E4620	**4615**
A4640*.............	55	187–235		4640
A4815.............	50	187–229	A4821	**4815**
A5045.............	65	179–229		
A5120.............	65	170–212		5120
A5140*.............	60	174–229		
A5150*.............	55	179–235	A5145, A5152	

TABLE 10. (CONTINUED)

Material	Machinability Rating in Per Cent	Normal Machinability Brinell Hardness	Closely or Approximately Comparable A.I.S.I. Spec. No.	Comparable 1943 S.A.E. Spec. No.
N.E. Steels				
NE8024	60	174–217		
NE8124	55	174–217		
NE8233*	60	179–229		
NE8339*	60	179–229		
NE8620	60	170–217		
NE8630*	65	179–229		
NE8724	65	179–229		
NE8739*	60	179–229		
NE8744*	55	183–235		
NE8749*	50	183–241		
NE8817	60	170–229		

Class III — Ferrous, Ratings 40 Per Cent to 50 Per Cent

Material	Machinability Rating in Per Cent	Normal Machinability Brinell Hardness	Closely or Approximately Comparable A.I.S.I. Spec. No.	Comparable 1943 S.A.E. Spec. No.
Irons†				
Cast Iron‡ — Soft	80 Per Cent	160–193		
Cast Iron‡ — Medium	65	193–220		
Cast Iron‡ — Hard	50	220–240		
Ingot Iron	50	101–131		
Wrought Iron	50	101–131		
Stainless (d)	45	179–212		
A.I.S.I. Steels				
C1008	50	126–163	C1006, CB1008, **C1010, C1012,** CB1012	1008
C1010	50	131–170	See 1008	**1010**
C1015	50	131–170	C1010, **C1012,** CB1012, **C1014,** C1017, CB1017	**1015**
C1050*	50	179–229	C1045, C1046, C1055	**1050**
C1070*	45	183–241		
A1320	50	170–229	A1321	
A1330*	50	179–235		**1330**
A1335*	50	179–235		**1335**
A1340*	45	179–235		**1340**
A2330*	50	179–229		**2330**
A2340*	45	179–235	A2335	**2340**
A3240*	45	183–235		**3240**
E4150*	45	269–321		4150
A4340*	45	187–241		4340
A6120	50	179–217		
A6145*	50	179–235		
A6152 (c)	45	183–241	**E6150**	**6150**
A9260*	45	187–255	A9255	**9260**

† These values established by the Handbook Committee and approved by Professor O. W. Boston.

‡ Unalloyed.

(*Table 10 is concluded on following page*)

TABLE 10. (CONCLUDED)

Material	Machinability Rating in Per Cent	Normal Machinability Brinell Hardness	Closely or Approximately Comparable A.I.S.I. Spec. No.	Comparable 1943 S.A.E Spec. No.
N.E. Steels				
NE8442*...............	45	187–255		
NE8447*...............	40	187–255		
NE8949*...............	50	187–255		

Class IV — Ferrous, Ratings 40 Per Cent or Below

Irons				
Ni-Resist*..............	30 Per Cent			
Special Steels				
Stainless 18–8*..........	25			
Manganese oil hardening steel (c)..............	30			
Tool Steel — Low Tungsten Chromium and Carbon (c)...........	30			
High Speed Steel (c).....	30			
High Carbon, High Chromium Tool Steel (c)...	25			
A.I.S.I. Steels				
A2515*...............	30	179–229	E2512, **A2514,** E2517	**2515**
E3310*................	40	170–229	E3316	**3312**
A5150*...............	37	287–341	A5145, A5152	**5150**
E52100 (c).............	30	183–229	E52098, E52099, E52101, E52107	**52100**

Class V — Nonferrous, Ratings Above 100 Per Cent

Alloys				
Magnesium Alloys.......	500–2000 Per Cent			
Aluminum 11-S.........	500–2000			
Aluminum 2-S.........	300–1500			
Aluminum 17-S.........	300–1500			
Brass, leaded...........	150– 600			
Brass, yellow............	200			
Brass, red..............	200			
Bronze, lead-bearing.....	200– 500			
Zinc...................	200			

Class VI — Nonferrous, Ratings Less Than 100 Per Cent

Alloys				
Gun Metal.............	60 Per Cent			
Bronze, manganese......	40			
Copper, cast............	70			
Copper, rolled..........	60			
Nickel.................	20			
Monel Metal, cast.......	35			
Monel Metal, rolled.... ˙.	45			
Monel "K" Metal.......	50			
Inconel................	45			
Everdur................	60			

CUTTING FLUID RECOMMENDATIONS

The following recommendations for cutting fluids follow those of a group of men eminent in this field.* They are intended to serve as a guide to the choice of a cutting fluid. It must be remembered that a cutting fluid should be selected for the individual operation, the material being machined, the tool material, size, and shape, and the conditions of operation, such as speed, depth of cut, feed, tool life desired, chip formation, and finish. These are all factors bearing on the final decision.

These recommendations represent the average practice of the majority of users of cutting fluids when normal operating conditions are maintained:

1. Generally speaking, mineral-lard oil and sulphurized oil mixtures of low sulphur percentages are interchangeable.

2. Sulphurized oils have a tendency to stain certain nonferrous materials, such as copper and its alloys.

3. Certain materials, such as carbon tetrachloride, chloroform, and other volatile solvents should not be added to cutting fluids as harmful physiological effects might follow.

4. In the machining of aluminum, cutting oils are often diluted with kerosene or mineral seal oil with satisfactory results. Kerosene up to 15 per cent is frequently added to emulsions to improve the quality of the finished surface.

5. Magnesium and its alloys are usually machined with mineral seal oil or dry. A supply of powdered asbestos should be kept handy to smother a fire, just in case. Tools should be kept sharp and heavy feeds used. Chips should not be permitted to accumulate on the machine.

6. In machining brass, it is advisable to apply a cutting fluid to function as a coolant.

7. In turning Monel Metal, it has been found that an emulsion gives a slightly longer tool life than a sulphurized mineral oil.

* The Independent Research Committee on Cutting Fluids, established in 1937, includes as members at present Joseph Geschelin, Chilton Company, Detroit, chairman; Professor O. W. Boston, University of Michigan, Ann Arbor; G. A. Beiter, Standard Oil Company (Indiana), Chicago; H. M. Fearon, Standard Oil Company of New Jersey, New York; Floyd Fritts, Standard Oil Company, Detroit; C. B. Harding, Sun Oil Company, Detroit; Dr. Raymond Haskell, The Texas Company, New York; W. D. Huffman, Chevrolet-Forge, Detroit; John F. Kennedy, Buick Motor Company, Flint, Michigan; C. M. Larson, Sinclair Refining Company, New York; H. E. Martin, E. F. Houghton and Company, Detroit; B. B. Mears, Petroleum Advisers, New York; James T. Beard, Socony Vacuum Oil Company, New York; H. L. Moir, Pure Oil Company, Chicago; F. F. Musgrave, The Lubrizol Corporation, Cleveland; W. H. Oldacre, D. A. Stuart and Company, Chicago; E. M. Slaughter, Republic Steel Corporation, Detroit; G. L. Sumner, Westinghouse Electric and Manufacturing Company, East Pittsburgh. The committee's findings were based on research work conducted for the committee by Professor Boston and Messrs. Moir, Oldacre, and Slaughter. These findings were published under the title "Machinability Ratings of Metals and Cutting Fluid Recommendations" in *Metal Progress*, October, 1943.

8. In general, cutting fluids should be applied in large quantities at the highest velocity possible without splashing. The fluid should be applied directly on the tool point where the chip is being formed.

9. When carbide tools are used, the cutting fluid should flood the tool before the start of the cut and must be applied continuously during the cut. The use of sulphurized oils on carbide tools is reported to be injurious to the tools.

10. Cutting fluids should be kept cool for satisfactory tool life, and the temperature of the fluid should not exceed 110 degrees Fahrenheit.

11. Cutting fluids should be kept clean — free from chips, bacteria, and high acidity.

12. Oils should be used on complicated machines where the lubrication of the machine, such as tool slides, must be provided for.

13. On some jobs, such as milling and drilling, the lubrication of the chips in the flutes or chip space is an important factor in chip removal.

14. On high-speed operations, cooling is more important than lubrication, inasmuch as the speed itself usually provides good surface quality.

Recommendations for certain types of machining operation, considering the severity of the cut, are shown in Table 11. This table should be used in conjunction with Table 10 for the grouping of the materials in the six general classifications.

Machining a welded gear case of C1020 steel on a horizontal boring machine.

By Independent Research Committee on Cutting Fluids

This table classifies machining operations in an arrangement indicating the order of their severity. Recommendations for cutting fluids consider the type of machining operation and the character of material being fabricated as expressed by the six classes of materials mentioned in the table. Preferred recommendations are in **bold face type**.

Symbols for Cutting Fluids

K. — Kerosene; L. — Lard oil; MO. — Mineral oils; ML. — Mineral-lard oils; Sul. — Sulphurized oils; see note (a); Em. — Soluble or emulsifiable oils and compounds; Dry — No cutting fluid.

Severity Rating	Type of Machining Operation	Ferrous Metals; Steels and Irons				Nonferrous Metals	
		Class I 70 per cent Plus*	Class II 50 to 70 per cent*	Class III 40 to 50 per cent*	Class IV Below 40 per cent*	Class V 100 per cent Plus* / 100 per cent*	Class VI Below 100 per cent*
(Greatest) 1	Broaching; internal	Em. Sul. (a)	**Sul.** Em.	**Sul.** Em.	**Sul.** Em.	MO. Em.	Sul. ML.
2	Broaching; surface	Em. Sul.	**Em.** Sul.	**Sul.** Em.	**Sul.** Em.	MO. Em.	Sul. ML.
2	Threading; pipe	Sul.	**Sul.** ML.	Sul.	Sul.	Em.	Sul. (c)
3	Tapping; plain	Sul.	Sul.	Sul.	Sul.	Em. Dry	Sul. ML.
3	Threading; plain	Sul.	Sul.	Sul.	Sul.	Em. Sul.	Sul.
4	Gear shaving	Sul. L.	Sul. L.	Sul. L.	Sul. L.	ML.	ML. MO. Sul.
4	Reaming; plain	ML. Sul.	ML. Sul.	ML. S.l.	ML. Sul.		Sul. ML.
4	Gear cutting (d)	Sul. ML. Em.	Sul.	Sul.	Sul. ML.	MO. ML. Em.	
5	Drilling; deep	**Em.** ML.	Sul. **Em.**	Sul.	Sul.	MO. ML. Em.	Sul. ML.
6	Milling; plain	**Em.** ML. Sul.	Em.	Em.	Sul.	Em. MO. Dry	Sul. Em.
6	Milling; multiple cutter	ML.	Sul.	Sul.	**Sul.** ML.	Em. MO. Dry	**Sul.** Em.
7	Boring; multiple head	**Sul.** Em.	**Sul.** Em.	**Sul.** Em.	Sul. Em.	K. Dry Em.	Sul. Em.
7	Multiple spindle automatic screw machines and turret lathes; drilling, forming, turning, reaming, cutting off, tapping, threading	Sul. Em. ML.	Sul. Em. ML.	Sul. Em. ML.	Sul. ML. Em.	Em. Dry ML.	Sul.
8	High speed, light feed automatic screw machines; drilling, form-ing, tapping, threading, turn-ing, reaming, box milling, cut-ting off	Sul. Em. ML.	Sul. Em. ML.	Sul. Em. ML.	Sul. ML. Em.	Em. Dry ML.	Sul.
9	Drilling	Em.	Em.	Em.	Em. Sul.	Em. Dry	Em.
9	Planing, shaping	**Em.** Sul. ML.	**Em.** Sul. ML.	**Em.** Sul.	**Em.** Sul.	Em. Dry	Em.
9	Turning; single point tool form tools	Em. Sul. ML.	Em. Sul. ML.	Em. Sul. ML.	Em. Sul. ML.	Em. Dry ML.	Em. Sul.
10 (Least)	Sawing; circular, hack	Sul. ML. Em.	Sul. Em. ML.	Sul. Em. ML.	Sul. Em. ML.	Dry MO. Em.	Sul. Em. ML.
	Grinding; 1. plain	Em.	Em.	Em.	Em.	Em.	Em.
	2. form (thread, etc.)	Sul.	Sul.	Sul.	Sul.	MO. Sul.	Sul.

NOTES: (a) Oils containing both sulphur and chlorine when carefully manufactured and sponsored may be used where sulphurized oils are indicated.

(c) In threading copper, palm oil is frequently used.

(d) It is reported by several observers that emulsions are usually unsatisfactory on some precision machines, like Fellows gear shapers and Gleason gear generators.

* Machinability rating based on 100 per cent for cold drawn Bessemer screw stock (specification B1112). See Table 10 for lists of metals in each class.

The reader's attention is directed to the Engineering Tables and Data toward the close of this volume. Those concerned with machining may find many items of general and specific interest, such as:

1. Tables for converting inches to millimeters, and to reverse the conversion.
2. Decimal equivalents.
3. Drill sizes for specific taps.
4. Details of screw threads.
5. Hardness tests.
6. Strengths of materials.
7. A.I.S.I. and S.A.E. steels.

XII

RECOMMENDATIONS TO USERS OF
MALLEABLE IRON CASTINGS

NEITHER malleable iron nor any other cast metal is bought at a fixed price per pound as a finished part.[53] Rather, the final cost of a machine part to the purchaser depends upon the price per pound of the casting, the cost of machining and assembling, and the service life of the part itself. All three elements which thus determine final cost can be effectively controlled by co-operation at the start between the foundryman and the purchaser of the casting.

Given full information about the ultimate use for which the casting is designed and about the pattern equipment with which it is to be produced, the foundryman at this early stage not only can prepare more accurate esti-

The ductility of malleable iron may be judged from this single continuous chip, obtained from a production casting.

mates but also can often suggest ways to decrease the cost and increase the usefulness of the casting. Future machining operations can often thus be simplified and assembly can be speeded up by minor alterations in the casting, or longer probable life can be assured for the finished part by a shrewd alteration in design based on first-hand knowledge.

For work already designed and ready for production, the purchaser when asking for quotations should, as for new work, give the foundryman full information about the casting wanted, the use to which it is to be put, the equipment furnished, the quantity desired, and the specifications which must be met. When a new casting is contemplated, the time to consult the foundry is as soon as the designing engineer has assembled information concerning the design and the pattern equipment. Too often a part is designed, drawings are made, and pattern equipment is finished and turned over to the foundry without this preparatory discussion, so that the opportunity for cutting cost and gaining efficiency is lost.

ESSENTIAL INFORMATION

The data [54] listed in this section should accompany inquiries and orders from buyers of castings; they are the necessary basis for sound estimates:

1. *Class of malleable iron required*

The minimum mechanical properties, or the A.S.T.M. specification to which the castings must conform, should be stated.

2. *Detailed drawing of casting and sample casting if available*

Whenever possible, the drawing should give the foundry the actual or estimated weight of the casting.

The drawing should show important dimensions, dimension tolerances, locating points, and machined surfaces, with the amount of finish to be allowed.

If a specific location is desired for symbol number, pattern number, and trademark, and if there is a preference between raised and sunken symbols, this information should appear on the drawing. Part and pattern numbers should be simplified and systematized as much as possible to avoid confusion in the foundry.

3. *Description of available pattern equipment and its condition*

The description should include the following:

A. Type of pattern:

Metal match plates — the number on the plate and the size of the flask, including depth

Mounted wood or metal patterns — the number in each mounting and the size of the flask, including depth

Cope and drag patterns (wood or metal) — the number of pieces per mold, the size of the flask, including depth, and the pin centers

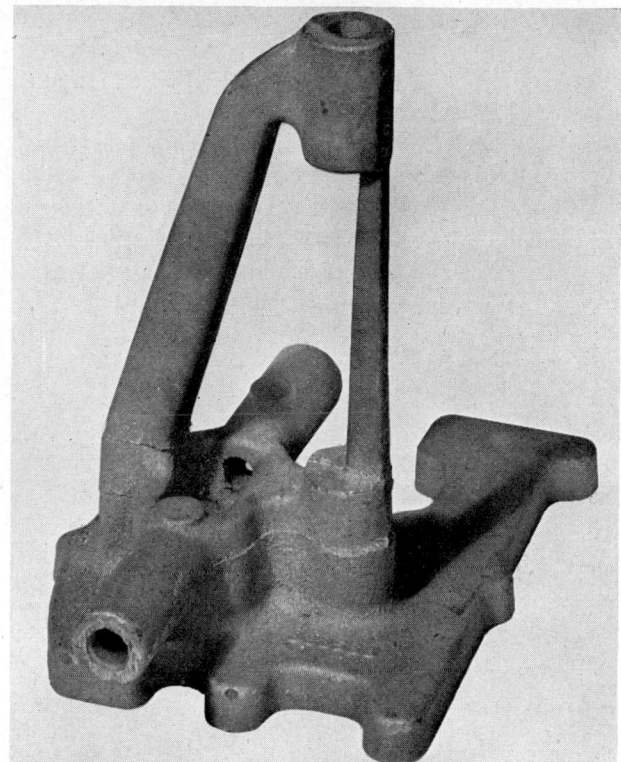

This casting of American malleable iron replaces an original welded assembly requiring one steel casting, one forging, three pieces of round bar stock, and one flat. The vertical bar in the center of the piece is a tie bar used to prevent any possible distortion in casting or in the anneal, and is cut out before the sections at its top and base are drilled.

Gated patterns in vibrator frames — the number in the frame and the size of the flask, including depth

Gated patterns — the number on the gate, the over-all size, and the size of the flask, including depth

Single loose patterns — the number of patterns, whether they are split or flatback and so suitable for mounting, and the over-all size

B. Material from which pattern is made:

Aluminum

Brass

Wood (hard or soft)

White metal

Cast iron

C. Number of cores per casting, with kind and type of core boxes:

Number of cores to each box

Material from which core box is made

Whether core box is rigged for use in core-blowing machine

Number and kind of core driers

The purchaser customarily furnishes pattern equipment, core driers, straightening dies, gauges, and any other such equipment needed for the production of the casting in question. Gating charges are paid by the purchaser, who sometimes also provides flasks.

If the customer does not supply patterns and wishes the foundry to make them at his expense, he should state the quantities that will be required and ask the foundry for recommendations as to suitable equipment.

If the customer is to furnish flasks, he should state their size, type, and construction. If new flasks are to be constructed at his expense, the foundry should recommend their size and type.

4. *Description of the service or use of the casting*

If the castings are to be subjected to pressure, shock, tension, abrasion, or other such use requirements, the foundry should be so informed.

If tests are to be made, the methods of testing to be followed should be specified.

If test bars are to be required in accordance with specifications of the A.S.T.M., the customer should so state. He should also state where and by whom inspection or testing is to be done.

Though not suitable for all gear applications, malleable iron was employed in this marine motor reverse-gear mechanism, at a substantial saving in machining cost over the material formerly used.

How well the properties of American malleable iron — physical, mechanical, and engineering — can cope with difficult design problems is illustrated in this part for a military installation. The character of the casting, particularly its nonuniform section, is such that malleable iron was specified for it after difficulty had been encountered in producing it in another cast metal.

5. *The number of pieces to be ordered of each pattern, with delivery dates and schedules, should be given.*

6. *Special requirements and finish*

When they are required, special operations such as pressure testing, drilling, drifting, gauging, coining or straightening castings, grinding gates, or special grinding should be specified.

Special tolerances, when required, should be specified.

Special surface finish, such as galvanizing, sherardizing, or plating, should be specified if it is required. Foundrymen can sometimes suggest special finishing operations which, though adding to the initial cost of the casting, will appreciably lower the cost of the finished part.

7. *The price basis desired whether per piece or per pound, should be stated, with the f.o.b. point for shipment.*

8. *Any special crating, packing, or marking desired should be specified.*

On the basis of full information from customers as outlined in the foregoing schedule, malleable iron foundries undertake to furnish castings free from injurious defects and of surface smoothness and dimensional accuracy to the extent permitted by good foundry practice. Quality of castings is determined by the foundries through regular tests and well-established laboratory supervision. Customary quality control, however, does not include the examination of test bars made as parts of individual castings or unusual inspection operations such as the x-ray, gamma-ray, or magnetic testing of each individual casting.

For commercial castings meeting these qualifications, cost estimates and price quotations can generally be directly determined. However, a group of special requirements exist which are outside the scope of usual foundry practice, and which lead to special costs that often cannot be finally determined in advance of manufacture. Today's industrial mass-production practices often require very close-fitting jigs and fixtures in finishing operations by machine tools and therefore necessitate special sizing operations on castings. Similarly, some critical equipment such as that involving contingent danger to human safety must be constructed of materials with no flaws whatsoever, even the inconsequential flaws that are ignored in usual operations; castings to be used in such equipment must undergo special tests and examinations. The special services involved in these operations are among the functions which many malleable iron foundries are prepared to perform when desired. They lead to additional direct and indirect costs, which necessarily are reflected in the price to the customer. Operations of this sort are the following:

1. Special sizing of castings by coining operations.

2. One hundred per cent gauging and inspection of individual castings.

3. X-ray, gamma-ray, magnetic, fluorescent, lacquer, or other similar special testing and examination.

4. Pressure testing.

5. Testing to destruction of a scheduled series of castings produced.

6. Elevated or depressed temperature tests.

Special rust proofing, lacquering, and painting of castings can be supplied by many malleable iron foundries, but at an additional cost.

XIII

THE MANUFACTURE OF MALLEABLE IRON

AMERICAN malleable iron is being made in more than 100 plants located in the various industrial areas of the United States. Plants vary in size from those manufacturing a hundred tons monthly and organized for the efficient handling of relatively small orders to those producing several thousands of tons monthly and mechanized for large-quantity continuous production. This chapter is devoted only to the fundamental divisions of the manufacturing process.

Metallurgically, the process consists of but two steps: manufacture of the white iron casting, and subsequent conversion of it into the tough malleable product.[1] The malleable iron foundry, however, necessarily includes a number of separate divisions corresponding to the various operations into which these two steps are separated to increase efficiency in the production of the final casting from the raw materials, pig iron and scrap. The major operations, which will be treated here in sequence, are melting; molding; core making; pouring and subsequent shaking out; hard iron cleaning and inspection; annealing; soft iron cleaning, finishing, and inspection.

MELTING

The first operation, that of melting, converts the raw materials into a molten metal of adequate temperature for casting and of suitable composition for the production of castings which are to be converted into malleable iron by subsequent heat-treatment.

RAW MATERIALS

The usual furnace charge for malleable iron production, regardless of the type of melting equipment, consists of pig iron, sprue (remelt), malleable and steel scrap. These components should contain silicon, manganese, carbon, phosphorus, and sulphur in amounts necessary to give the desired final composition, due allowance being made for oxidation loss of silicon, manganese, and carbon, and some sulphur increase, during melting.

[157]

The proportion of metal in a typical charge for the manufacture of standard malleable iron is:

	Air Furnace	*Duplexing*
Pig iron	32 per cent	18 per cent
Sprue	50 per cent	50 per cent
Malleable scrap	14 per cent	10 per cent
Steel scrap	4 per cent	22 per cent

These proportions are varied according to individual foundry practices, particularly in duplex melting, and according to the quality and availability of scrap. Coke and limestone of course form part of the cupola charge in the duplex process.

In the old days before blast furnace control was as accurate as it now is, malleable iron foundrymen felt that pig iron from ore originating in certain districts in the country was necessary for the production of good malleable iron. Today most blast furnaces make a "malleable" pig iron. The main requirement is that it must have low phosphorus, preferably under 0.20 per cent, except in duplex melting where the large amount of low-phosphorus scrap customarily used permits higher content in the pig iron.

The composition of the pig iron suitable for the production of direct air furnace melted malleable iron usually runs about as follows: silicon, 1.25 to 2.50 per cent as required; manganese, 0.50 to 1.00 per cent; phosphorus, 0.20 per cent maximum; and sulphur, 0.05 per cent maximum. The carbon content of the pig iron is, of course, dependent upon the blast furnace operation and is generally in inverse ratio to the silicon content, with a carbon range of approximately 3.80 to 4.40.

The sprue used in the melting furnace charge includes gates, runners, risers, and scrapped hard-iron castings, all from earlier heats of known composition, and therefore introduces no variable into the charge.[1] It is important to understand that great care must be taken in separating and segregating the sprue and scrap from special types of malleable iron. If an alloyed malleable iron is being produced, the sprue and scrap must be marked and segregated to protect the regular malleable iron from the introduction of foreign elements.

Malleable scrap includes castings which for some reason have been rejected after annealing, as well as the malleable iron parts of scrapped cars, machines, or other equipment which have been purchased as malleable scrap in the open market.

Steel scrap, consisting of rails, splice bars, crop ends, heavy sheets, and flashings, is of low carbon content and is included to reduce the percentage of carbon in the mixture. It must be carefully selected to insure against a detrimental content of elements such as chromium, vanadium, sulphur, tin, tellurium, and molybdenum, which are undesirable in malleable iron because they may interfere with the anneal unless carefully controlled.

Fig. 1. A 10-ton malleable iron air furnace, fired with pulverized coal.

FURNACES

Air Furnace. The air furnace, which is largely used in this country for the manufacture of malleable iron, is of the acid-hearth reverberatory type. The charge is melted in a fairly shallow-walled hearth by flame from fuel in a burner or firebox at one end of the hearth. Passing over the hearth, the flame is drawn off by a stack at the opposite end of the furnace. The first air furnaces were of about 800 to 1,000 pounds' capacity.[55] Today they are usually of 20 to 40 tons or larger, and efficiency is possible with furnaces of capacity as high as 75 to 80 tons through modern control methods, mechanical charging equipment, and mechanical equipment for conveying the molten metal.[3]

The design of a malleable iron furnace is simple. The walls are of neutral firebrick, supported and enclosed by cast iron or steel plates. The bottom is of either silica sand or firebrick. The top is a series of removable firebrick arches known as "bungs." Held in place by adjustable metal frames, the

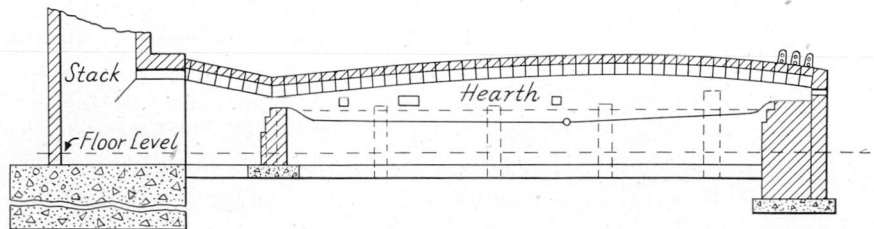

Sectional view of a typical air furnace.

Fig. 2. Replacing the bungs of an air furnace after charging.

bungs are rather flatly arched, their contour being calculated to reflect heat down upon the charge on the hearth, from which function the furnace gets its name "reverberatory." Removal of some of the bungs permits charging the furnace from the top. Charging and handling are generally mechanical.

Usual practice in charging air furnaces is to distribute the sprue on the furnace bottom in a fairly uniform layer extending well over the entire area. The malleable and steel scrap are placed on top of the sprue, and pig iron is charged last. This method puts the smaller material near the bottom so that the larger protects it from excessive oxidation, and also puts the materials with the lowest melting point at the top. When charging has been completed, the bungs are replaced and firing is started. Air furnaces are fired mechanically with pulverized coal and with oil, and some manually with lump bituminous coal.

A 30-ton heat can be melted in an air furnace at a faster rate per ton than a 15-ton heat, because less heat is dissipated through the walls and up the stack. However, though the melting rate is faster, the total elapsed time for one cycle of operation is necessarily longer. This fact frequently leads to the use of smaller furnaces to provide more heats per day even though their rates of melting are slower than for the larger furnace and they produce a smaller total daily tonnage.[3] Melting proceeds from the top down, the pig iron at the top of the charge melting and dripping down to alloy with the scrap and sprue and thus lower the melting point of the mass. In a furnace of average efficiency, a 25-ton charge is generally completely melted in about six hours. Increased melting speed and some saving in fuel cost may be obtained with a recuperator to preheat incoming air, but such an installation necessitates somewhat more costly melting equipment.

As the metal reaches the molten state, impurities contained in the original charge, ash from the fuel, and any silica and clay eroded from the refractory lining, rise and combine to form a coating, called slag, on the surface of the liquid iron. This blanket of slag, which has an insulating effect, is removed through a skim door, after which superheating of the metal progresses rapidly. It may be interesting at this point to note that all ferrous metals in the liquid state, when subjected to an oxidizing flame, first lose some manganese and silicon, and then carbon. After the slag has been skimmed off, the bath becomes more directly exposed to the heating and oxidizing effects of the flame. At this time, in part because of the higher temperature, most of the carbon loss occurs. Further loss during pouring of the heat is controlled by converting the flame to give a reducing rather than an oxidizing effect. Subsequent reactions may require supplemental skimming.

Following the skimming operation, test sprues are poured, cooled, and broken to determine the progress of the heat in arriving at a point where samples from it will no longer contain primary graphite. Test sprues are generally 1¾ to 2 inches in diameter.[2] Chemical tests usually made between 30 minutes and an hour prior to pouring indicate what if any adjustments of silicon and manganese in the form of ferro-silicon and ferro-manganese and of carbon in the form of petroleum coke should be made to the bath to control the chemical progress of the heat and produce the desired white-iron analysis for silicon, manganese, and carbon. Temperatures are judged by experienced operators with suitable instruments. In some plants, test specimens are poured into special types of molds to measure fluidity.

Duplexing. As the name implies, duplexing consists of melting in a double unit. The actual melting is done in a cupola which provides a metal too high in carbon for use in producing standard malleable iron. This hot metal is therefore transferred to a second furnace where it is refined and elevated in temperature. The secondary furnace may be an air, open hearth, or electric furnace. Of these, the air furnace is the most widely used.

Fig. 3. Test sprues. The sprue at the left, taken at the beginning of a heat, shows gray fracture. The slight mottling of the sprue in the center indicates that the heat is nearly ready for pouring. At the right is the pure white fracture showing that the iron is ready to pour.

Duplexing may be continuous, semi-continuous, or intermittent. When the method is continuous, the hot metal flows continually from the cupola to the air or open hearth furnace and is taken from the opposite side of this furnace to be poured into the molds. As these secondary or holding units are sufficiently large to hold at least an hour's supply of metal to be poured, the metal from the cupola stays in the refining furnace at least that long.

A semi-continuous operation consists of the same units, but in this case the refining unit is much larger in relation to the metal to be poured, so that after the holding furnace is once filled up, the cupola is shut off and the holding furnace is operated as a batch furnace. In intermittent duplexing, the cupola is used in conjunction with an electric furnace. In this case a batch of iron is taken from the cupola and put in an electric furnace from which, after refining and superheating, a quantity is removed and distributed to various molding floors for pouring. The process is then repeated.

The duplexing method has the advantage of furnishing a continuous supply of molten metal. It is not generally found to be economical, however, unless the daily melt exceeds 50 tons. The composition of the iron can be controlled closely by the use of either oxidizing or reducing flame. By means of many new types of control for cupolas, the metal entering the refining unit may be made more uniform, thus simplifying the work in the refining unit. As a check on the operation of the refining unit, metal analyses are made regularly during the operation, usually every 30 minutes, thus indicating silicon or manganese additions or reversal of type of flame.

The raw materials used are the same as for air furnace practice, except that coke and limestone are added to the cupola charge, this being done in layers. The coke is necessary for fuel and is low in ash and sulphur, high in British thermal units, and sufficiently strong to support the weight above it in the cupola. The limestone is used to provide a fluxing material and is tapped off as slag. Melting rates in duplexing vary from six to 30 tons an hour. As indicated in the charge formula, a high proportion of scrap may be used.

Open Hearth. The open hearth furnace has been used for the melting of malleable iron for many years, though not extensively. It is either oil- or gas-fired and has an acid lining. Among the advantages of the open hearth are ease of control of the chemical composition during the melting and refining operations, and the fact that the furnace does not require frequent repairs.

Rotary Furnace. The rotary furnace, the only type in which both top and bottom of the charge are heated at the same time, was installed in several American malleable iron foundries between 1934 and 1940. Fired with pulverized coal, it has low fuel consumption and permits rapid melting and superheating.[3] But since it produces only small batches of metal — four to eight tons — the rotary furnace is not widely used in malleable melting. As its silica brick lining must be maintained at temperature at all times, it is most efficient with multiple-shift operation.

Fig. 4. Tapping a malleable iron heat from an air furnace into a large ladle, in which it is conveyed to the pouring floor.

Cradle Furnace. A new development in melting equipment is the cradle type of air furnace, which is a sort of modified rocking furnace, being mounted on rollers. It may be tilted 22 degrees in either direction. In this country the cradle furnace has as yet been used only for duplexing. As the tilting feature permits lip pouring, tapping is unnecessary, delivery of metal from the furnace is faster, and the temperature drop between the spout and the ladle is less than that which occurs with a stationary furnace using a necessarily smaller pouring stream.

Electric Furnace. Electric furnaces are employed mostly for duplexing, although some melting is done in small electric furnaces.

Refractories. Many types of refractory brick are in use in the melting and annealing departments of malleable foundries. Improvements in the refractoriness of brick available for lining air furnaces and cupolas make possible much longer life today than 15 years ago. For the sides of air furnaces, modern super-duty fire-clay brick or a 60 per cent alumina brick with high refractory value is often installed.[56] In addition to refractoriness, the density and maximum strength of the side-wall brick in air furnaces must be considered, for they are important factors in service. Bung brick must withstand severe temperature changes and the abuse of mechanical handling during the charging operation.

MOLDING

Molding, the second of the major operations into which the fundamental process of manufacture of malleable iron is divided, involves a number of important considerations. Prominent among them are:

(1) The pattern equipment from which the molds are made;

(2) Effective gating and feeding;

(3) Molding and facing sand and methods of molding.

Patterns. The original "wood pattern" which is made in accordance with the accurate dimensions of the drawing of the part to be cast may be either a working pattern for the manufacture of very small lots of castings, or a master pattern from which metal working patterns or metal master patterns may be made.

The metal working pattern is used without fixed gates to produce very small quantities of castings, or is gated, generally with several duplicates if size allows, for the manufacture of fairly substantial quantities.

For quantity production of castings, match plates, which consist of light metal plates with pattern halves affixed diametrically opposite to each other, or with the patterns cast integral with the plate, are employed. A detailed discussion of pattern equipment is found in Chapter X.

Gating and Feeding. Although the original patterns for the production of many cast metals may be of a generally similar type, there is great variation in requirements and practices in gating and feeding, depending upon the metal in which the part is to be made. With malleable iron, substantial and adequate feeding of the castings is of paramount importance. The objective, consequently, is both so to feed and gate the castings that all will be sound throughout and to obtain the greatest number of castings from a mold of a given size. Many factors warranting consideration in this connection are discussed in Chapters IX and X.

Molding and Facing Sand. The requisites of a molding sand for the manufacture of malleable iron were originally considered to be (1) a natural clay bond of enough strength for the mold to hold its shape when the sand contained about 6 per cent of water, and (2) sufficient refractoriness to prevent the sand from "burning on" the casting. Of course, it was found that a fine-grained sand imparted a smooth surface to a light casting, but with heavy castings a coarser sand was generally required because of its probable greater refractoriness and because it served to eliminate the possibility of "blows."

In more recent years, however, studies of the properties of foundry sands have brought out clearly the importance of permeability, moisture, green bond strength, dry bond strength, hot strength, grain size, and refractoriness. The interrelation of these properties is now also largely understood. The foundryman is keenly interested in tests to indicate and control the various factors, as he realizes their prime importance in reducing rejections due to defects, most of which in the past have been occasioned by improper sand control. Most large production foundries and especially those making relatively heavy castings now use synthetic sands in which a sand with low original clay content is bonded with bentonite or another type of clay.

In the conventional open floor foundry, sand which is to be placed next to the pattern and thus to form the surfaces of the casting, is generally run through a sand muller and aerator prior to use. In the muller, very finely pulverized coal, called "sea-coal," or oil is added, to improve the casting surface and prevent the possible tendency of the sand to fuse to the surface of the casting. This sand is customarily called "facing sand." When necessary to distinguish between it and the sand which forms the remainder of the mold, the latter is referred to as "backing sand." In foundries using continuous conveyor systems delivering sand to molding stations, all of the sand is generally mulled and aerated, so that special facing sand is not required.

The varying properties of foundry sands, which should be accurately controlled, are outlined as follows:

(1) Permeability is the physical property of sand which permits the passage of gases. The natural characteristics of the sand and its binders, the density with which these are packed, and the percentage of moisture used for tempering, are important factors in regulating the degree of permeability. If the permeability is too high, the surface of the casting is rough; if too low, there is danger of porosity or scabs.

Fig. 5. Sand-conditioning machines in operation. Above, conventional sand cutter. Below, conditioning equipment integral with sand slinger.

Fig. 6. A hand molder at work.

(2) Green bond strength is the property which holds the mold in shape and enables it to withstand the forces exerted by the molten metal.

(3) Dry bond strength is the strength of the sand after it has been dried. This property enables it to resist the cutting and washing action of the molten iron.

(4) Hot strength is the strength of the sand at elevated temperatures.

(5) Grain size is expressed by average fineness number. This is a relative figure derived from the amount of sand retained on each of the standard screens specified by the American Foundrymen's Association, and gives an indication of the venting properties and surface which may be expected.

(6) Refractoriness is a measure of the resistance the sand offers to fusion and to breaking down into smaller particles when heated.

Today, instead of following the old practice of squeezing a handful of sand to ascertain whether it will give good results, the foundryman tests various properties of the sand with standard equipment which is simple of operation.[57, 58, 59] When the best sand for a certain class of work has been determined and its properties have been tested and recorded, it may then be duplicated at any future time. Testing also makes it possible to keep the sand uniform. The variations which naturally might appear in different heaps of sand can be controlled. Sand control in the modern foundry helps production, improves finish, and decreases scrap. Many foundries find that control may be adequately maintained by testing a few of the sand heaps daily for moisture, permeability, and green compressive strength, thus testing each sand heap at least once a week.

Pouring molten metal into molds affects the sand by burning out some of its clay content and driving off moisture, both of these being needed for bond, which permits the sand to form a sufficiently strong mold. In addition, pouring raises the temperature of the sand so that unless it is cooled before being used again it will be dry and crumbly. Broken cores and pieces of metal tend to accumulate in the sand as a result of pouring, and continued use develops dust which reduces the permeability of the sand, that is, its ability to permit gases to pass away through the mold from the casting.

To be reused, molding sands therefore must be reconditioned. In open-floor shops, reconditioning is done by hand labor or by mechanical sand cutters on each floor. In mechanized foundries, it is done by a central sand-conditioning system employing conveyors to carry used sand from the shakeouts and to return reconditioned sand to the molders' stations. The steps usually included in conditioning are: (1) cleaning and screening, to remove metallic iron, core butts, and other refuse; (2) restoring correct bond and moisture; (3) removal of excess fines at muller and shakeout; (4) aeration to produce coolness, softness, and lightness.

Types of Molding. The actual making of the mold is accomplished by the molder's ramming the sand which he has placed in the flask enclosing the pattern, by machine squeezing of the mold, by machine jolting of the mold, or by a combination of these operations. Removal of flask and pattern may be manual or mechanical.

In some foundries where tonnages are very large or where certain patterns are in continuous production, mechanical conveyors are used to move the molds to the pouring station, where pouring is continuous. In other foundries the molders or carry-out men spread the molds over an area adjacent to their machines and accumulate a "floor" of molds for pouring at "heat time."

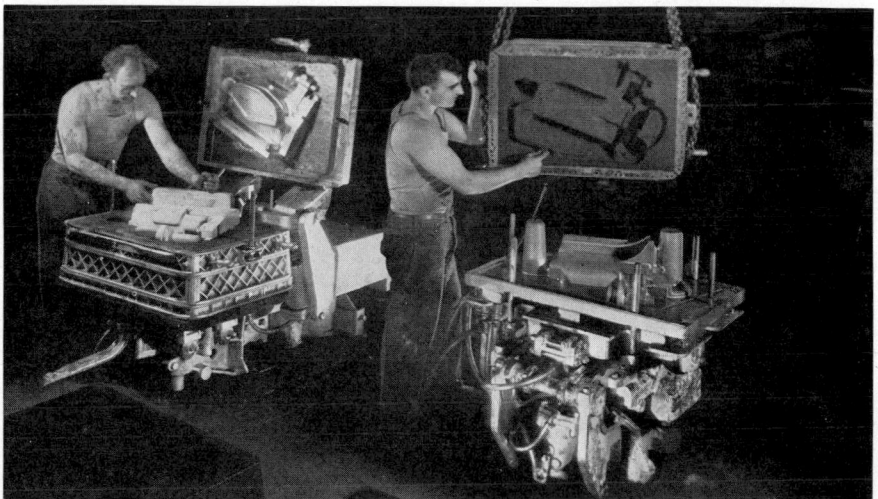

Fig. 7. Molders using power molding machines. The drag is being molded at left, the cope at right. Cores are in position in the drag half of the mold.

Fig. 8. Machine production of large castings, the sand with which the tight flasks are filled being supplied by overhead hoppers. At the right, the molder is placing cores, with the plate pattern swung up out of his way. At the left, peening is being done pneumatically.

Some foundries do not employ mechanical handling and conveying equipment because production quantities do not warrant it. The degree of mechanization affects the ease of production and the labor involved, but of course in no way guarantees nor adversely affects the quality of malleable iron produced. Many malleable iron foundries have foremen and superintendents whose years of experience have given them outstanding skill in the proper gating and molding of castings. Some of the best molders in the industry, real journeymen who are artists in their work, are found in malleable foundries where more dependence is placed upon the individual workman's skill and less upon machines.

Fig. 9. Continuous mold conveyor handling snap flask molds.

Fig. 10. Typical coreroom of a malleable iron foundry.

As earlier indicated, in the malleable iron industry manufacturing methods may vary in accordance with such factors as the exact type of product, the tonnage melted, and the equipment used. Some large companies having several plants have a different layout and plant organization at each of their subsidiaries.

COREMAKING

Cores are employed to form cavities in castings or to produce openings which cannot be practically made with the pattern alone. Refractory properties of cores must be quite high. Other properties, such as hardness and collapsibility, vary with the type of casting being made. Cores are generally made up of sand held together by a binder, either a water-soluble mix, a cereal binder, a resin binder, a straight or compounded oil, or any combination of these. The core sand mix is made by adding the constituents in the following order: sand, dry binders, water-soluble binders, water, and oil binders. Mixing may be done by hand, paddle mill, or muller.

Cores are made either by hand, rollover machines, or core-blowing machines. When large quantities of cores are used, core-blowing machines save much time and produce more nearly uniform cores than those made by hand. Cores are then baked in core ovens, at a temperature of about 400 degrees Fahrenheit, until thoroughly dry. A typical coreroom is shown in Fig. 10.

POURING

After the molds are made and necessary cores are set, they are then ready to be filled with molten iron, or "poured." The molten metal is frequently taken from the furnace in overhead-rail or buggy ladles holding several hun-

Fig. 11. Pouring castings on the floor of a typical malleable iron foundry. An air furnace is at the left rear. Molders are pouring from hand ladles; helpers are placing weights on top of molds to be poured. Molds which have been poured are in the right foreground, and the molders' benches may be seen at the right rear.

dred pounds and poured into the hand ladles of the molders or pourers at a location near their respective "floors." In some large foundries, as has been mentioned, conveyor systems are so arranged that pouring is continuous. Pouring temperatures, as determined by means of optical pyrometers, are 2750 to 2850 degrees F. at the spout of the furnace.

Although most light castings are poured with 50-pound hand ladles as shown in Fig. 11, with the floors of molds as near the furnace as possible, heavier castings are poured from large ladles. When the distance from the furnace to the mold is great, a covered ladle is sometimes employed to keep the molten metal up to the correct pouring temperature.

Some heavy castings must be poured from two ladles at once. This method is illustrated in Fig. 13.

Fig. 12. Pouring heavy castings from an 800-pound covered ladle.

Fig. 13. Two ladles in use in the pouring of a heavy casting.

Shaking Out. After the molds are poured and the metal is sufficiently cool, the castings are shaken out of the sand. In some foundries, shaking out is done by hand. Other foundries use mechanical shakeouts, located at the end of the conveyor system and consisting of grilles through which the sand falls, leaving the castings. Such a vibratory shakeout is shown in Fig. 14. The molds are taken on a conveyor from the pouring station and are shaken out under a hood which carries off any gas and dust.

Spruing. Removal of gates, runners, and other sprue is done, in many foundries, at the molder's floor, the castings being placed in one container for transfer to the hard iron cleaning department, the sprue in another, to be used as part of subsequent furnace charges. In mechanized foundries, the castings with sprue attached are moved by conveyor to the hard iron inspection department, the sprue being broken off while the castings are on a conveyor such as the one shown in Fig. 16 on the following page.

Fig. 14. Vibratory shakeout.

Fig. 15. "Spruing," or knocking off castings — in this picture chain-links — from the sprue, which here includes runners, feeders, and gates. The sprue, or remelt, is thrown in the wheelbarrow to be remelted. The worker uses a wooden stick, to prevent cracking the castings while they are still in the hard state.

HARD IRON CLEANING AND INSPECTION

White iron castings are cleaned by tumbling, or by sand-, grit-, or shot-blasting to remove sand from the surface. Castings are then inspected, and light gate connections and any fins at parting lines are trimmed off. Men at the left in Fig. 17 are inspecting hard iron castings and placing them in containers for annealing. At this time, some of the scrapped heavier white iron castings are broken as an additional check to assure that no primary graphite is present and to inspect for soundness.

ANNEALING

The castings are then taken to the annealing department, where the exact practice depends upon the type of equipment used in the plant and

Fig. 16. Apron conveyor carrying hot castings to the cleaning room of a mechanized foundry.

upon the end product desired.[60] As a first general classification, annealing furnaces are of either the periodic (batch) or continuous type. Periodic furnaces include the conventional pot-type, muffle furnaces, car-type, and elevator-type furnaces. They are heated by pulverized coal, oil, gas, radiant tubes, or electricity. The tunnel car-type gas-fired furnace and the roller-tray type heated by electricity or by radiant tube are continuous furnaces.

It is important in annealing that the castings be protected against the scaling and excessive decarburization produced by an oxidizing furnace atmosphere, or that the atmosphere in the furnace be rendered nonoxidizing by sealing against any excessive entry of air or by the admission of regulated amounts of treated gas. Packing to prevent oxidation and warpage increases

Fig. 17. Men at the left are inspecting and trimming white iron castings preparatory to annealing. At the right are stands ready to go into the annealing furnace.

the mass to be heated and cuts down the readiness of heat transfer. It therefore increases the annealing time, principally through the delay in bringing the castings to the proper annealing temperature and, after annealing, through the added time necessary for the castings to cool down to just below the critical temperature and later to room temperature for handling.

Conventional Pot-Type Periodic Furnace. The conventional periodic-type annealing furnace, which is built of brick, is well insulated, and is direct-fired by coal, oil, or gas, is used in a large number of malleable iron plants and produces about 70 per cent of the tonnage of malleable iron.[61] Usually the castings are packed — that is, placed in suitable metal pots or rings surrounded by a packing material. Slag, sand, silica gravel, pebbles, or mill scale is used as packing. Either air furnace or blast furnace slag is suitable. The object of the packing material is to prevent oxidation and to support the castings in order to avert warpage. Many malleable iron annealing pots have no top or bottom. The first pot is placed on a stool and another pot is superimposed on it, followed by a third and often a fourth, to make what is known as a "stand." Flat plates are placed on top of the stands, clay being plastered over the top and at the joints of the rings. The stands are placed in the furnace, which usually is of 20 to 40 tons' capacity, by means of an electric or gasoline-powered lift truck. The furnace is then closed and firing is started. The flue drafts are arranged to produce a uniform temperature and proper circulation throughout the furnace.

Pots and packing material cause a lag of eight to 20 hours between the temperature of the furnace and that of the castings. Because of this, the total annealing cycle in such furnaces is from five to nine days with packing; when separator plates or pots with bottoms and no packing are used, some saving in time results. The temperature is controlled in accordance with pyrometer readings, at least one thermocouple being located inside one of the pots in the coldest part of the furnace.[62] The time necessary to bring the castings up to the annealing temperature varies with the size of the furnace and the kind of fuel used, but after the annealing, or holding, temperature of about 1600 degrees F. is reached by the castings in the pots, the remainder of a typical cycle may be given as: Hold the castings about 40 hours at 1600 degrees, F. cool to 1400 degrees F. in 15 hours, cool to 1275 degrees F. in 15 hours, hold 20 hours at 1275 degrees F., then cool to a temperature at which the stands can be handled. This entire cycle may be controlled automatically.

Muffle-Type Periodic Furnace. The muffle-type periodic furnace in construction is essentially one brick shell inside another. As the inner shell is sealed against the products of combustion, neither pots nor packing material is necessary as a safeguard against oxidation. Cost of pots is therefore eliminated, and a greater tonnage may be annealed in a given space. Oil, gas, or coal is used as fuel. The time required for loading, cooling, and reloading the muffle-type furnace results in a longer average annealing cycle than with pot-type furnaces. The muffle cycle generally requires from seven to 10 days.[63]

Car-Type Periodic Furnace. The car-type periodic furnace fired with oil, gas, or pulverized coal is so designed that the stands may be loaded onto cars which are moved into the furnace when it has been brought to a fairly high temperature. Since the cars may be removed for cooling or be quickly transferred to a furnace of lower or higher temperature, the annealing cycle may be shortened by several days.[64]

Smaller car-type periodic furnaces, generally heated by radiant tubes or electricity and effectively insulated against temperature loss, are employed for the annealing of small or medium tonnages with a very short cycle. These may be furnaces of the elevator type. They require neither pots nor packing material, for those electrically heated may be effectively sealed to prevent scaling, and those heated by gas-fired radiant tubes utilize a prepared essen-

Fig. 18. Typical batch annealing furnaces for malleable iron. Of 32-ton capacity, they are fired with pulverized coal. Castings have been stacked in stands in the furnace at the right.

tially neutral atmosphere to protect the castings against oxidation. Light trays or boxes are generally used to hold very small castings in these furnaces. An annealing cycle of two to four days is possible with such furnaces.

Annealing furnaces of the batch type have been developed in which the castings are assembled in a stand under a hood, which is heated up. When the batch has been annealed and brought down below the critical temperature, the hot hood is placed over a second stand, thus shortening the heat-up period by taking advantage of the residual heat. Pots and packing are unnecessary, since the atmosphere is controlled to be neutral or non-oxidizing.

Continuous Furnaces. The continuous annealing furnace of the tunnel and car type, typified by the oil- or gas-fired Dressler kiln, has double-walled

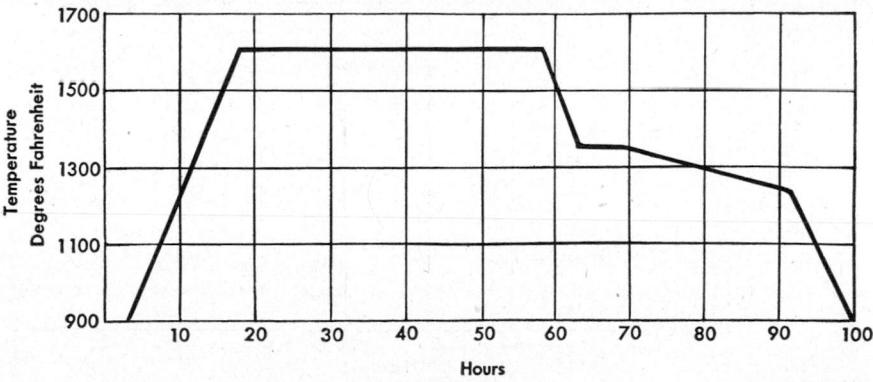

Fig. 19. Annealing cycle used in some pot-type periodic furnaces in annealing standard malleable iron.

chambers, combustion taking place within a tile muffle, and hot gases being forced from one end to the other by a fan.[65] In such furnaces, a car full of castings packed in pots is pushed in one end and is rapidly brought into the high temperature zones. When the next car is pushed in, each car in the furnace moves one car-length forward. Obviously, such a furnace is suitable only for large production. The annealing cycle may vary from three and a half to six days.

Continuous conveyor or roller-type furnaces,[66] which may be heated either by gas-fired radiant tubes, by electric heating elements, or by a combination of both, are new types of continuous furnaces, in which controlled atmosphere obviates the necessity for pots. Basically, they are similar to the tunnel and car type of annealing furnace in that the castings move through various zones of temperature, entering one end of the furnace as white iron castings, and emerging from the other end completely malleableized. Since temperature control is extremely accurate, and since only small quantities of castings are entering the various zones of temperature at one time, the annealing period is cut to a minimum. This type of equipment is often used

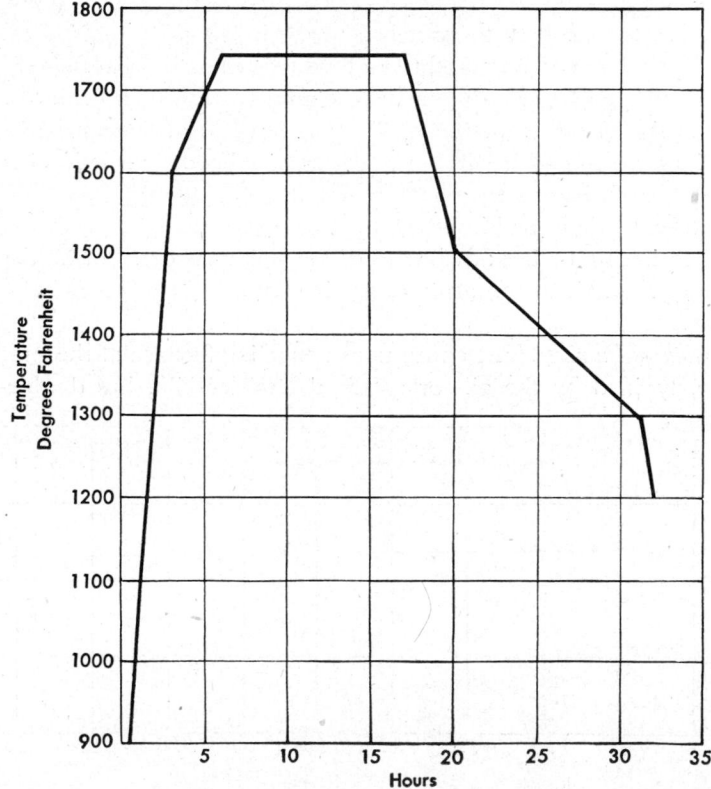

Fig. 20. A typical annealing cycle for gas-tight annealing furnaces heated by radiant tubes. Iron suitable for such a short cycle usually has a high silicon content.

for high-silicon, short-cycle malleable iron, requiring total annealing cycles of from 15 to 60 hours.

Short-Cycle Annealing. "Short-cycle malleable" is malleable iron which because of its composition can be thoroughly annealed in one or two days rather than the four to nine days required in the conventional batch-type periodic furnaces. Many factors enable the foundryman to reduce the annealing time safely: (1) using smaller ovens, so that less weight of metal is raised to temperature at one time, with a correspondingly small lag between the temperature of the furnace and that of the castings; (2) having ovens so well insulated that they retain from the previous load a heat of 1200 degrees F. when a new batch of castings is introduced, thus saving several hours of heating-up time; (3) having ovens well controlled, so that temperature can be dropped sharply at the end of the soaking period; (4) having castings of such size and shape that they can be annealed without packing, because time is required to heat all the packing; (5) having the composition of the metal such that graphitization proceeds at a rapid rate, this usually being accomplished by a high silicon content.[67]

Annealing Pearlitic Malleable Irons. The characteristic structure of pearlitic malleable irons, which differ from standard malleable in that they contain some combined carbon in the matrix, depends primarily upon the heat-treatment used in production. The pearlitic structure is generally secured in one of three ways: (1) by preventing or retarding second-stage graphitization through adding to the composition a suitable alloy or through quenching and reheat-treatment or through a combination of alloy and quench; (2) by arresting graphitization before it is complete, through reduction of the time of second-stage graphitization; or (3) by heat-treatment of a completely graphitized malleable iron. Equipment for these processes must be

Fig. 21. Soft iron cleaning room, showing a variety of malleable iron castings being cleaned and readied for shipment.

Fig. 22. Closer view of a shot-blast machine used to clean castings.

capable of accurate control. It generally consists of smaller units, since the tonnage of pearlitic malleable produced is smaller than that of standard malleable iron. Electric or gas-fired furnaces are customarily used in this heat-treatment.

Fig. 23. Large malleable iron castings being given final inspection after the removal of gates and parting lines. Straightening press is shown at the left.

Fig. 24. The pads left by gate and feeder connections on malleable iron castings may be removed by a milling operation, as here shown.

SOFT IRON CLEANING, FINISHING, AND INSPECTION

After the anneal, castings are removed from the furnace, freed from packing, and cleaned of any sand which may adhere. Many methods are used for cleaning the surface of castings. Tumbling or blasting by shot, sand,

Fig. 25. A hydraulic press applies heavy pressure to a casting for the purpose of straightening within close limits.

grit, or water removes any sand or scale and leaves the castings clean for plating, painting, or any further finishing operations.[68]

Gates and any irregularities which may exist at the parting line on castings are customarily ground following the anneal. Standard aluminum oxide or high-speed rubber-bonded or bakelite-bonded abrasive wheels are used. Grinding before the anneal — hard-iron grinding — is restricted to small castings and to other castings which do not have large gates. Where substantial gate connections are to be ground, the abrasive wheel cost is less if the work is done after the anneal. Shearing and milling are also used to decided advantage in removing gates from castings after the anneal.

Castings tend to warp during the anneal, especially if they are long and of light section. Such warpage as may be caused by the relief of internal strains within the castings cannot be prevented by any known packing. Any deformation which occurs through lack of proper care in packing can be prevented or minimized. Such castings as are warped may be straightened either with hand hammers and forming blocks or in presses with special dies. Pressure of 20,000 pounds per square inch is enough to straighten warped or deformed castings of standard malleable iron.[69] For coining, a permanent set

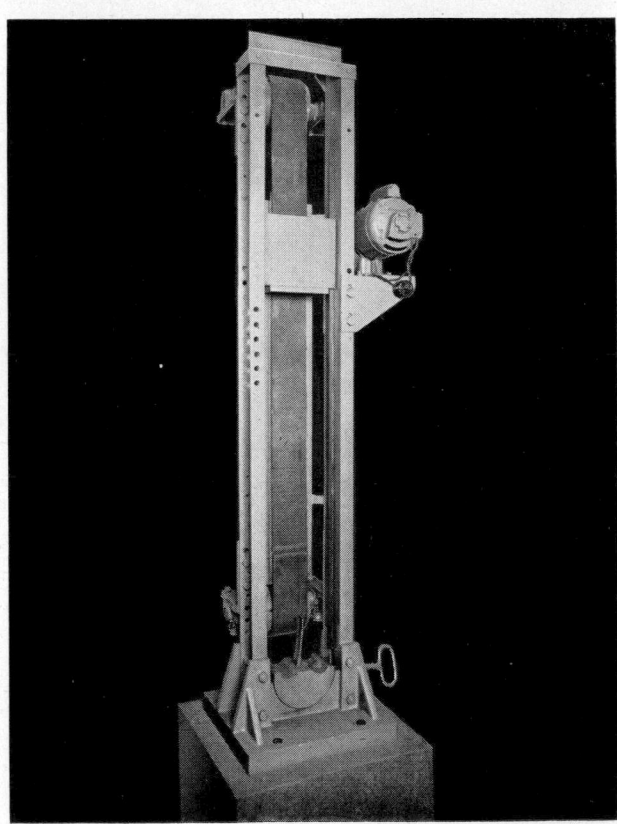

Fig. 26. The wedge test machine, with a wedge in place.

Fig. 27. Malleable iron wedges before and after the test.

of approximately 6 per cent must be imparted, which requires 60,000 pounds per square inch.[69]

The many different operations involved in the production of malleable iron castings afford opportunity for frequent inspections at various stages in the process. Thorough final inspection, however, including gauging and other special operations, is also performed previous to shipment. As a final operating test to measure the reaction of malleable iron to sudden and repeated impact, many foundries employ the wedge test.

In this test, the specimen is a wedge six inches long and one inch wide, tapering from one-half inch thick at the large end to $\frac{1}{16}$ inch thick at the thin end. With a hand hammer, about one-half inch of the thin end of the wedge is bent over, starting a "curl," and the wedge is then held upright and firmly fastened by the butt in a clamp forming part of an anvil. It is then subjected to repeated blows of a 21-pound tup falling through a distance of $3\frac{1}{3}$ feet, representing 70 foot-pounds of energy. The tup strikes the curled edge of the wedge. The clamp is so made that the wedge can be tilted gradually so that

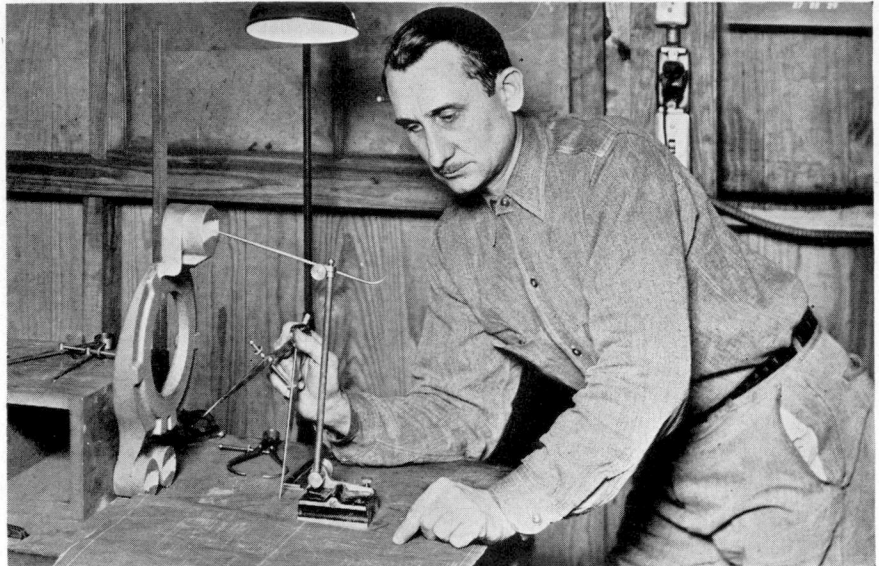

Fig. 28. Checking a sample casting against the blueprint.

the tup will always strike on the highest point of the curl. As deformation of the wedge takes place, the distance through which the tup falls becomes greater, and the energy of the blow increases. The number of blows required to produce fracture is recorded, and is usually 17 or more. It is customary to end the test if no sign of fracture occurs after 30 blows.

While this test is an arbitrary one, it seems to be a fairly reliable measure of the metal's ability to resist shock. The test results check with experience.

CHEMICAL AND METALLURGICAL CONTROL

The manufacture of malleable iron must of necessity be subject to close chemical and metallurgical control at all times. In the course of the process, checks are made for the following:

1. Suitable chemical composition of melting stock and coal.

2. Proper chemical composition of white iron.

3. Freedom from primary graphite in heavy castings while still in the white iron state.

4. Freedom from porosity or cracks.

5. Completeness of anneal.

6. The possession of adequate strength and toughness.

7. Satisfactory mechanical test results as indicated by values obtained from standard test bars.

The malleable foundry organizations are well qualified and equipped for the maintenance of this product control. In addition, the Malleable Founders' Society maintains an engineering staff which is available for consultation and technical assistance.

XIV

THE METALLURGY OF MALLEABLE IRON

ALL IRONS and steels are iron-carbon alloys and are made up of varying proportions of substantially the same group of elements, which pass through various metallurgical changes during the process of manufacture. The properties peculiar to a particular ferrous alloy such as malleable iron are functions primarily of the chemical composition of the melt and the metallurgical form in which the components are fixed by that chemistry and the manufacturing procedures used. Brief discussion of the metallurgical constituents [86] of iron-carbon alloys will aid understanding of the metallurgy of malleable iron. The constituents are:

Ferrite — carbon-free iron. Ferrite, which is almost pure iron, is tough, ductile, and fairly strong. It has an ultimate strength of approximately 40,000 pounds per square inch, elongation of 50 per cent, and Brinell hardness number of about 80. Wrought iron is practically all ferrite and is therefore tough and ductile.

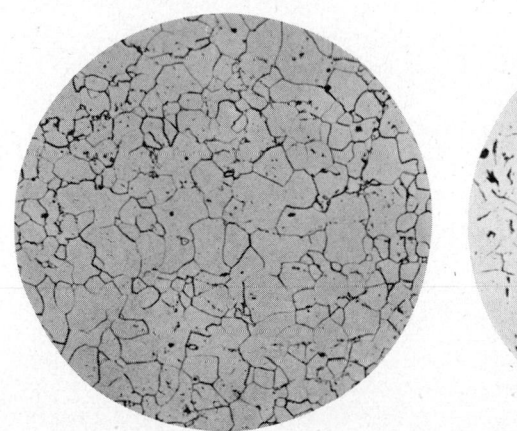 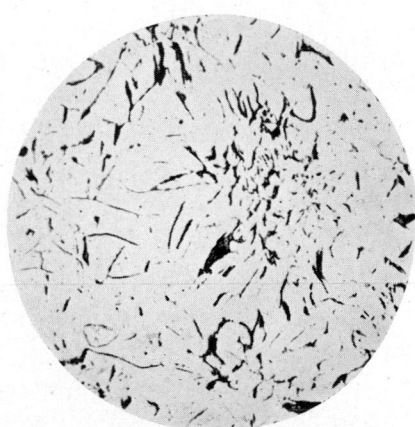

Fig. 1. Ferrite in cross section of wrought iron, x100, etched. Dark spots are slag inclusions.   *Fig. 2. Graphite flakes in gray iron, x100, unetched.*

Graphite — free carbon in flakes. Graphite is characteristic of gray cast iron. The graphite flakes aid machinability but weaken the iron, since they have very little strength themselves and because of their form break up the continuity of the matrix, or structure, of the iron.

Temper Carbon — free carbon in nodules. Temper carbon is characteristic of malleable iron. It differs from graphite not only in shape but also in the fact that in malleable iron production it does not appear on solidification of the casting, but rather is precipitated by subsequent heat-treatment. Because of this fact and because of their round shape, the nodules of temper carbon do not lessen the strength of the matrix as the flakes of graphite do. Temper carbon also increases machinability, which fact explains why malleable iron so greatly excels wrought iron in machinability.

Cementite — carbon combined chemically with iron, forming Fe_3C, iron carbide. Cementite in the massive state is hard, brittle, and very difficult to machine. When occurring as a constituent of pearlite or sorbite, as in medium and high-carbon steels, it is machinable.

Pearlite — a mechanical mixture of ferrite and cementite in alternate layers. Characteristic of steel and some pearlitic malleable irons, pearlite is strong and can be machined, but is less ductile than ferrite.

Austenite — a solid solution of cementite in iron. Austenite is a true solution, just as is a solution of sugar in water, except that it is a solid rather than a liquid. Although composed of the same materials as pearlite, austenite is quite different in characteristics, being a homogeneous mixture rather than two separate parts. Another difference is that in the carbon range used in production of malleable iron, pearlite is stable from room temperature to 1330 degrees Fahrenheit, while austenite exists mostly at temperatures above 1370 degrees F. and is stable at room temperature only when alloyed with large amounts of nickel or manganese. Moreover, the ferrite and cementite in

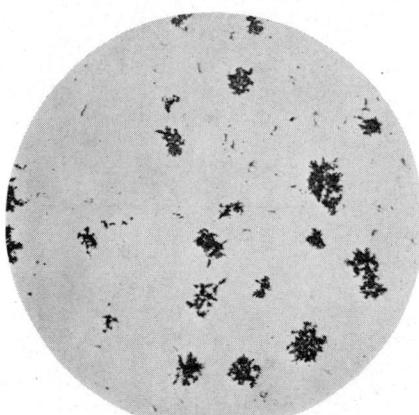
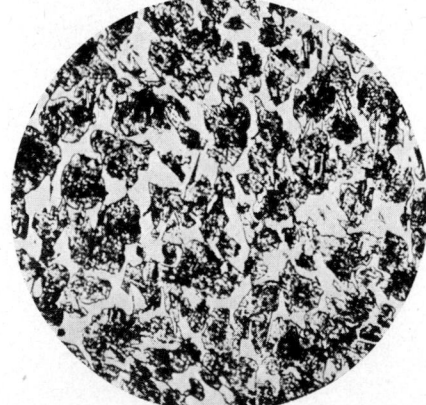

Fig. 3. Temper carbon nodules in American malleable iron, x100, unetched.

Fig. 4. Cementite (white) and pearlitic matrix (dark) in white iron, x100, etched.

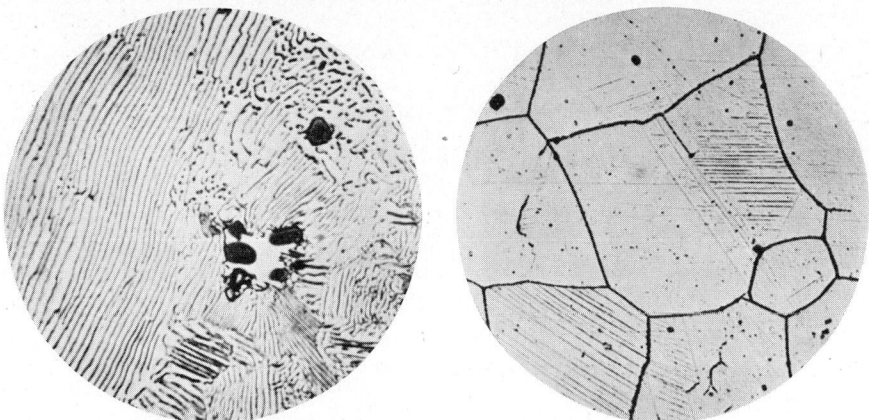

Fig. 5. Pearlite, x1000, etched.   Fig. 6. Austenite, x800, etched.

pearlite for any given metal composition are always present in a definite proportion, whereas in austenite the amount of carbon depends on the temperature because the solubility of cementite in austenite rises with increasing temperature. At the critical range for malleable iron, between 1330 and 1370 degrees F., austenite contains in solid solution about 0.60 per cent carbon, equivalent to about 9.00 per cent cementite. Just short of the melting point at about 2050 degrees F., austenite can dissolve 25.50 per cent cementite.

Martensite, troostite, sorbite — various structures intermediate between pearlite and austenite, which are produced by different heat-treatments or alloys.

ALLOTROPIC FORMS OF IRON

Iron, like water, may exist in different forms,[87] depending upon temperature. Ice, water, and steam are all chemically the same, but their forms are entirely different because of their different temperatures. Iron also exists in different forms at different temperatures, even while still in the solid state.

ALPHA IRON

Ferrite, the form which is stable at room temperatures, is called alpha iron. Alpha iron is magnetic, will dissolve only minute amounts of carbon or carbide (although it is possible to have such alloying elements as silicon, manganese, copper, nickel, and so on in solid solution in the ferrite).

GAMMA IRON

When iron is at temperatures above 1328 to 1360 degrees F., it no longer exists in the alpha form; though still solid, it is in the form known as gamma iron, chemically the same as alpha iron, just as steam and water are chemically identical, but of quite different properties. Gamma iron is nonmagnetic and can dissolve and hold in solid solution carbon up to 1.7 per cent. Austenite is the name given to the solution of iron carbide in gamma iron.

METALLURGY OF MALLEABLE IRON

The metallurgy of malleable iron can be discussed naturally in two divisions:

1. The metallurgy of the melting process:
    (a) Raw materials.
    (b) Fuel.
    (c) Effect and control of chemical composition.
    (d) Pouring temperatures.

2. The metallurgy of the anneal:
    (a) Effect of temperature time cycles.
    (b) Effect of changes in composition.

METALLURGY OF THE MELTING PROCESS

RAW MATERIALS

Raw materials for the manufacture of malleable iron consist of pig iron, sprue (remelt), malleable and steel scrap in such proportions as will result in a predetermined desired chemical composition.

The *pig iron* in general use is of a composition within the following range: Silicon 1.25–2.50 per cent, manganese 0.50 to 1.00, phosphorus 0.20 maximum, and sulphur .05 maximum. The carbon content depends on silicon content and blast furnace operation, ranging from 3.80 to 4.40.

Sprue is the term commonly applied to all remelt consisting of gates, runners, risers, and rejected white iron castings.

Malleable scrap consists of selected and graded malleable components taken from worn out or obsolete automobiles, freight cars, farm implements, and other equipment.

Steel scrap consists of selected sizes of carbon steel scrap suitable for charging into the melting unit. The most common forms of steel scrap used are short rails, angle bars, cut structural, billet crop ends, etc.

FUEL

The fuels in the melting process are:

1. Pulverized coal
2. Coke (duplex process)
3. Coal (lump)
4. Oil
5. Electricity
6. Gas

EFFECT AND CONTROL OF CHEMICAL COMPOSITION

Experience indicates the usual losses of silicon, manganese, and carbon which occur in the melting process; hence the relative amounts of pig iron, sprue, malleable and steel scrap must be adjusted to compensate for these losses, to arrive at the desired white iron composition.

Carbon. The amount of carbon is one of the most significant factors in ferrous alloys. Gray iron owes its excellent castability to its high carbon content, but this carbon precipitates out as graphite flakes on solidification. Steels which contain comparatively high carbon are much more fluid than the low-carbon steels, but are still not so fluid as the white iron from which malleable iron is made. Malleable iron alone has the advantage of high carbon content at the pouring stage, with neither flake graphite nor combined carbon in the final product, because the carbon becomes temper carbon during the annealing process. Pearlitic malleable irons have the same carbon as is customary for other malleable iron, with all the advantages in foundry properties resulting therefrom, but as some of the carbon is in the combined form in the final product, pearlitic malleables are more like cast steel in strength and hardness.

The usual carbon content of white iron castings from which malleable iron is made is between 2.00 per cent and 2.70 per cent. With high carbon, a low silicon content is necessary to avoid primary graphite.

Silicon. Silicon has a very powerful effect upon graphitization of iron-carbon alloys. When silicon is extremely low, annealing the castings is difficult, if not impossible.[1] When silicon is too high, graphitization takes place when the molten metal solidifies. For this reason, silicon is controlled carefully, and in general varies inversely with the carbon. For instance, an iron with 2.60 per cent carbon and 0.80 per cent silicon has about the same tendency toward graphitization on solidification as an iron with 2.20 per cent carbon and 1.10 per cent silicon. The percentage of carbon and silicon allowable in white iron without primary graphite is always influenced by the size of the casting and by the cooling time. Very light work can tolerate a higher total of carbon plus silicon than can castings of heavier section, because the lighter the section, the shorter the cooling time and the greater the tendency of the metal to solidify white. In the higher carbon ranges for extremely light work, which may sometimes be as high as 2.70, the cooling time is the predominant factor in determining whether primary graphite is formed on solidification, and silicon has relatively less influence.

Manganese and Sulphur. Some sulphur is always present in the iron, not only that contained in the metal charged but also that resulting from pick-up from the melting fuel. Since if it is present in substantial amounts sulphur retards graphitization, low-sulphur fuels are used, and when necessary manganese is added to form a harmless compound with the sulphur, manganese sulphide, which exists in small inclusions both in the white iron and in the resultant malleable iron. These inclusions have no effect on the properties or graphitization of the iron. In commercial practice, an amount of manganese slightly in excess of that required to combine with all the sulphur to form manganese sulphide and thus prevent any harmful effect on the anneal, is always used. However, the manganese additions should be limited, for when present in amounts excessively above that required to neutralize the sulphur content, manganese acts as a retarder to graphitization.

Phosphorus. It is desirable that the white iron composition contain at least 0.10 per cent phosphorus, for below this content the metal's strength is decreased. In the ranges used commercially, the phosphorus exerts no other effect, except that near the top of the range, especially when high silicon is present, there is a tendency toward embrittlement in hot-dip galvanizing, or through the blue heat range. Conversely, when the silicon is low, the tendency toward galvanizing embrittlement is diminished, as is explained in Chapter IV. It may also be prevented by a quench in air, water, or other medium from 1200 degrees F. prior to galvanizing.[27]

POURING TEMPERATURES

Molten iron is usually at a temperature of 2600 to 2800 degrees F. when poured into the mold. Since the fluidity of the iron varies directly with its temperature, light-section castings are generally poured at the highest temperatures. Iron which has been superheated to a temperature substantially higher than that at which it is poured has less tendency to form primary graphite upon solidification, because of the stabilizing effect of the high temperature. Advantage of this principle is taken in the production of high-silicon, short-cycle-anneal irons.

MICROSTRUCTURE OF WHITE IRON

The microstructure of white iron castings is almost independent of chemical composition unless the composition is extremely abnormal. The microstructure is always crystalline, consisting of white cementite in a matrix of dark pearlite. The grain of the structure, whether coarse or fine, depends upon the rate of freezing and on the composition. Castings cooled rapidly and those of low carbon content have the finer grain.

THE METALLURGY OF THE ANNEALING

EFFECT OF TEMPERATURE TIME CYCLES

White iron castings at room temperature consist of free cementite in a matrix of pearlite. When such castings are heated to just above the critical temperature, between 1330 and 1370 degrees F., the pearlite is transformed into austenite, the cementite of the original hard iron being unaffected by the rising temperature. Thus above the critical range, the iron consists of free cementite in a matrix of austenite.[88] As the temperature continues to increase, the solubility of cementite in austenite also increases. By the time the temperature reaches 1550 degrees F. or more, a considerable amount of the free cementite is in solution.

First-Stage Graphitization. First-stage graphitization involves the solution of free cementite in austenite, and the depositing of some temper carbon nodules, at a holding temperature about 1550 to 1700 degrees F. The austenite will dissolve all the cementite it can at a given temperature, say 1650 degrees F. If it is held

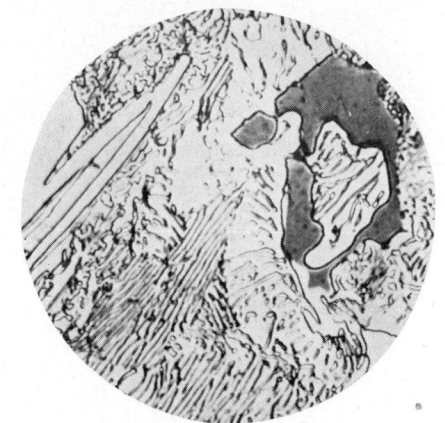

Fig. 7. White iron, x1000, etched.

at that temperature for a considerable time, some of the carbon which was in the cementite begins to separate out of the solid solution, in the form of temper carbon. Then the austenite, no longer saturated with cementite, dissolves more cementite. These two reactions, namely, dissolving of cementite and precipitation of carbon by the austenite, proceed simultaneously

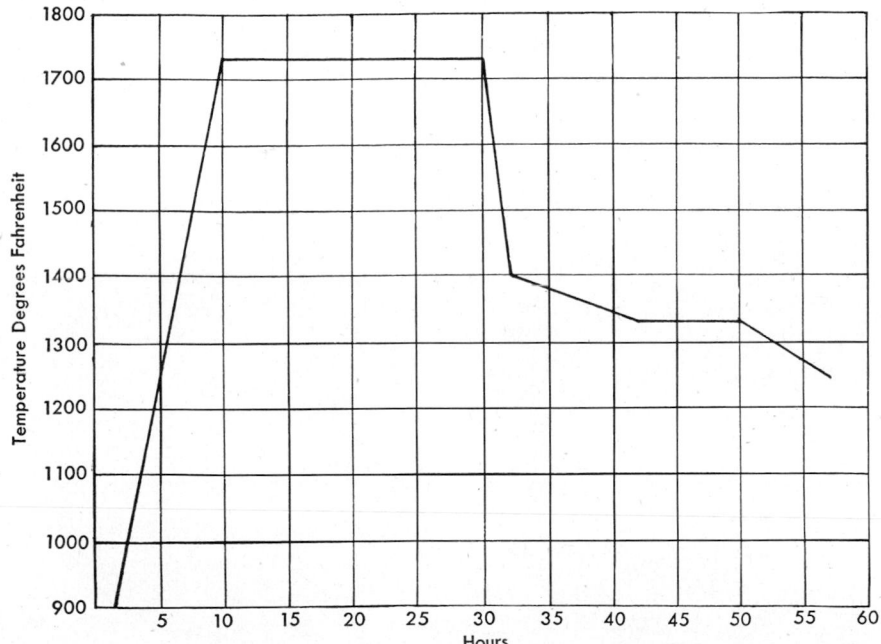

Annealing cycle in a gas-tight periodic annealing furnace heated by radiant tubes and equipped with controlled atmosphere. First-stage graphitization is complete after 30 hours, and second stage takes place during the slow cooling from 1400 to 1250 degrees F.

at the holding temperature until all the free cementite has by degrees been dissolved and most of the carbon has been precipitated as described.[89] At this point, first-stage graphitization is said to be complete. Because the temperature is held constant to effect the solution of cementite and precipitation of temper carbon, the heat at which first-stage graphitization takes place is called the "holding temperature."

Temperatures Used in Annealing. The higher the holding temperature, the faster the solution of cementite in austenite. But there is a practical limit to the temperatures employed, since costs of fuels and refractories will rise and warpage will cause higher straightening cost. Also, the mechanical properties will be adversely affected, the drop in general being about 5 per cent for each 100 degrees F. increase in holding temperature over the range normally used.[89]

Second-Stage Graphitization. Second-stage graphitization, the breaking down of austenite into temper carbon and ferrite, takes place at or slightly below the critical range of 1330 to 1370 degrees F.[86]

When the temperature is lowered from the holding temperature, the solubility of cementite in austenite decreases. The temperature then should be lowered as rapidly as practical for the type of oven used, until a temperature of about 1400 degrees F. has been reached, during which cooling period more carbon is precipitated. A very slow rate of cooling should now be adopted, because somewhere between the temperature of 1400 degrees F. and, say, 1290 degrees F., the metal will be passing through its critical range. It is essential that the drop in temperature through this range should not exceed 10 degrees per hour, and preferably it should be somewhat less. At this point, the austenite is of eutectoid composition, the eutectoid point being the lowest temperature at which two alloys will combine in the solid state. This

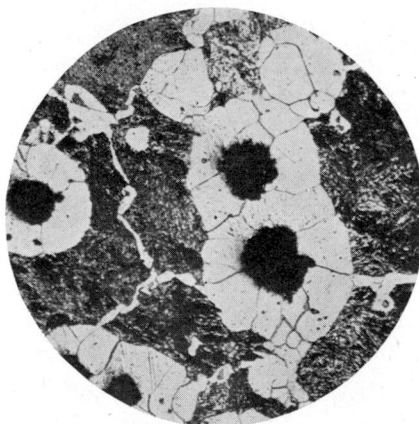

Fig. 8. Bull's-eye structure of white ferrite surrounding nodules of temper carbon, x100, etched.

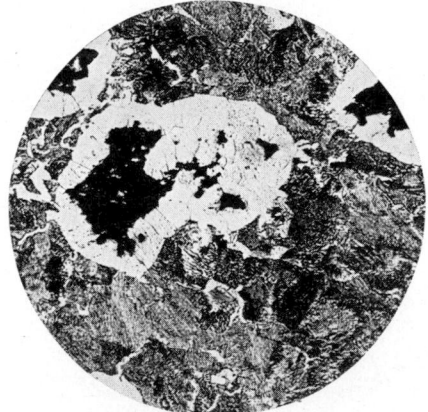

Fig. 9. An incompletely annealed malleable iron which contains considerable pearlite, x100, etched.

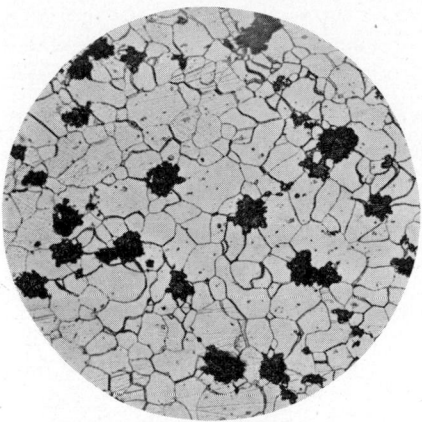

Fig. 10. Completely annealed American malleable iron, x100, etched.

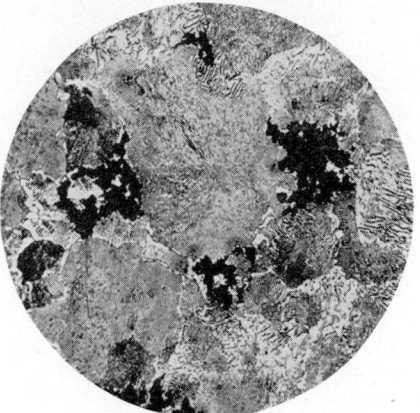

Fig. 11. Pearlitic malleable iron of Class 1
type, x100, etched.

austenite is unstable, for as the temperature of the product drops through the lowest critical point, the tendency is for the austenite to revert to pearlite. This action is retarded by the high silicon and a very slow rate of cooling. Under the critical temperature, some pearlite is formed and at the same time the iron has been changed from the gamma to the alpha form. On holding at a temperature close to but under the range, the cementite of the pearlite is spheroidized and, in time, decomposed into ferrite and temper carbon. To effect complete precipitation of the carbon, a very slow rate of cooling to about 1275 degrees F. or a holding period just below the critical temperature should be maintained.

The ferrite which is characteristic of malleable iron does not appear in the iron until it has cooled to near the critical range. In irons quenched from temperatures of around 1380 degrees F., ferrite first begins to grow around the grain boundaries [90] and adjacent to the temper carbon nodules, which have a local "decarburizing" effect. As the temperature decreases slowly, the ferrite develops and begins to appear as "bull's eyes" around the temper carbon nodules. [91] In other words, the temper carbon nodules grow at the expense of the iron carbide dissolved in the surrounding austenite or ferrite. When the structure consists entirely of temper carbon in a matrix of ferrite, second-stage graphitization is complete.

If the castings have not had enough time for first-stage graphitization at the holding temperature, some cementite may remain in them. If cooling is too rapid during second-stage graphitization, or if the iron was not held long enough just below the critical range, some pearlite remains.

Effect of Changes in Composition. The chemical composition of the white iron has an important effect on the rate of graphitization. The most common variable, silicon, alters graphitization not only when the castings are subjected to heat-treatment but also on solidification of the molten white iron. [92] For that reason, the use of higher silicon than usual to speed up the graphitization process entails a great deal of care to avoid primary graphite.

All alloys have more or less effect on graphitization, as mentioned in Chapter VII. Some are strong retarders which interfere with annealing so markedly as to make it practically impossible; others promote graphitization to such an extent that primary graphite is unavoidable; and there are all grades between these two extremes.

In commercial practice, three alloying elements are added to malleable iron — copper, manganese, and molybdenum.

Copper reduces the required time for both first- and second-stage graphitization.

Manganese retards graphitization and finds use as an alloying element in some pearlitic malleable irons.

Molybdenum retards both primary and secondary graphitization. When malleable iron is alloyed with both molybdenum and copper, which latter favors graphitization, the retarding effect of molybdenum is neutralized, and a completely graphitized metal is obtained after a normal annealing cycle.

Atmosphere in the Annealing Oven. Castings which are of such shape and dimensions that they may safely be annealed without packing, of course, anneal faster than those which are surrounded by packing material. A controlled or essentially neutral atmosphere in the annealing furnace has no direct influence on annealing time, but indirectly reduces it because in the case of castings not susceptible to warpage it eliminates the necessity for heavy pots and packing material and prevents decarburization. A slight decarburization nearly always present on the extreme outer rim of the casting is not harmful to the properties and is not commercially significant.

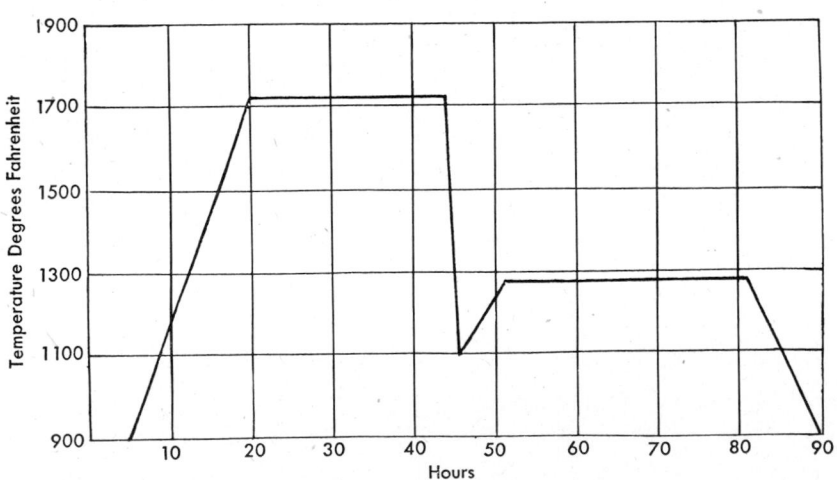

Annealing cycle for spheroidized pearlitic malleable iron containing 0.90 per cent manganese. Note the long holding time in the spheroidizing range just below 1300 degrees F.

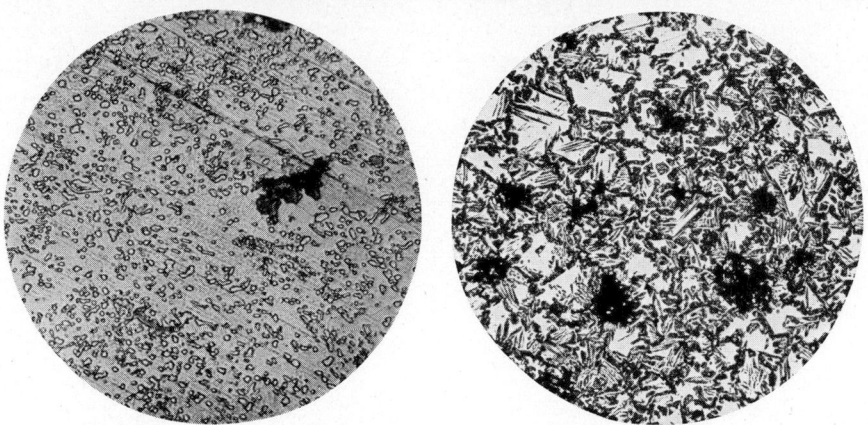

Fig. 12. Pearlitic malleable iron of Class 2   Fig. 13. Pearlitic malleable iron of Class 3
type, x500, etched.   type, x100, etched.

METALLURGY OF PEARLITIC MALLEABLE IRON

The metallurgy of annealing pearlitic malleable irons [93] is the same as that for standard malleable irons through the completion of first-stage graphitization.

Pearlitic malleable irons may be divided into three classes: (1) those that are produced by preventing or retarding second-stage graphitization through adding to the composition a suitable alloy or through quenching and reheat-treatment or through a combination of alloy and quench; (2) those that are produced by arresting graphitization before it is complete, through reduction of the time of second-stage graphitization; or (3) those that are produced by the heat-treatment of a completely graphitized malleable iron.

CLASS 1

The alloying element most commonly used in pearlitic malleable iron is manganese. It is used in amounts between 0.50 and 0.80 per cent for the purpose of holding the carbon combined during second-stage graphitization. Manganese has three advantages in pearlitic malleable iron: (1) It slows up second-stage graphitization; (2) it prevents graphitization from continuing to completion while the pearlitic matrix is being spheroidized; and (3) it permits the retention of some combined carbon even when the standard annealing cycle is used.

CLASS 2

When the massive cementite is all decomposed at the end of first-stage graphitization, the iron consists of austenite and temper carbon nodules. The metal is then allowed to cool to the upper portion of the critical range, about 1370 degrees F. The percentage of combined carbon in the final product is determined by the amount of time the metal remains at or just below the critical temperatures, because that is the region where the final graphitization to ferrite and temper carbon takes place.

If pearlitic malleable iron is taken through the critical range at a drastically high cooling rate, as for instance by a liquid quench, the resultant metal will have an entirely martensitic matrix. It will be wear resistant, very hard, and fairly brittle. Such a metal with a martensitic matrix can be tempered to any lesser degree of hardness desired. If the cooling rate is rapid, say 400 degrees F. an hour, the matrix of the resultant metal will be pearlitic or sorbitic. If the metal is cooled more slowly, coarse pearlite will result. Such metals with a pearlitic matrix may be spheroidized by a reheat-treatment. Spheroidal structures consist of round particles or spheroids of carbide in a ferritic matrix, instead of lamellar pearlite composed of alternate layers of ferrite and carbide. They have superior ductility, and for that reason irons with pearlitic matrices are frequently subjected to heat-treatment for the purpose of spheroidization.

Class 3

When completely graphitized malleable iron is reheated to a point above the critical, some of the temper carbon is redissolved to form iron carbide. This recombination of carbon is selective, occurring first at the grain boundaries and about the temper carbon nodules. The amount of recombined carbon can be controlled by the temperature and time factors of the heat-treat cycle. It may be retained in the matrix by a liquid quench or by regulation of the cooling rate to produce the desired microstructure in the final product. If a liquid quench is employed, it is usually followed by a high reheat or tempering operation to form a spheroidized cementite structure.

Hardened Malleable Irons

The metallurgical principle on which the surface hardening of malleable iron is based is simply the fact that when the metal is heated above the critical range, carbon redissolves in the matrix. Then a fast cooling rate through the critical range results in the redissolved carbon's remaining combined with the iron. This fact is utilized commercially in the employment of a very short heating period and a liquid quench immediately following to produce martensite instead of the normal ferrite–temper carbon structure.

XV

HISTORY OF THE MALLEABLE IRON INDUSTRY

THE SEARCH for a metal that could be cast to shape and yet would be tough and ductile was already an old one when in the Eighteenth Century R. A. F. deRéaumur made known his process of heating iron castings in an oxidizing packing to malleableize them. This was, as pointed out in Chapter I, but a partial answer to the quest, and though the French scientist's disclosure became the basis of a limited industry, several others before him had had the same idea. Almost a hundred years before Réaumur's publication of his process in 1722, an English patent for a way "to make hard iron soft" had been issued to David Ramsey. There is no record of commercial application of Ramsey's process, which was patented on June 21, 1630.[11] Nor is there indication that ironmongers of that century were interested in English patents Nos. 161, 164, and 165 issued in 1670[11] to Prince Rupert von der Pfalz, then living in England, although he claimed "a new invention or art of prepareing and softening all cast or melted iron, soethat itt may be fyled and wrought as forged iron is."

These Seventeenth Century patents were in fact so mysterious that even a limited industry could not have been built on them. Réaumur hence is generally considered the father of the idea of malleabilization, for his was the first real treatise explaining a practical approach toward it. His publications of 1720, 1721, and 1722 were the first technical discussions of malleable castings.[70] The process which he described consisted of melting and pouring iron castings, packing them in pulverized hematite, and heating them to bright redness for many days. The metal thus produced was almost free from carbon and was quite similar to wrought iron. An industry developed in Europe for the manufacture of this whiteheart malleable iron. Since decarburization was the basis of Réaumur's process, only small castings could at first be made malleable. Larger ones were liable to be hard and brittle in the center. Though present-day whiteheart malleable has advanced beyond these limitations, decarburization is still basic to its manufacture. Some graphitization takes place during the heat-treatment, but small castings — say up to a half inch in section — are almost entirely decarburized. Heavier sections consist of a white rim and a pearlitic core containing nodular graphite. The properties of the rim differ greatly from those of the core of the casting, and so the size of casting which can be made successfully in whiteheart malleable is still limited.[71]

BOYDEN'S AMERICAN MALLEABLE IRON

American malleable iron — a mixture of free iron and free carbon — thus is quite a different thing from whiteheart malleable iron. The American iron, of black fracture, owes its valuable properties of strength and ductility to the fact that its primary constituent is ductile ferrite in which are contained nodules of temper carbon.

This iron, as Chapter I pointed out, is a typically American product, originally developed by an American for use in American industries, and brought to its present high standard of quality and uniformity by the continued co-operation of its producers. In its adaptability to a multitude of uses, American malleable iron parallels the versatility of the man who invented the process by which it is made — Seth Boyden.

Boyden, whom Thomas Edison called "one of America's greatest inventors," was born at Foxborough, Massachusetts, on November 17, 1788, into a family skilful in the use of metal and ingenious in the use of inventive wit.[72, 73, 74] Our Boyden's father was another Seth, who ran a small forge and machine shop in Foxborough, and was the inventor of a leather-splitting machine. That Seth's father, Uriah, is said to have cast some of the first cannon ever made in America, and was operating a foundry in Foxborough during the youth of his grandson Seth, the future inventor and the future founder of at least two American industries.

Seth Boyden of malleable iron fame had little schooling in the formal sense, but had an excellent opportunity for sound training in metals in the parental forge and machine shop and the grandparental foundry. He made good use of his opportunity; by the time he was 15 years old, he had built up considerable local renown for his skill in repairing clocks, watches, and guns, and for general ability as a mechanic. By the time he had reached his majority, he had constructed machines for making nails and cutting files. Four years later, in 1813, he went to Newark, New Jersey, with an improved leather-splitting machine of his own invention, to enter the business of supplying split sheepskins and leather to the bookbinding trade. In 1819, having succeeded in duplicating the lacquer of a piece of European ornamental leather, he opened the first factory in this country for the manufacture of varnished or "patent" leather, establishing the industry in America. He was 31 years old.

Maybe because he had gone far enough with leather to lose interest in it, maybe because simply as a good Yankee he had to be starting a new enter-

Fig. 1. The manufacture of iron cannonballs in the late 18th century, as depicted in a colored engraving by Pyne. Réaumur's furnace was much like this small affair, blown with air supplied by a hand bellows.

prise, maybe because he experienced an inner homesickness for the forge and the foundry of Foxborough, Boyden set up a foundry of his own in Newark in the next year. Here, at 26 Orange Street, he was to be in business for the next 17 years, and here, beginning on Independence Day of 1826, he was to start the experiments creating the second industry which America owes to him — the manufacture of American malleable iron.

His record of experiments [55, 75] extends over the six years from 1826 to 1832, and like most summaries of pioneering undertakings, it is a record of ups and downs. But bit by bit he worked out the problems through trial and error. He had started to duplicate Réaumur's process and to malleableize iron castings by decarburization. Instead, he found he had developed an alloy which graphitized when properly heat-treated. It gave him a malleable casting which had properties superior to those of the best whiteheart and which was more easily made and was more uniform. Continuing empirically, he evolved the process which, refined and developed, produces American blackheart malleable iron today. He was a hard worker; only two years after he had started the experiments, he won the silver medal offered by the Franklin Institute for the best exhibit of "annealed cast iron," the conditions specifying that the exhibit should include not less than 12 separate pieces.[55] In 1831, he was granted the first American patent for malleable iron.

Having thus once again done what he had set out to do, he sold his foundry business in 1837 in order to begin the manufacture of locomotives, and after he had built three of them turned to the making of stationary steam engines, in which he made the first application of "cut-off" governing. Ten years later, in 1847, he adapted a grate bar for the manufacture of oxide of zinc — the grate bar which is still used today in the "American process" in the zinc industry. When the gold rush of 1849 had the East in a fever of excitement, Boyden, possibly deciding that he had earned a vacation, went West. The trip did not result in any gold mine for him, and in 1850 he returned to Newark. In the years remaining before his death on March 31, 1870, he developed a process for the inexpensive manufacture of "Russian" sheet iron, invented an important hat-forming machine, invented a goldlike alloy known as "oroide," published a book on atmospheric electricity, contributed to the development of the famous Hilton strawberry, and all in all more than lived up to the traditions of Yankee ingenuity. He is reported to have made the first daguerreotype produced in America, and to have aided Samuel F. B. Morse, the inventor of the telegraph.

During his period as a founder, Seth Boyden made over a thousand different articles of malleable iron, including castings for coachmakers, for harness and saddlery, for gunsmiths, blacksmiths, and machinists. His first melting furnace was a crucible, but soon the rising demand for his castings led him to build an air furnace having a capacity of 1,000 pounds. Eight heats a day were sometimes taken from this furnace, which was not tapped but was emptied by the molders, who dipped iron out in their clay-washed ladles. About 1832, when he built his large furnace, Boyden employed 60 molders in the Orange Street foundry. His first annealing furnace was of a beehive shape, with the pots inserted from the top. Next, to meet production schedules, he built a continuous annealing furnace with a sloping floor. Because pots were pushed in at the upper end and out at the lower end, this was known as the "shoving furnace." [55]

Seth Boyden's original foundry on Orange Street in Newark was operated under his own name until 1835, when it became known as the Boston Malleable Cast Iron and Steel Company. After two years under this management, it was operated by Daniel Condit, J. H. Barlow, and others, under various firm names. It became the Barlow Foundry Company in 1907, and in 1914 removed from the original site to 357 Wilson Avenue, Newark, where the Newark Malleable Iron Company today is operating — direct descendant of the pioneer foundry established by Boyden. Three of Seth Boyden's brothers — Otis, Alexander, and Frank Boyden — also became malleable iron foundrymen.[1] Otis had a foundry in Newark from 1835 to 1837, when it was absorbed by the Boston Malleable Cast Iron and Steel Company. Alexander and Frank were in business in East Boston, Massachusetts, until the former went to Easton, Massachusetts, to work for Frederick Fuller. Under the name of the Belcher Malleable Iron Company, the plant in Easton is still producing malleable iron castings. It is the oldest malleable iron foundry in continuous operation at the same site in the United States.[76]

Small malleable iron foundries began to spring up all over the East in the 1830's. Within a few years, eight plants were operating in Newark, New Jersey, alone. Between 1830 and 1880, a number of other malleable iron plants were started, most of them in New England and New York, though some were in Ohio and Illinois.

The procedure for the location of new plants was nearly always the same: A town would find that it could use a considerable tonnage of malleable iron, one to three thousand tons a year being considered enough. Capital would be subscribed, largely among the prospective users, and a superintendent would be hired from the personnel of a plant then operating successfully somewhere else. He would bring with him a melter and an annealer and possibly some other workmen. Then the foundry would start. So many of these foundries were located in New England and they did so much to train the men who later established and operated foundries in the Middle West, that New England may be considered the mother of the malleable iron industry.

In the early days of the industry, very little was understood about either the melting or the annealing operations, and each workman carried his secrets with him. It is said that Alexander Boyden used to squirt some secret

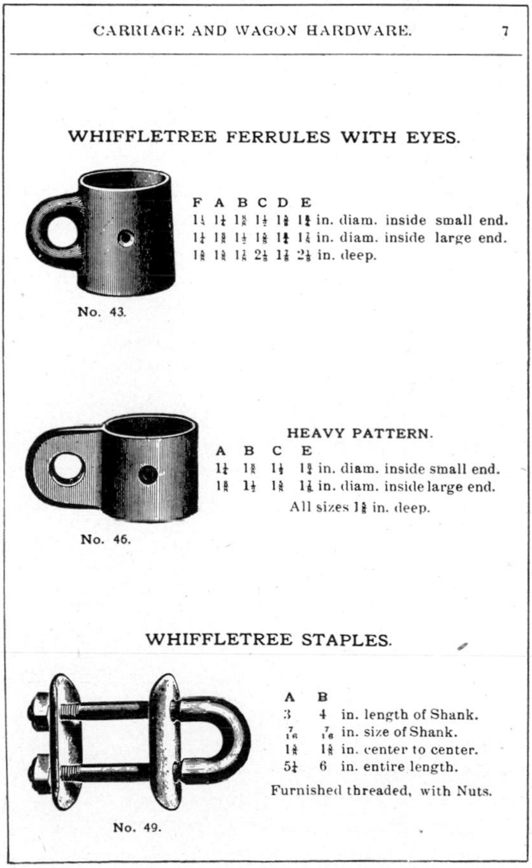

CARRIAGE AND WAGON HARDWARE. 7

WHIFFLETREE FERRULES WITH EYES.

F	A	B	C	D	E	
$1\frac{1}{8}$	$1\frac{1}{4}$	$1\frac{3}{8}$	$1\frac{1}{2}$	$1\frac{5}{8}$	$1\frac{3}{4}$	in. diam. inside small end.
$1\frac{1}{4}$	$1\frac{3}{8}$	$1\frac{1}{2}$	$1\frac{5}{8}$	$1\frac{3}{4}$	$1\frac{7}{8}$	in. diam. inside large end.
$1\frac{5}{8}$	$1\frac{5}{8}$	$1\frac{7}{8}$	$2\frac{1}{8}$	$1\frac{7}{8}$	$2\frac{1}{8}$	in. deep.

No. 43.

HEAVY PATTERN.

A	B	C	E	
$1\frac{1}{4}$	$1\frac{3}{8}$	$1\frac{1}{2}$	$1\frac{5}{8}$	in. diam. inside small end.
$1\frac{3}{8}$	$1\frac{1}{2}$	$1\frac{5}{8}$	$1\frac{7}{8}$	in. diam. inside large end.

All sizes $1\frac{5}{8}$ in. deep.

No. 46.

WHIFFLETREE STAPLES.

A	B	
3	4	in. length of Shank.
$\frac{7}{16}$	$\frac{7}{16}$	in. size of Shank.
$1\frac{3}{8}$	$1\frac{3}{8}$	in. center to center.
$5\frac{1}{4}$	6	in. entire length.

Furnished threaded, with Nuts.

No. 49.

Fig. 2. Page from one of the earliest catalogues of malleable iron, showing carriage and wagon hardware. Castings like these were made in Seth Boyden's foundry in Newark in the 1830's.

substance into the stack with a little pump.[55] While other foundrymen were perhaps not so obviously mysterious, they were quite secretive. Any improvements in methods of melting or annealing were regarded as trade secrets, to be zealously guarded lest a competitor discover them.

Malleable iron in those days was melted either in a crucible furnace or in a type of cupola, and charcoal pig iron was generally used. A low-silicon, high-carbon white iron resulted. Because with them the composition could be controlled more easily, air furnaces gradually supplanted the cupola, and because they had greater production capacity and cost less to run, they also displaced crucible furnaces. Early air furnaces were of 800 to 1,000 pounds' capacity, and when one daring foundryman put in a charge of 1,500 pounds, the others viewed it with alarm as being too large to handle.

In some of the earlier foundries, the furnace was built in a pit. When the heat was ready, instead of tapping and letting the metal flow out as is done today, a man stood beside the furnace with his arm protected by an old boot-leg and lifted up the bung so that the molders could dip their ladles in the furnace to take out the iron, as Seth Boyden's molders had done.

As little was known in those days about temperature control, the anneal was a process of guesswork, with good results hoped for but not necessarily assured. Cycles varied from six to ten days. The annealing temperature was judged by eye, and references to the heat's being too cold and requiring another anneal occur in the notebooks of early founders. From the decarburized condition of some of the castings made about the middle of the Nineteenth Century, it is evident that a very oxidizing packing such as mill scale or iron ore was used. Such packing continued in general use until the 1920's and is still employed in the production of certain castings requiring sharp bending.

APPLICATIONS

SADDLERY

The first application of malleable iron was in saddlery hardware such as buckles, bits, snaps, and stirrups. Many of these are made and sold in malleable iron today.

VEHICLE PARTS

From its success in saddlery hardware came the use of malleable iron for carriage and wagon parts.[1, 55] Whiffletree tips and hooks, fifth wheels, bolster plates, braces and brackets, hubs, hub bands, flanges, and steps [77] were a few of the parts made of malleable iron then, as they are today. The use of this metal made possible greater production of vehicles; the malleable iron castings were far more nearly uniform in size than the handmade product of the blacksmith, and could be produced in quantity.

AGRICULTURAL IMPLEMENTS

The third large use for malleable iron in the early days of the industry was in agricultural implements. Small farm tools such as hoes and rakes of

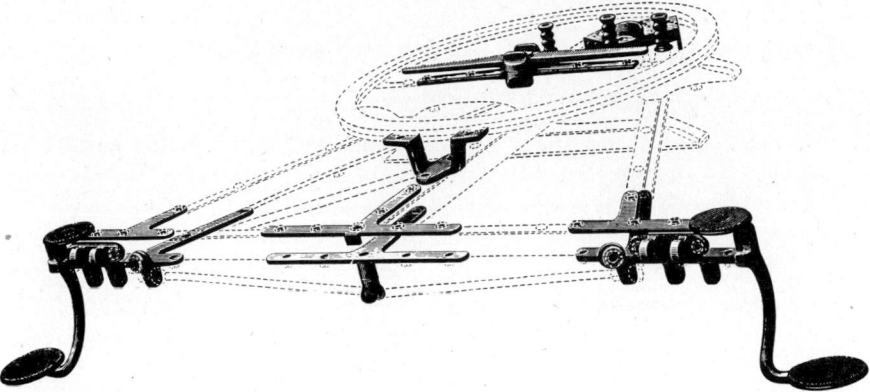

Fig. 3. Malleable iron platform gear of the type used on heavy one-horse wagons about 1885. The dotted outlines indicate woodwork, save for the circles on which the gear turned, which were usually of wrought iron. All solid lines indicate malleable iron.

malleable iron had met with great success, as the toughness and shock resistance of the metal gave good service at relatively low cost, and when the manufacture of farm equipment on an industrial scale began, malleable iron was selected for a large number of parts. As early as 1868, a catalogue [77] of malleable iron castings for the agricultural-implement trade listed a considerable number of satisfied customers, many of whom almost 80 years later are still in business and still using a good proportion of malleable iron castings (see Fig. 4). Parts for plows, reapers, mowers, binders, cultivators, and spreaders were made of malleable iron then, and are today.[4]

PERIOD OF EXPANSION, 1880–1910

By 1880 or thereabouts, the worth of malleable iron had become recognized by both manufacturers and users of saddlery and carriage hardware, plumbing supplies, garden tools, wagon parts, and agricultural implements. More orders were coming in than the industry could handle, even by expanding its capacity. This condition naturally led to the establishment of many more malleable iron foundries.

INFLUENCE OF THE RAILROAD INDUSTRY

Much of the increased demand for malleable iron was due to a new purchaser, the railroad industry. By 1890, the railroads were taking a substantial part of the tonnage of malleable iron foundries for such castings as journal boxes and lids, wedges, draw-bars, brackets, hooks, oil-box frames, brake equipment, door fasteners, stake pockets, turnbuckles, switch castings, and many others.

As the railroads were the largest customer of the malleable iron industry during the period between 1890 and 1910, it is natural that the expansion of the industry took place along their routes. Many of the new plants were established through the Midwest. In general they were built in the area east

OFFICE OF

Forbes' Malleable Iron Works

(MALLEABLE DEPARTMENT ESTABLISHED 1864.)

Rockford, Illinois, Sept. 1868.

Dear Sir:

We would most respectfully call your attention to the accom-
panying catalogue of Plow Clevis &c. and the fact that we have this sum-
mer largely increased our facilities for the manufacture of Malleable Iron
Castings. Heretofore we have been obliged to refuse a great many orders
every year, now we are prepared to extend our trade with due regard to the
wants of our present customers. We shall continue to use the best kind of
STOCK and WORKMANSHIP and give our business in all its details per-
sonal attention. Our prices will always be as low as good work can be done
for at fair profit. Orders should be made thirty days ahead of your actual
wants.

Thankful for the patronage we have received, we would say to our old
customers, that we will try to merit a continuance of their favors.

To those who have not used our castings we would refer to the following
well known firms.

Emerson & Co., Rockford, Ill.	Geo. Fawcett & Co. Farmington, Ill.
F. H. Manny, Rockford, Ill,	S. D. Morrison & Son, Ft. Madison, Io.
N. C. Thompson, Rockford, Ill.	Burg Funck & Co. Burlington, Io.
Skinner Briggs & Enoch, Rockford,	McColl Richter & Hensler, Daven-
Furst & Bradley, Chicago, Ill.	port, Iowa.
Hapgood Young & Co. Chicago, Ill.	Keokuk Plow Co. Keokuk, Iowa.
C. H. McCormick & Bro. Chicago, Ill.	O. M. Hofford. Millwaukee Wis.
Theron Cummins, Grand Detour, Ill.	Fish Bros. Racine, Wis.
B. D. Buford & Co. Rock Island, Ill.	Firmin & Billings, Madison, Wis.
Deere & Co. Moline, Ill.	P. Gormly & Co. Delevan Wis.
Candee, Swan & Co. Moline, Ill.	M. J. Althouse, Waupun, Wis.
W. Lintner & Co. Decatur, Ill.	Barber & Hawley, Manufacturing Co.
Richards & Vandegrift, Princeton, Ill.	Pekin, Illinois.
Lowth & Howe, Owatonna, Minn.	

All communications will be answered promptly. Soliciting your patronage we are.

Very Respectfully Yours.

D. FORBES & SON.

*Fig. 4. A page from the
1868 catalogue of a mal-
leable iron foundry, with
a long list of satisfied
customers.*

of the Mississippi and north of the Ohio, roughly along the lines of the
present Pennsylvania and New York Central railroads.[1]

INFLUENCE OF THE AUTOMOBILE INDUSTRY

At the turn of the century, the automobile and allied industries were
rapidly developing, and by 1910 they had come to be heavy consumers of
malleable iron castings. In such critical parts as rear axle housings, differential
cases, spring shackles, and hubs, as well as in utilitarian parts such as brackets,
hangers, cover plates, and so on, malleable iron is utilized in passenger cars
and trucks. Electric starters for automobiles later offered another important
application of malleable iron.

PERSONNEL

Among the men who followed Boyden and who were influential in the
industry during the period of mushroom growth was J. H. Whittemore of

Naugatuck, Connecticut, who established a foundry there in 1858 and later became president of the Eastern Malleable Iron Company, formed in 1912 by the merger of five New England malleable iron foundries.[1] Duncan Forbes, a Scotch foundryman, came to this country in 1853, worked for a short while in a foundry in western New York state and then moved to Rockford, Illinois, where he started the foundry his descendants still operate. A. E. Hammer of the Malleable Iron Fittings Company and B. J. Walker of the Erie Malleable Iron Company were among the first to study the chemistry of malleable iron. A. A. Pope, who entered the industry in 1869, became president of the National Malleable and Steel Castings Company.

It is impossible to mention all the eminent industrialists and foundrymen who helped build the malleable iron industry of the country, or to trace the history of their companies through the years. A partial list of the oldest foundries which are still producers of malleable iron follows.

Company	Began Production of Malleable Iron	Original Name
Newark Malleable Iron Company Newark, New Jersey	1826	Seth Boyden's Foundry
Westmoreland Malleable Iron Company Westmoreland, New York	1833	Oak Hill Malleable Iron Company
Belcher Malleable Iron Company Easton, Massachusetts	1837	Easton Iron Foundry
Meeker Foundry Company Newark, New Jersey	1843	Gardner, Harrison and Company
Frazer and Jones Company Syracuse, New York	1845	Frazer, Burns, and Jones
Arcade Malleable Iron Company Worcester, Massachusetts	1850	Arcade Malleable Iron Company
Malleable Iron Fittings Company Branford, Connecticut	1854	Totoket Company
Eastern Malleable Iron Company Naugatuck, Connecticut	1854	American Malleable Iron Company
Stanley G. Flagg and Company, Inc. Stowe, Pennsylvania	1857	Stanley G. Flagg and Company
Gunite Foundries Corporation Rockford, Illinois	1864	Forbes Malleable Iron Works
The Dayton Malleable Iron Company Dayton, Ohio	1866	The Dayton Malleable Iron Company
Rhode Island Malleable Iron Works Hillsgrove, Rhode Island	1867	Rhode Island Malleable Iron Works
National Malleable and Steel Castings Company, Cleveland, Ohio	1868	Cleveland Malleable Iron Company

CAPTIVE FOUNDRIES

During the second half of the Nineteenth Century, the captive foundry first appeared, to produce castings primarily for use in the final product of the parent company. Though a captive foundry may do some jobbing work during periods when not all its capacity is required for its own company, its main aim is to furnish castings for the parent company. Since a malleable iron foundry requires considerable investment in equipment and personnel, it is not practical for any except a large company with a steady demand for a substantial tonnage of malleable castings to establish its own foundry. Such companies as Chain Belt, General Electric, General Motors, International Harvester, and Link-Belt are among those which have their own malleable foundries.

ADVANCES IN MANUFACTURE

During the period between 1880 and 1910, the increase in the number of malleable iron foundries and in tonnage produced was paralleled by improved methods of manufacture. Up to that time, the deepest secrecy surrounded any knowledge of either melting or annealing processes. A worker going from one plant to another carried his knowledge in his head. Few records were kept, and those extant were considered valuable trade secrets. Since raw materials were graded by fracture only, and since both melting and annealing were done without temperature measurements or controls, it is really a remarkable feat that good metal was produced.

Most of the malleable iron of those days was melted in air furnaces which were of one to five tons' capacity. Later, furnaces of 10 to 15 tons' capacity became common. Charging was generally done by hand. Only a few of the early air furnaces had forced draft, and the dependence on natural draft sometimes led to very slow melting. Starting a heat of 10 to 15 tons at 1:30 A.M., and finishing at 6:00 or 7:00 P.M., was not an uncommon occurrence in the malleable iron foundry of the Nineties.

One of the old-time foundries had only a single furnace with a melt capacity of one ton. As orders increased, the founders tried to get more heats from that furnace, till they were getting six heats a day. This capacity of six tons a day was still not adequate to take care of the demand, and so they decided they were working along the wrong lines and should increase the size of the furnace, rather than the number of heats per day. Starting with a one-ton furnace and natural draft, they built up the capacity to 40 tons per heat and then began to expand the number of furnaces. This one furnace of 40 tons' capacity was installed in 1900 and was the largest furnace in use in the industry until 1925.[3]

In the Eighties and Nineties, patterns were made of brass, gated for standard long running work; for shorter runs, white metal was used. The chief concern of the patternmaker was to gate a pattern so as to obtain the greatest number of pieces in a mold. On smaller work, there were often 40 to 60 pieces in a mold. Very little attention was given to locating the gate in order to produce a sound casting, as is the practice today. Molders were apprenticed for four years. About 1900, molding machines were introduced and were immediately tried in some of the more progressive foundries. The natural prejudice of the molders against the machines, combined with lack of knowledge as to

Fig. 5. A three-spring express wagon built about 1885, completely ironed with standard malleable iron castings.

how the machines might best be used, retarded adoption of them. But grad-ually more molding machines were employed, until by 1910 they were fairly common.[78]

Sand-handling machinery was introduced into malleable iron foundries about 1905. Although the real importance of the condition of the sand was not then recognized, the use of machinery to cut in new sand and temper the heaps was a good step toward uniformity. To clean the hard-iron castings, the custom for many years [79] had been to use a stiff brush to remove the sand. After the brush followed tumblers or rattlers. Then in 1900, sand-blasting machines entered the picture. Pulverized coal was first used between 1898 and 1900 as a fuel for annealing furnaces; it was used to fire melting furnaces about 1914.

For straightening annealed castings, the hydraulic press was introduced about 1903, supplementing the drop hammer in use before that. Along with other industries, foundries were becoming more mechanized during this period. Credit for the successful development of many of these advances in manufacturing goes to John Francis Hay of the Erie Malleable Iron Company of Erie, Pennsylvania, during his 52 years in the malleable iron industry between 1880 and 1932.

TECHNICAL RESEARCH

During most of its first half-century, the manufacture of American malleable iron, like much of the industrial activity of the nation during this period, was mainly empirical in its approach. The age of industrial research as we know it had not begun. But by the 1870's, inquiry into the reasons behind the practical success of particular methods in various industrial operations began to come into prominence. In the malleable iron industry, the early lines of investigation had as their goal some at least quantitative understanding of why certain proportions of the constituents in the melt produced better castings than others did; the objective was to determine the chemical basis of the malleable process.

Probably the first scientific investigator of American malleable iron was Alfred E. Hammer of the Malleable Iron Fittings Company at Branford, Connecticut.[1] He had begun to study the chemistry of the process in 1872, and three years thereafter he established at the Branford plant the first chemical laboratory in the industry. Studying the effect of different proportions of carbon and silicon and of manganese and sulphur, he worked out chemical ratios for each pair, and subsequently applied these in the selection and mixing of irons, where they were the more valuable in view of the fact that at the time pig iron was not made and sold by analysis. B. J. Walker of the Erie Malleable Iron Company actively fostered studies similar to those in which Mr. Hammer engaged, as did A. A. Pope of the National Malleable and Steel Castings Company of Cleveland, Ohio. Publication of the kind which is customary today was by no means frequent in the years around the Centennial Exposition, so that it was entirely natural for an investigator to hold confidential the useful results which he attained. Mr. Hammer and Mr. Walker nevertheless began in the 1880's to share their knowledge of malleable iron and the science underlying it. Mr. Walker's contribution to the increase of information about the chemistry of malleable iron was highly important, and probably of even more lasting significance was the influence which he constantly exerted for more liberal policies governing the exchange of information.

Other laboratories were established by some of the larger malleable iron manufacturers after 1890. Enrique Touceda, who had come from Cuba to study the arts at Georgetown University and the sciences at Rensselaer Polytechnic Institute, and who as later discussed was to play a dominant part in the improvement and consolidation of malleable iron techniques, entered the work in 1894, when he was engaged as consultant by the Walter A. Wood Mowing and Reaping Machine Company of Hoosick Falls, New York. The Wood firm established a well-equipped laboratory at the time.

In 1904, the National Malleable and Steel Castings Company instituted a works and experimental laboratory at Indianapolis. Here Dr. Harry A. Schwartz, using as a nucleus the information which Mr. Pope had assembled, commenced investigations looking toward the establishment of a sound theoretical basis for works control. The quantitative effect of carbon on the melt was determined in the first year of this research, and subsequently the lack of effect of manganese sulphide was established. The theoretical explanation thus derived for the practical observations which Mr. Hammer and Mr. Pope had made 20 years before was similarly arrived at by other investigators, prominent among whom was W. R. Bean, then of The T. H. Symington Company of Corning, New York, later of the Eastern Malleable Iron Company of Naugatuck, Connecticut. Further studies of the effect of the carbon content on the strength of castings, and of the carbon-silicon, sulphur-manganese, and silicon-phosphorus relations were carried on in the period after 1903 by Dr. Schwartz, Mr. Bean, and other investigators. Much of this work was vigorously supported and encouraged by Allen Bixby of the Indianapolis Works of the National Malleable and Steel Castings Company. Except for early publications by Professor Palmer C. Ricketts and Enrique Touceda, general publication remained a rare thing until Dr. Richard Moldenke, after having been associated with the laboratories of two malleable iron concerns, established himself as an independent consultant and commenced frequent contributions to technical journals. For a considerable number of years, his were almost the only published treatments of malleable iron and its chemistry, and he was a stout advocate of greater exchange of ideas.

Through work of this sort and through subsequent research which turned from the chemistry to the physics, metallurgy, and metallography of American malleable iron, further progress was made toward assured control of the product. The more progressive manufacturers thus were determining not only the proportions and chemistry of the charge and the melt, but also the temperatures and periods most effective in the annealing process, and the mechanism of the anneal itself. Others, however, were still not familiar enough with the product or the process to secure consistent results. Occasional poor castings thus produced were a reflection on the whole industry.

AMERICAN MALLEABLE CASTINGS ASSOCIATION

To correct this condition, a group of forward-looking manufacturers, meeting in New York in 1897 under the chairmanship of O. P. Letchworth of Pratt and Letchworth, founded the American Malleable Castings Association. One of the first co-operative industrial groups in the country, this was an association whose members agreed to share knowledge of practice and thus improve the product of all. E. C. Metcalf of the Westmoreland Malleable Iron Company, Westmoreland, New York; Fred Frazer of the Frazer and Jones Company, Syracuse, New York; Harry Forbes of the Rockford Malleable Iron Works, Rockford, Illinois; B. J. Walker of the Erie Malleable Iron Company; Amos Whiteley of the Muncie Malleable Foundry Company, Muncie, Indiana; Frederick W. Sivyer of the Northwestern Malleable Iron Company, Milwaukee, Wisconsin; W. H. Osborne of the Wisconsin Malleable Iron Company, also of Milwaukee; and John J. Llewellyn of Belle City

Malleable Iron Company, Racine, Wisconsin, were among the group concerned in the formation of the association. Other leading malleable foundrymen who made their influence felt throughout the industry during the period from 1890 to 1920 were John Haswell of the Dayton Malleable Iron Company, Dayton, Ohio; Frank J. Lanahan of the Fort Pitt Malleable Iron Company, Pittsburgh, Pennsylvania; J. H. Whittemore, under whose guidance several foundries merged into the Eastern Malleable Iron Company with headquarters at Naugatuck, Connecticut; and A. A. Pope, who founded and developed the group of plants constituting the National Malleable and Steel Castings Company, Cleveland, Ohio.

After a few years' work had demonstrated to the association the diversity of opinion existing among even the best informed about the manufacture and properties of malleable iron, a program of intensive research was decided upon. For that purpose the association in 1913 retained Enrique Touceda who, as we have seen, had become associated with American malleable iron through the Walter A. Wood Company nearly 20 years before. Professor Touceda, who was recognized as a consulting metallurgist of great skill, was commissioned to carry out a series of fundamental researches and to report to the members of the Association the information thus gained. The group agreed to forego the long-established custom of individual safeguarding of trade secrets, and to turn over to Professor Touceda all the knowledge then available to the industry. As far as is known, this was the first co-operative research project undertaken by any industrial group in the country. Investigation was carried out along three lines, chemical, metallographic, and mechanical tests and examinations being made and recorded.[80]

Though much of his work was necessarily concerned with the particular problems of individual manufacturers, Professor Touceda undertook and published a great deal of research on basic questions involved in the production and properties of malleable iron. Studying the annealing process, he established fundamental principles for control and uniformity. Through constant publication in technical journals, he made plain what could be expected of American malleable iron, and how it should be used. In terms of publication of basic knowledge, he soon came to be the leader.

Others too continued the active study of malleable iron and the processes employed in manufacturing it. To summarize even by topic the papers which appeared during the latter part of this period is not possible here. Among the subjects discussed were the problem of comparative strength of machined and unmachined bars (by-product again of the old error of confusing American blackheart with European whiteheart malleable), the microstructure of fractures of American malleable iron, the question of high iron oxide in sands as a possible source of surface troubles in castings, which included the problem of gas entrapment, the use of powdered coal as a fuel, and galvanizing embrittlement. Prominent among those contributing were Dr. Schwartz, W. R. Bean, W. H. Highriter, and E. K. Smith.

Enrique Touceda, for half a century foremost contributor to the development of American malleable iron.

Oliver Storey of the Wisconsin Malleable Iron Company, in studies of the graphitizing reaction during the latter part of this period, was among the first to show in published writings about 1912 and 1913 a thorough understanding of the reaction as related to the iron-carbon diagram. Slightly later was pioneer work by Paul Merica, National Bureau of Standards, in the theoretical metallurgy of malleable iron. The University of Michigan about 1917 sponsored work on the measurement of the effect of graphitizing rates, the investigations being under the charge of A. B. White. Anson Hayes and his graduate students at the Iowa State University somewhat later published a considerable amount of information dealing with the effects of various alloy elements. Joining with the inventors of a type of annealing furnace, Dr. Hayes later was active in the advancement of the manufacture of the type of pearlitic malleable iron known as "Z" metal.

The wedge test was developed during this period as a practical means of studying the toughness of malleable iron. Devised by B. J. Walker of the Erie Malleable Iron Company, it is regarded as particularly valuable from a performance point of view because of the fact that it tests shock resistance, a quality which the more conventional tests measure primarily as to notch effect. Through this test and the standard mechanical tests which were performed by Professor Touceda on daily test bars supplied to the association laboratory by members, the maintenance of high standards of production and performance was fostered. Trained technical men from the laboratory, making periodic visits to each company for the purpose of inspecting practices in the foundry, aided the adoption of approved methods.

Duplexing, the process of melting the stock in a cupola and then running the cupola melt into another furnace for refining, was developed between 1912 and 1930. The National Malleable and Steel Castings Company made the first experiments with the process in 1912, an electric furnace being the refining unit. This combination was not successful at that time, because the high carbon obtained in the cupola iron could not be reduced to the range of 2.40 to 2.60 per cent then necessary for the production of malleable castings for railroad use. In order to overcome this difficulty, a third type of furnace was introduced, so that the process became a triplex rather than duplex one, involving (1) melting white iron in the cupola, (2) reducing carbon in the Bessemer converter, and (3) refining in an electric furnace. The triplex process is no longer used. In 1921, the Ohio Malleable Iron Company, Columbus, Ohio, employed cupola–air furnace melting for a period, but the first permanent application of duplexing was at the Southern Malleable Iron Company, East St. Louis, Illinois, in 1928. Walton Woody of the National Malleable and Steel Castings Company in 1931 was the first to employ duplexing to supply continuous metal. By the mid-1930's, 13 per cent of American malleable iron melted was duplexed with cupola and air furnace, and 8 per cent by cupola and electric furnace.

IMPROVEMENT IN PROPERTIES

Probably the best record of the success of the American Malleable Castings Association program of technical improvement is in the constant advance in both the quality and the uniformity of malleable iron which appears from a review of published test data.

The first published test results on malleable iron in this country were those by Professor Palmer C. Ricketts [81] which appeared in Van Nostrand's *Engineering Journal* in 1885. Professor Ricketts' assistant in conducting these early tests was Enrique Touceda. An average value for the bars then tested would be about 38,000 pounds per square inch tensile strength and 3 per cent elongation.

In 1903, Richard Moldenke [82] gave 45,000 pounds per square inch and 4 per cent elongation as probable values for malleable iron. Some plants were making iron with a tensile strength of over 50,000 pounds per square inch and elongation of 7 per cent in two inches, whereas others were able to obtain only 35,000 pounds tensile and 2 per cent elongation as in the Eighties and early Nineties. [83] This situation was partly due to the great demand for malleable castings, which encouraged expansion at the expense of trained personnel and often meant that castings were pushed through the anneal without due regard for time and temperature.

Fig. 6. A woodcut of about 1890, showing a malleable iron foundry, complete with pattern vault, barn, and all appurtenances.

For this reason, the first specification which the American Society for Testing Materials adopted for malleable iron castings in 1904 called for 40,000 pounds per square inch tensile strength and 2.5 per cent elongation in two inches. Transverse strength was also specified, the requirement being that the breaking load on a bar on 12-inch supports should be 3,000 pounds with one-half inch deflection.[78]

Then, as the work done by Professor Touceda and the American Malleable Castings Association began to bear fruit, a marked upward trend in the properties of the product occurred. Today malleable iron has reached the point where castings can be bought from any of more than a hundred foundries with confidence in the uniformity and reliability of the metal. The list of the specifications made by the American Society for Testing Materials through the past 40 years and the fact that each upward revision has been at the request of the manufacturers themselves, who thus continually set high standards for their product, tell better than words what has been done.

TABLE 1. PROPERTIES OF AMERICAN MALLEABLE IRON (1885–1933)

Date	Tensile Strength (Pounds per Square Inch)	Yield Point (Pounds per Square Inch)	Elongation (Per Cent in 2 inches)
1885 [81]	38,000		3
1900 [83]	42,000		4
A.S.T.M.			
1904 [78]	40,000		2.5
1915 [80]	38,000		5
1919 [84]	45,000		7.5
1924	50,000		10
1927	50,000	30,000	10
1930	50,000	32,500	10
1933 (Grade 32510)	50,000	32,500	10
and Current (Grade 35018)	53,000	35,000	18

PRESENT ORGANIZATION OF THE MALLEABLE IRON INDUSTRY

The American Malleable Castings Association was succeeded in 1927 by the Malleable Iron Research Institute, which emphasized especially improvement in properties and practice of manufacture of malleable iron. The activities of the institute were turned over to the Malleable Founders' Society in 1934. In general, the aims of all the organizations have been product improvement, research, and market development. Today the Malleable Founders' Society, which retains an expert engineering staff, continues the plant inspection and technical research carried on by the earlier groups and maintains its own chemical and metallurgical testing laboratory.

MODERN MANUFACTURE

The manufacture of malleable iron is now governed by both laboratory and production control throughout the entire process. As was shown in detail in Chapter XIII, every step of the manufacture is accurately checked by the most modern control equipment. Naturally, this practice leads to uniformly high quality in the final castings.

The modern trend toward larger, more efficient industrial organizations is felt in the malleable iron industry as in others. One of the largest firms in 1865 produced 152 tons a year. Today the average individual plant production is approximately 10,000 tons annually. In 1943, 100 companies operating 108 plants throughout the nation supplied malleable iron castings. Of these, 76 make castings primarily for sale as such; 10 plants make specialties using malleable castings but do not regularly engage in jobbing foundrywork; and 14 are owned by large companies for which they supply castings almost exclusively. The 108 plants are scattered throughout the country, many in the East and Midwest, and malleable iron is manufactured also on the Gulf and Pacific coasts.

TABLE 2. MALLEABLE IRON FOUNDRIES BY STATES [85]

Alabama	1
California	2
Connecticut	7
Delaware	1
Illinois	16
Indiana	9
Iowa	1
Massachusetts	2
Michigan	8
Minnesota	1
Missouri	1
New Hampshire	1
New Jersey	2
New York	12
Ohio	17
Pennsylvania	13
Rhode Island	1
Texas	1
West Virginia	1
Wisconsin	11

The wide utility of American malleable iron as an engineering material has been recognized abroad, to such extent that the American product before the second World War was on the way to displacing whiteheart malleable iron in its European homeland. American malleable iron producers were exporting, and have continued in some measure, not only to England, France, and the Scandinavian countries, but also to South America and Asia. Establishment of the manufacture of American malleable iron in Europe before the war is another evidence of the acceptance of the metal.

Naturally, in 1942 and 1943 most of the tonnage of the malleable iron industry was for war material. In 1941, the approximate classification [85] of total production of malleable iron castings by principal users was as follows:

Automotive (including passenger cars, trucks, trailers, accessories, and repair parts) . . . . 45.3 per cent
Railroad . . . . 8.7 per cent
Agricultural implements . . . . 7.4 per cent
Electrical fittings . . . . : 4.4 per cent
Pipe fittings . . . . 17.0 per cent
All other uses . . . . 17.2 per cent

USE IN AUTOMOTIVE INDUSTRY

Despite the lowered weight possible today because of the high mechanical properties available in modern malleable iron, there was an average of 183 pounds of malleable iron castings on every automotive vehicle produced in 1941. Table 3 [85] shows the approximate production of automotive malleable iron and automotive production figures from 1930 to 1941:

TABLE 3. APPROXIMATE PRODUCTION OF AUTOMOTIVE MALLEABLES AND THE PRODUCTION OF AUTOMOTIVE VEHICLES, 1930–1941

Year	Approximate Tonnage of Automotive Malleables *	Production of Automotive Vehicles †	Pounds per Vehicle
1930	301,000	3,355,986	179
1931	198,000	2,389,738	166
1932	112,000	1,370,678	163
1933	174,000	1,920,057	181
1934	240,000	2,753,111	174
1935	326,000	3,946,934	165
1936	372,000	4,454,115	167
1937	371,000	4,808,974	154
1938	173,000	2,489,085	143
1939	291,000	3,577,292	162
1940	339,500	4,469,354	152
1941	441,000	4,838,561	183

* Includes passenger cars, trucks, truck tractors, truck trailers, passenger-car trailers, accessories, and repair parts.

† Includes sales of passenger cars and trucks to distributors and dealers in the United States, exports from United States factories, plus number of vehicles assembled abroad from parts produced in United States plants.

The tonnage of malleable iron dropped in 1942 because of the many changes in patterns and the conversion to war production. In 1943, 975,000 tons of malleable iron was produced.

TABLE 4. APPROXIMATE PRODUCTION OF MALLEABLE IRON CASTINGS IN THE UNITED STATES, 1924–1943 [85]

	Tons
1924	790,000
1925	901,000
1926	889,000
1927	800,000
1928	895,000
1929	947,000
1930	572,000
1931	342,000
1932	207,000
1933	316,000
1934	430,000
1935	538,000
1936	665,000
1937	688,000
1938	334,000
1939	565,000
1940	662,000
1941	972,000
1942	880,000
1943	975,000

XVI

APPLICATIONS OF AMERICAN
MALLEABLE IRON

To ITEMIZE one by one the thousands of commercial applications and industrial uses of American malleable iron is outside the scope of this handbook; the list would be impressive, but it would run to unwieldy length.
Castings are being made daily from thousands of patterns representing hundreds of product classifications, for in practically every industry where toughness, shock resistance, and resistance to corrosion and rust are important in
metal parts and appliances, American malleable iron finds wide utilization.

This chapter therefore will describe representative uses to which the
material is put and will classify the major industrial and commercial fields
in which it is employed. The classification will give a suggestion of the range
in which malleable iron serves, and description of typical applications will
indicate ways in which it has provided effective answers to design problems
in many industries. Malleable iron's machinability, its entire freedom from
casting strains, the facility with which it can be cast in intricate shapes involving both extremely thin and heavy sections, its high strength, and its unique
combination of the ability to be accurately cast and yet to be ductile and
shock-resistant are the primary reasons for such extensive use of it as the discussion in this chapter will indicate.

Aeronautical Castings

In the plane itself, malleable iron is used in aircraft for many critical
parts where strength and ductility are of such extreme importance as to offset
the weight of ferrous materials, as for instance in the brackets and forks of
swivel tail-wheel assemblies. Another comparable use is in the famous B-17
light bomber which, weighing seven tons without load, imposes tremendous
stresses on landing gear both in taking off and in landing. In the wheel assembly of this plane, malleable iron is used in drive ring and the supporting
rings for the hydraulic brake disk, where the toughness and shock-resistance

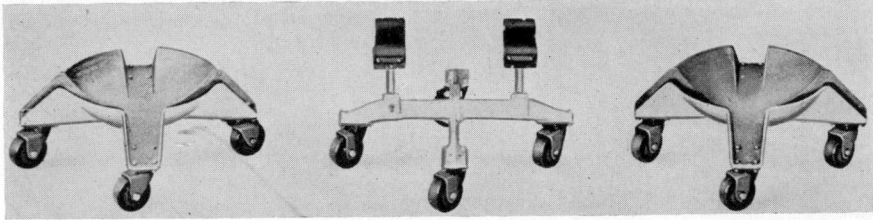

Fig. 1. Wheel and nose cradles of American malleable iron, used in the storage and handling of small aircraft.

of the metal are extremely valuable. Elsewhere throughout aircraft, fittings for doors and cargo compartments, bomb-bay door clips and hinges, bomb racks, angle brackets in wing assemblies, engine brackets, and similar components are made of malleable. In airfield operation again, malleable is found in refueling trucks and pipe line couplings, in lighting fixtures, in hangar brackets and swivels. Wheel and nose cradles of malleable are employed in handling planes in the hangar.

Agricultural Castings

The agricultural implement industry, among the earliest heavy purchasers of malleable iron nearly a century ago, continues today to be a leading user. The industry's steady utilization of malleable is due in large measure to the fact that the metal has more than kept pace with the increasingly exacting demands for performance made by the motorization and mechanization of farming. Resistance to normal wear and to deterioration from abuse or from lack of protection from weather is of great importance in agricultural machinery, and is a quality which malleable iron readily affords. Hence malleable iron castings form parts in farm machinery ranging from the plows and harrows that start the crops to the combines and other harvesters, the diggers and huskers, that get them in for market. Similarly, malleable is extensively used in cotton-ginning machinery and in machinery for the processing of food products such as sugar cane. In cane-processing machinery especially, the metal's resistance to corrosion is particularly valuable. Hand farm tools of all sorts are made of malleable, and malleable iron castings are utilized in scores of equipment units for poultry houses, dairies, and barns. Fencepost parts and fittings, chains, ferrules, clevises, and swivels are comparable farm materials manufactured of malleable, as are binder-needles, mower shoes and guards, and draft brackets. Harness fittings, earliest application of malleable iron, still are made of it.

Automotive Castings

Up to 300,000 tons of malleable iron have been used by the automotive industry in a year of normal production. The average passenger automobile contains about 140 pounds of malleable iron castings in strategic places. In a single truck, as much as a ton and a half of malleable may be used. The steering gear housing through which the car is directed and the differential gear case through which it is driven are but two of the vital spots in which the strength and dependability of the material are utilized. The ability of malleable iron to withstand impact loads applied with split-second suddenness is a prime reason for the use of it in such applications. The moderate finish-stock requirement imposed by malleable iron, its ready machinability, uniformity, castability, and low cost per pound combine to make it practically universally specified in passenger cars for a wide variety of parts here listed:

Adjusting nuts	Motor supports
Bearing caps	Pinion cages
Bearing retainers	Radiator inlets and outlets
Brake pedals and brackets	Rear-axle housings
Brake supports	Shifter forks
Body brackets	Shock-absorber brackets, housings, and liners
Bumper brackets	
Combination hub and brake drums	Spring hangers, seats, and seat-caps
Clutch pedals and brackets	Steering-gear brackets and cases
Differential carriers	Steering knuckles
Differential cases	Steering-post brackets and lock-bodies
Exhaust-pipe flanges	
Generator and fan supports	Spare-tire lock-bodies
Hubs	Spare-wheel brackets
Master cylinder brackets	Vibration dampener plates

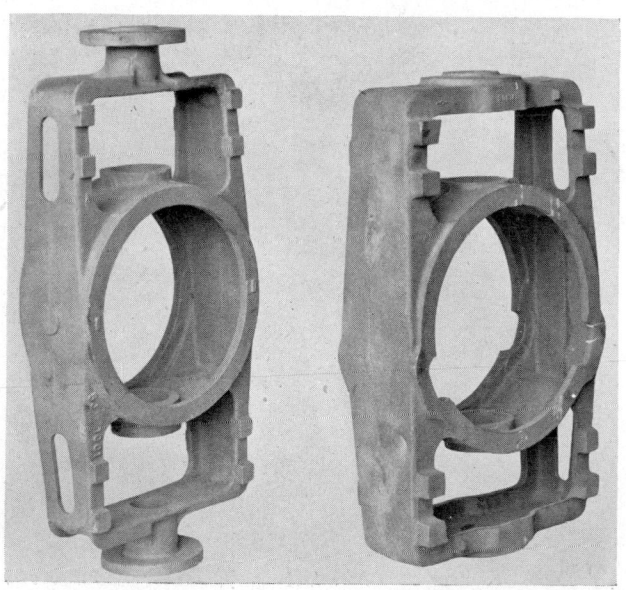

Fig. 2. Automotive differential housing castings made of pearlitic malleable iron.

Fig. 3. Wheel and wheel cover castings used in converting 1½-ton trucks to four-wheel drive for military use.

The parts listed for passenger cars are similarly used in truck construction. In addition, many dual-wheel hubs are of malleable iron, as are wheels themselves, rear-motor supports, power take-offs, fifth wheels, brake spiders, and winches. Malleable iron is likewise employed in the cross-members of frames, in shims, and so on, in the construction of heavy-duty vehicles.

Pearlitic malleable iron is used for camshafts, gears, pistons, piston rings, valve rocker-arms, propeller-shaft flanges, universal-joint yokes, bearing caps, fan-pulleys, clutch parts, Diesel injector plugs, levers, and brackets, in heavy automotive construction.

Fig. 4. Army four-wheel drive scout car.

Boiler, Tank, and Engine Castings

Where resistance to corrosion and the combination of high tensile properties with relatively light weight are important, malleable iron finds application in parts for boilers and tanks. Manhole and handhole covers and frames, outlet valve frames, manifolds, and similar parts are fabricated from malleable iron castings. The development of pearlitic malleable iron with higher strength and hardness than standard malleable has extended the usefulness of malleable castings in the engine field. Connecting rods of malleable iron, as well as Diesel valve rocker arms, piston and cylinder heads, motor end plates, and other engine parts are made in the material, which likewise is extensively employed in outboard motors and in propeller-mechanism parts.

Building Equipment Castings

In the manufacture of all forms of building hardware where efficient and economical production demands long runs from molding equipment, slight necessity for finishing operations, and low cost to the ultimate user, malleable iron has been found to be a thrifty as well as rugged material. As a result, malleable iron fitments are to be found nearly everywhere one turns in the modern dwelling. In furniture and household and office appurtenances likewise, malleable is extensively used. Window and door fittings, hangers, tracks, and other equipment for garage doors, awning hardware, and plumbing fittings are but a few representatives of these applications of the metal. Others are in door checks, window catches, radiator nipples, gutter hooks, latches, drawer pulls, lock parts, keys, desk brackets, shelf supports, and the like. The swivel chair which is the symbol of the business executive and the

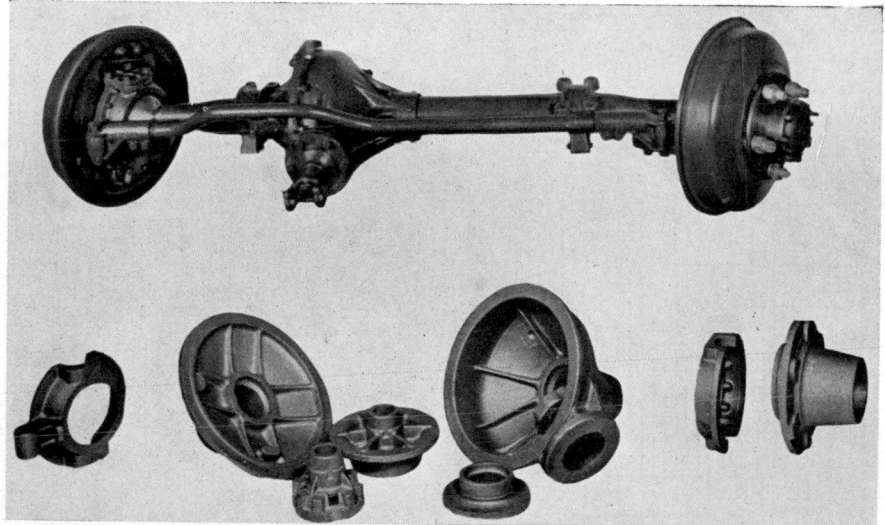

Fig. 5. Axle assembly of malleable iron used in the scout car shown in Fig. 4.

Fig. 6. Propeller mechanism parts for tank carrier barges, made of malleable iron.

football stadium seat which he occasionally occupies both are constructed with malleable iron in essential parts. Folding-chair brackets also are made of malleable. In builder's equipment it finds much work to do, from the clamps that hold concrete forms together to expansion-bolt shells, pipe hangers, staging and shoring clamps, hinges, and ladder fittings. Manufacturers of heavy screw jacks converted to malleable for the shells of their product in order to gain greater strength and toughness and at the same time to make the jacks lighter and easier to handle. The machinability of malleable, which speeds and simplifies finishing operations, is regarded as of decided importance in finished building equipment.

Conveyor and Handling Equipment Castings

In such installations as conveyor systems, where a very large number of uniform elements must be combined, and where the installations, to be efficient, must have rugged dependability without clumsy heaviness of parts, malleable iron castings offer an effective solution. In rollers, pulleys, guides, and other components of movable belt conveyors, particularly in the chain-links, malleable castings are widely used, being produced in an extremely large variety of special shapes for particular kinds of work. The pearlitic malleable irons are often used in chain-links where abrasive wear is encountered and some added strength is needed. Industrial truck wheels cast as units in malleable iron have replaced composite wheels of other materials, thus freeing manufacturers from design limitations. Storage equipment involving the use of ranges of racks and shelves employs unit castings of malleable iron which are readily assembled in multiples as needs require. The accuracy of dimension and smoothness of cast surfaces possible with malleable iron are of pronounced value in such installations. Equally important is the freedom of design which malleable iron allows in such castings as those used as truck frames in overhead crane-conveyor systems, where the necessity of conserving overhead space must be reckoned with.

Electrical and Industrial Power Equipment

Malleable iron castings have quite a range in the electrical field, from outlets and switchboxes, for example, to insulator caps. In addition, parts for electric motors and generators are made of malleable iron, and the high permeability of the material at and below moderate intensities of magnetizing fields makes it useful in magnetic circuits. The numerous malleable iron parts employed in the construction of electric locomotives and tractors anticipate in our listing the very wide use of malleable iron in regular railroad equipment. Such supplementary units in electrical installations as pole brackets, mounting hooks, and other equipment which must withstand exposure to the atmosphere are made of malleable. Its high resistance to soil corrosion is exploited in the use of it in expanding earth anchors to hold transmission towers in position, and in telegraph pole supports. A comparably critical application, in which malleable's equally high resistance to atmospheric corrosion is im-

Fig. 7. A chain drag conveyor of pearlitic malleable iron used in a cement mill for handling ground limestone into silos.

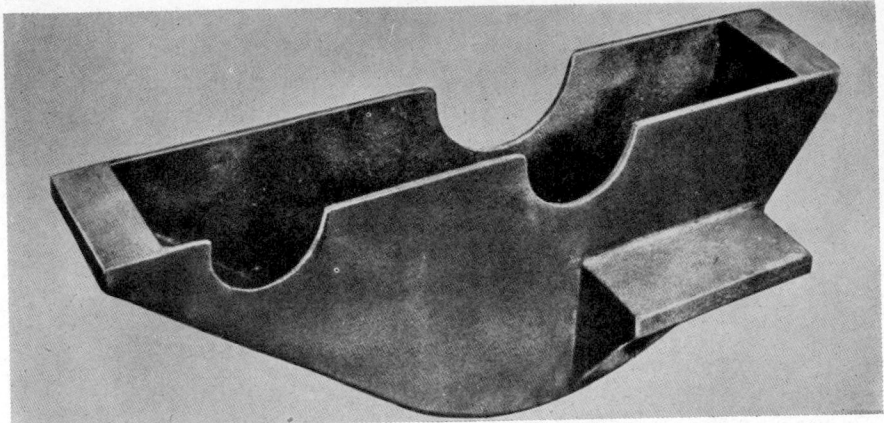

Fig. 8. Large malleable iron electric motor gear case.

portant, is in insulator caps for high-tension transmission lines. A string of insulators using these caps must carry a weight of 12½ tons, and the caps must resist all kinds of sleet loads as well as withstand corrosion by the atmosphere.

Hardware and Appliance Castings

Light weight and resistance to sudden impact are extremely important qualities in pneumatic and portable tools, in small shop equipment, and in domestic appliances and utensils. Malleable iron therefore is found in a very great number of such castings. To stand the strain of continuous use and extreme fatigue and vibration imposed on aircraft riveting tools, for example, malleable iron, already widely used in the bodies of other rivet guns, has been specified as the material for tool bodies. Impact resistance which can scorn the sudden bumps tools and appliances must undergo in the shop and the home, plus light weight for easy handling and good surface texture without costly finishing operations, have led to the use of malleable iron in many miscellaneous tools including wrenches, vises, breast drills, hand drills, hatchets, hammers, rakes, and andirons, and in such household appliances as stoves, sewing machines, refrigerators, washing and ironing machines, vacuum cleaners, dishwashing machines, oil burners, electric fans, electric toasters, automatic stokers, and radios. Hardened pearlitic malleable iron is used in many of the tools listed. Many motors such as those of washing machines and refrigerators have connecting rods, gears, and crankshafts of standard or pearlitic malleable iron. Malleable iron castings are important in the construction of lawn-mowers. The base and hydraulic mechanism of the barber chair, like that of the operating chairs used by dentists, are fabricated of malleable, which likewise is used in such hospital equipment as beds, x-ray apparatus, elevators, and so on. Typewriters and other business machines employ many malleable castings.

Machine Tool and Machinery Castings

Machine tools obviously require the most substantial of materials and the most rigorous engineering care in construction, for the stresses — torsional, tensile, compressive, and complex — which are thrown on their members are severe. Accuracy is essential in each component part, since exact alignment is imperative if the machine tool is to do its work properly. The accuracy with which malleable iron castings are made and the ease with which the material is machined, as well as its natural freedom from internal or casting strains, make it well adapted to use in machine tool parts. It is used in lathes, planers, shapers, grinders, screw machines, gear cutters, drills, and other machine tools. Likewise, malleable iron castings are extensively employed in the special machinery utilized in such industries as textile, cement, rubber, shoe, mining, quarrying, grinding, forging, foundry, bakery, woodworking, oil-refining, tobacco-processing, oil-drilling, bottling, icemaking, and laundry. Alloyed malleable iron is often specified when corrosive conditions present a problem.

Marine Equipment Castings

On cargo ships and luxury liners, malleable iron castings had won a place as old seadogs years ago, and in the special demands for seagoing equipment which World War II imposed they more than justified that place. The resistance to corrosion which malleable offers takes on special value when

Fig. 9. Mill type motor end plate casting.

Fig. 10. Malleable iron mine transition rail joints withstand both the corrosive attack of acid mine water and the wear and shock of track service.

ocean atmospheres, fog, and smoke are to be considered. The toughness of the metal in its resistance to shock renders it particularly suited to use in deck fittings and cargo-handling equipment, and in anchors, chains, capstans, fastenings, towing bitts, portlight covers and frames, winch parts, and hardware such as turnbuckles and cleats. In addition, the metal finds its place in parts for marine motors such as those used in motor torpedo boats, and in the propeller mechanism parts of invasion barges and tank carriers.

MINING AND OILFIELD CASTINGS

In mining equipment, not only extremely severe service conditions but also a high corrosion hazard must be met by metal. Malleable iron's toughness and resistance to corrosion and rust have led to its being employed in many kinds of equipment in the minefields, from safety devices and tools to

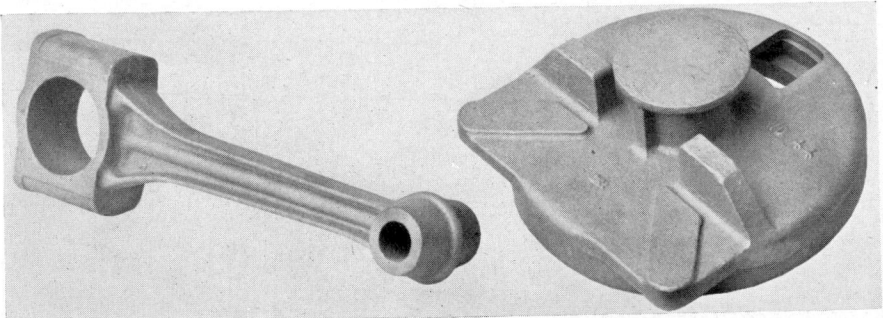

Fig. 11. Left, connecting rod used in ice-making machinery. Right, gear case used on crawler shovel. Both are made of pearlitic malleable iron.

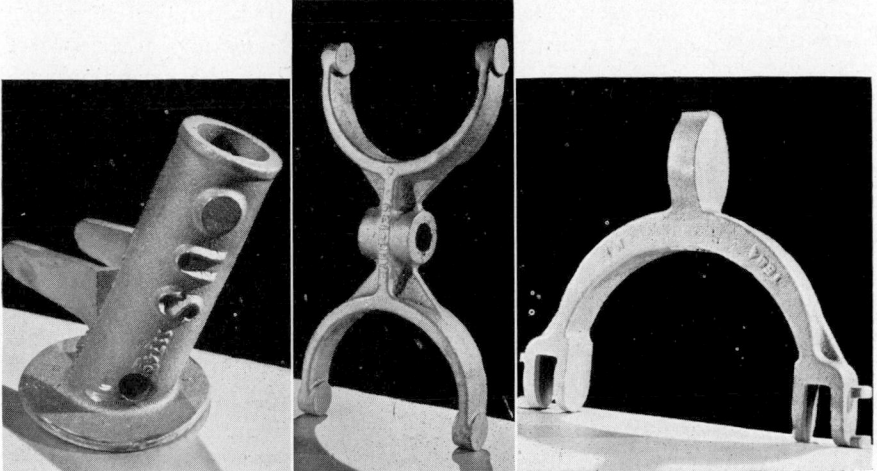

Fig. 12. Marine hardware castings for cargo ships.

conveying apparatus. Malleable castings in mine cars appear in many of the applications which are listed in a later section devoted to railway castings. Malleable is used in pumps, in air-hammers, in track supports and equipment, in joint equalizers in mine railways. Wherever wear conditions are particularly heavy, pearlitic malleable iron is specified, and for highly corrosive conditions, the special malleable irons, notably the copper-alloyed, are used.

Fig. 13. This oil well pump incorporates malleable iron castings in the equalizer, the pitmans, the brake drums, the brake operating assembly, and the rod line clamp.

Oilfield drilling and production equipment is probably subjected to more unpredictable stresses, strains, and pressures than almost any other type of equipment. As one designing engineer put it, "All of the exceptions are concentrated in the oilfield." Malleable castings are used extensively in oilfield equipment, for they stand up well under the impact of the unpredictable and the exceptional. Parts for pumping equipment such as brake assemblies and brake shoes, equalizers, hanger yokes, operating levers, and saddles; parts for draw works such as bearing caps, brake assemblies, end caps, and levers; parts for derricks such as angle irons, brackets, and buses; parts in general use such as gas burner castings, glands, hand wheels, insert packer rings, pipe clamps, snatch blocks, stuffing boxes, thread protectors, tong line blocks, valve bodies for gate and plug valves, and wire line clamps, are made of malleable. The manufacturers of oilfield pipe unions and couplings are among the largest users of malleable castings. These unions are made from one to ten inches in diameter, with test pressures ranging from 1000 to 4500 pounds per square inch, and working pressure one-half the test pressure.

MUNICIPAL, STATE, AND PUBLIC SERVICE CASTINGS

The list of specific applications of malleable iron in municipal, state, and public service utilities is a very large one. In highway construction, malleable iron is widely used in guardrail parts, where its toughness and resistance to sudden shock make it particularly effective. In brackets, turnbuckles, anchors, load-transmission devices, drainage inlets, and traffic markers, its strength and its lasting resistance to corrosion are valuable. Catch basin and manhole covers of malleable, as well as bridge railings, expansion castings, and scuppers demonstrate malleable's ability to compete more than successfully with other materials. As has been noted in our survey of the uses of malleable iron in electrical installations, insulator caps are made of it, as are guyline anchors and various fittings for electric street railways.

ORDNANCE CASTINGS

Nearly all applications of malleable iron in ordnance are either highly stressed or subject to sudden greatly increased stresses; as a consequence, the substantial use of the metal in ordnance castings is a good measure of its dependability in heavy-duty installations.

Army ordnance uses include tank track guides; body rollers (pearlitic malleable iron); parts for tank engines and bodies; the many castings in Army reconnaissance cars, scout cars, trucks, troop carriers, and so forth, which meet in intensified form the service requirements leading to the extensive use of malleable iron in civilian automotive equipment listed earlier; base pedestals and other parts for antiaircraft guns; parts for trench mortars; castings for motorcycles; parts for field stoves; machine gun tripods, barrage balloon winches; and castings for small arms.

Naval uses for malleable iron include marine hardware on troopships, cargo ships, and motor torpedo boats; parts for many types of naval ordnance,

Fig. 14. This decorative panel for a superhighway bridge is made of malleable iron.

from 20-millimeter antiaircraft guns to 14-inch guns on battleships; engine parts for motor torpedo boats, for invasion boats, and for the landing barges that carry our tanks ashore; as well as the general uses listed in the section of this chapter devoted to marine equipment.

Pipe Fittings and Plumbing Supplies

An increasing amount of standard malleable iron is used for pipe fittings and plumbing supplies. The excellent foundry properties and machinability of malleable iron produce sound, true castings with sharp, accurate threads. Elbows, unions, reducers, flanges, valves, bolts, nuts, and valve handles constitute a notable part of the tonnage of standard malleable iron. Special malleable iron of exceptionally high resistance to corrosion is produced for similar installations in oilfields and mines.

Railroad Castings

In railroad equipment, practically all of the individual service conditions which lead to the selection of malleable iron castings in other fields are summed up. Here are to be found in combination the requirements of meeting heavy continued stress, of withstanding sudden impact loads and sudden in-

Fig. 15. The malleable castings at the left, used in the Army truck shown above include (1) differential carrier, (2) differential case, (3) bearing cap, (4) adjusting ring, (5) right steering knuckle bracket, (6) left steering knuckle bracket, (7) steering knuckle flange, (8) steering gear case, (9) clutch pedal, (10) brake pedal.

creases in stress, of meeting exposure to all kinds of weather, of resisting highly corrosive industrial atmospheres, of encountering frictional and abrasive wear of unusual severity. Here also is found in emphasized form the vital necessity for dependability and safety. The fact that railroad use of malleable iron throughout its history led long ago to the development of the name "railroad malleable" is good evidence of the effectiveness with which the metal has met such demands. Railroad castings, constantly subjected to severe strains, are therefore today usually made of Grade 35018 standard malleable iron. Specific applications of these castings run the gamut in railroad equipment, from the locomotive water scoops that take the shock of picking up water from track reservoirs at 80 miles an hour to the humble picture-framelike card-holders that need only take what sleet and storm have to offer. The list which follows suggests the range of railroad applications:

Freight-car parts: drop-bottom gondola operating-mechanism parts, hinge butts, brake-beam parts, brake-beam supports, draft-gear parts, side bearing braces, hopper-car door-operating castings, brake wheels, power-brake cast-

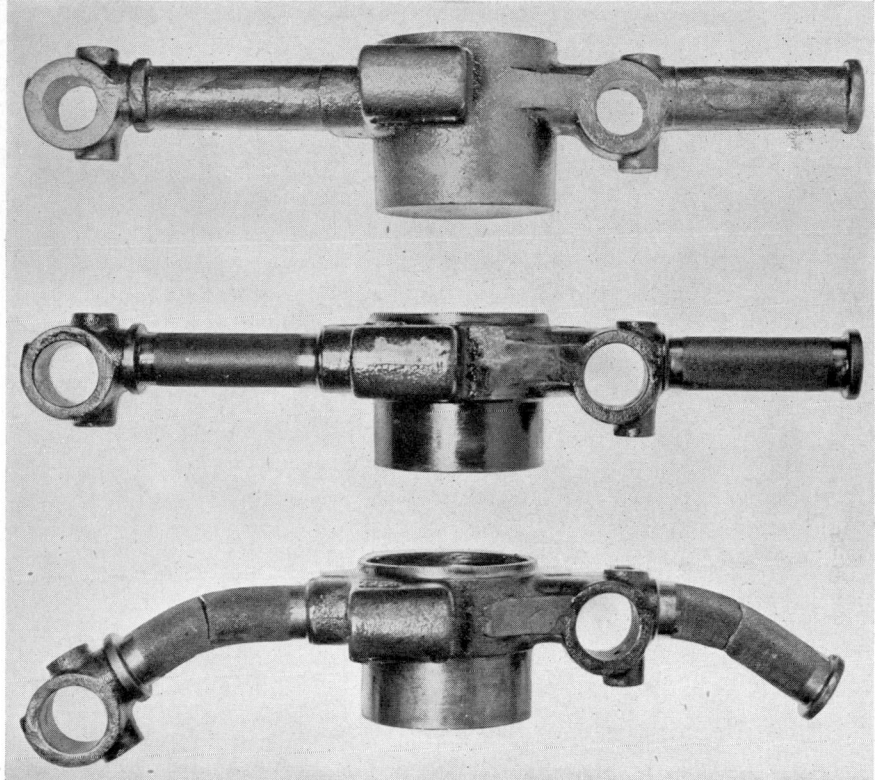

Fig. 16. At the top in this figure is a rough malleable iron casting. In the center is the finished part — a component of an Oerliken 20-millimeter antiaircraft gun. At the bottom is the same part tested to destruction.

ings, uncoupling lever brackets, journal-bearing wedges, journal-boxes and lids, draft lugs, push-pole pockets, door-fixture castings, centerplates, striking-plates, doorpost pockets, brakeshaft bearings, coupler carriers, card-holders, ownership and brake-diagram badge plates.

Tank car parts: dome covers and rings, outlet valves, truck springplates, safety-valve flanges, safety-valve housings, tank band anchors, body side-bearings, slabbing castings, card-holders, valve handwheels, and pipe brackets.

Refrigerator-car parts: ice-rack supports, door hinges, hatch-door hinges, and drain castings.

Track and switch castings: rail braces, adjustable rail braces, guardrail braces, combined rail brace and tieplate, special tieplates, filler blocks, rail anchors, gauge-rod ends, track-gauge ends, switch stands, bell cranks, turn-buckles, clevises, pipe connectors, pipe supports, derailers, and track pans.

Passenger-car parts: journal boxes and lids, buffer plates, buffer stem brack-ets, queen posts, side bearings, uncoupling-lever guides, draftsill filler blocks, flexible steam-heat connectors, air- and signal-hose clamps, signal-lamp and flag brackets, and window hardware.

Locomotive parts: water scoops, air-, steam-, and tank-hose clamps, flexible steam connectors, valve handles, oil cups, cab ventilator castings, cab storm-window parts, cylinder cocks, smoke-box lugs and hinges, handrail columns, grease-cup bushings, grease plugs, unions and union fittings, and reverse-lever handles.

ROAD MACHINERY CASTINGS

Few machines have to stand more of a beating as part of the regular day's work than that which is dealt out to rollers, scrapers, scarifiers, bulldozers, shovels, mixers, graders, pavers, and so on. The work they are called on to do and the materials they are expected to handle demand great ruggedness. Add to this the fact that road crews generally are working against time and are not disposed to coddle the equipment they are using. Consequently the ability to stand up under rough work and rough handling, as well as to meet adverse conditions of exposure and corrosion, is extremely important in the castings used in the manufacture of such machines. Malleable iron castings, in addition to those specified as used in the automotive industry, are extensively employed in road machinery. Parts are made in malleable for rollers, excavators, cranes, hoists, tractors, graders, scarifiers, mixers, and pavers. Tractor parts include malleable iron track spring-retainers and housings, and roller supports, equalizer spring-pads, sprocket drive gear covers, front idler guides, and sprocket-drive carriers. Differential cases, steering segments, and hand levers for road rollers are made of malleable. On power shovels, pearlitic malleable has been found the most economical material performing satisfactorily in the gibs or wearing blocks which are mounted inside the dipper-stick sleeve and must withstand the constant wearing action of the dipper stick as it shoots up and down when the shovel takes a bite out of loam and ledge and swings it over a waiting truck.

APPENDIX I

A.S.T.M. SPECIFICATIONS FOR MALLEABLE IRON CASTINGS

S PECIFICATION A47-33 of the American Society for Testing Materials is reprinted in entirety in this appendix. This standard was adopted in 1904 and revised in 1915, 1919, 1924, 1927, 1930, and 1933. In accordance with the practice of the Society, the standard is issued under the fixed designation A47; the final number indicates the year of last revision. The text below, however, was editorially revised and rearranged in 1939.

SCOPE

1. These specifications cover malleable iron castings for railroad, motor vehicle, agricultural implement, and general machinery purposes.

PROCESS

2. The iron shall be made by one of the following processes: air-furnace, open-hearth, or electric-furnace.

PRIMARY GRAPHITE

3. Castings shall be free from primary graphite.

TENSILE PROPERTIES

4. (a) The tension test specimen specified in Section 6 shall conform to the following requirements as to tensile properties:

	Grade No. 32510	Grade No. 35018
Tensile strength, min., psi.	50,000	53,000
Yield point, min., psi.	32,500	35,000
Elongation in 2 in., min., per cent.	10	18

(b) The yield point, defined as that load under which the specimen has an elongation in 2 in. of 0.01 in., may be determined by the drop of the beam or halt in the gage of the testing machine, or by the dividers method.

SPECIAL TESTS

5. (a) All castings, if of sufficient size, shall have cast thereon test lugs of a size proportional to the thickness of the casting, but not exceeding $\frac{5}{8}$ by $\frac{3}{4}$ in. in cross-

section. On castings which are 24 in. or over in length, a test lug shall be cast near each end. These test lugs shall be attached to the casting at such a point that they will not interfere with the assembling of the castings, and may be broken off by the inspector.

(*b*) If the purchaser or his representative so desires, a casting may be tested to destruction. Such a casting shall show good, tough, malleable iron.

TEST SPECIMENS

6. (*a*) Tension test specimens shall be of the form and dimensions shown in Fig. 1. Specimens whose mean diameter at the smallest section is less than $1\frac{9}{32}$ in. will not be accepted for test.

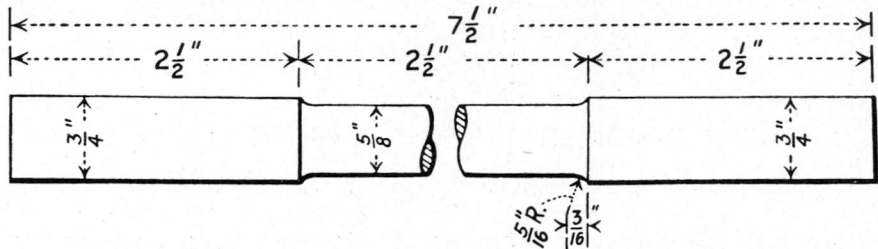

Fig. 1. The standard tension test specimen.

(*b*) A set of three tension test specimens shall be cast from each melt, without chills, using heavy risers of sufficient height to secure sound bars. The specimens shall be suitably marked for identification with the melt. Each set of specimens so cast shall be placed in some one oven containing castings to be annealed.

NUMBER OF TESTS

7. (*a*) After annealing, three tension test specimens shall be selected by the inspector to represent the castings in the oven from which these specimens are taken.

(*b*) If the first specimen conforms to the specified requirements or, if in the event of failure of the first specimen, the second and third specimens conform to the requirements, the castings in that oven shall be accepted, except that any casting may be rejected if its test lug shows that it has not been properly annealed. If either the second or third specimen fails to conform to the requirements, the entire contents of that oven shall be rejected.

(*c*) In case one of the retest specimens contains a flaw which results in the failure of the specimen to conform to the requirements, additional specimens from the same oven may, at the discretion of the inspector, be substituted; or specimens cut from the castings may be tested.

REANNEALING

8. Any castings rejected for insufficient annealing may be reannealed once. The reannealed castings shall be inspected and if the remaining test lugs, or castings broken as specimens, show the castings to be thoroughly annealed, they shall be accepted; if not, they shall be finally rejected.

PERMISSIBLE VARIATIONS IN DIMENSIONS

9. A variation of $\frac{1}{8}$ in. per ft. in any dimension will be permitted.

WORKMANSHIP

10. The castings shall be made in a workmanlike manner and shall conform substantially to the patterns or drawings furnished by the purchaser, and also to the gages which may be specified in individual cases.

FINISH

11. The castings shall be free from injurious defects.

MARKING

12. The identification mark of the manufacturer and the pattern numbers assigned by the purchaser shall be cast on all castings of sufficient size, in such positions that they will not interfere with the service of the castings.

INSPECTION

13. (*a*) The inspector representing the purchaser shall have free entry, at all times while work on the contract of the purchaser is being performed, to all parts of the manufacturer's works which concern the manufacture of the material ordered. The manufacturer shall afford the inspector, without charge, all reasonable facilities to satisfy him that the material is being furnished in accordance with these specifications. All tests and inspection shall be made at the place of manufacture prior to shipment, unless otherwise specified, and shall be so conducted as not to interfere unnecessarily with the operation of the works.

(*b*) The manufacturer shall be required to keep a record of each melt from which castings are produced, showing tensile strength and elongation of test specimens cast from such melts. These records shall be available and shown to the inspector whenever required.

REJECTION

14. Material which shows injurious defects subsequent to its acceptance at the manufacturer's works may be rejected, and, if rejected, shall be replaced by the manufacturer without charge to the purchaser.

PROTECTIVE COATINGS

TECHNIQUES to be followed in the application of standard coatings as further protection against corrosion, and the results to be expected from them, are summarized in the outlines which follow, prepared by firms manufacturing representative materials. Essentials in the outline of one company are:

Finish. The rougher the casting is to begin with, the heavier the final paint film must be to produce a smooth film.

Cleaning. The surfaces to be coated should be effectively cleaned to remove all traces of grease and oil to insure satisfactory adhesion of the finishing system. Cleaning should be accomplished by degreasing, alkali cleaning, or solvent wiping.

The Priming Coat. The function of the priming coat is to act as an anchorage for the entire system. It is advisable, therefore, to select a durable primer that will retain its elasticity under exposure to heat. A primer utilizing iron oxide and rust-inhibiting pigments in an alkyd resin vehicle has proved to be an excellent all-around primer for this purpose. It may be applied by brush or spray and dries in six to eight hours for recoating. For a fast-drying finishing system, a pyroxylin primer may be used, which must, however, be applied by spray and will air-dry in one-half hour.

Iron and Steel Filler. If the casting surface is rough, it is customary to use an iron and steel filler over the primer to fill up the indentations in the metal. These fillers are applied in a buttery consistency and may be applied in heavy coats up to three-sixteenths of an inch without cracking and still dry thoroughly overnight.

The deeper depressions are spot puttied, a glazing knife being used with material as it comes in the container. After the puttying, a brush coat of filler reduced with a small amount of mineral spirits to a creamy consistency may be applied immediately. This is allowed to set up for one to one and a half hours, after which it is "leathered." This operation can be most satisfactorily accomplished through using a chamois moistened with mineral spirits, and rubbing in a circular motion. This removes brush marks so that a smooth finish is presented, requiring minimum sanding. After the filler has been allowed to dry overnight, it is ready to sand.

For fast drying systems, a pyroxylin filler is available. This is applied by knifing in the deeper depressions and then applying a brush coat, reducing approximately 10 per cent with thinner. The pyroxylin thinner is ready to sand after air drying three to four hours.

Top Coats. The choice of top coats depends principally on what the ultimate exposure conditions are for the finished casting.

For general, all-around exposure to heat, gasoline, and oil, enamels made with an alkyd resin vehicle have proved far superior to those made with conventional oils and varnishes. Because of the relatively porous nature of the filler, it is advisable to use a coat of primer-surfacer prior to the application of the enamel. This seals up the porosity of the filler and prevents the top coat of enamel from sinking in. This is air dried approximately four hours and dry- or wet-sanded; then the final coat of enamel is applied.

For fast drying systems, a special pyroxylin sealer is provided to seal the porosity of the film, and is followed by two spray coats of pyroxylin enamel.

A second company's recommendations of surface finishes for malleable iron are embraced in the following:

Coatings for malleable iron castings may be classified as:
1. Controlled black oxides
2. Rust preventatives including the oily, waxy, and hard drying
3. Lacquer finishes

The principal reason for the application of any of these coatings is to resist or retard corrosion. A secondary but important reason is the improved appearance of the part.

Combinations of these methods are often used. The black oxide coating on polished steel enables the surface to hold a paint or lacquer bond better, and affords longer protection should the lacquer be abraded or chipped off. Also, a rust preventive coating affords greatly increased protection when added after treatment in a blackening bath. The black oxide coating, while corrosion resistant indoors, will not protect for as long periods under extreme conditions, such as accelerated salt spray test.

Wartime shortage of critical plating materials brought black oxide coatings into considerable favor. To avoid the possibility of obtaining a brown, rather than a black, coating, a prior dip in hydrofluoric acid is suggested. This has a pickling effect and provides a chemically clean surface. Overpickling should, of course, be avoided. The same preparation as for plating is customarily followed.

Black Oxide Coating. A black oxide coating creates Fe_3O_4 chemically at the boiling point of the solution into which work is immersed (about 295 degrees F.). The penetration into the metal ranges from 0.00002 inch to not more than 0.0001 inch. The blackening salt is a high caustic combined with an active oxidizing agent such as sodium nitrate or nitrate. The coating is jet black, dull or lustrous depending upon the finish to which it is applied.

Steel tanks are used, heated by steam, gas, or electricity. Water is placed in the blackening tank and the salt added before heating. The operator should be protected by customary equipment against splash or eruption during heating and while operating.

The usual cycle of tanks is alkaline cleaning, (hot) rinse, pickling (which is a good safeguard for clear black results) rinse, blackening bath, cold water rinse (with overflow), hot water rinse. For added protection against corrosion the blackened parts may be immersed in a hot solution of water-soluble oil (10 to 1), or in a hard drying wax bath, or lacquer.

Aside from chemical cleanliness of work, the other essential for assured blackening is maintenance of the solution at boiling point. Automatic means for adding water to make up for evaporation can readily be provided.

The black oxide finish causes no perceptible change in dimensions and will be found to be durable and lasting. Work is immersed in the blackening bath from 5 to 30 minutes, time to be determined by prior test.

APPENDIX III

SELECTED BIBLIOGRAPHY ON THE EFFECT OF ALLOYS IN MALLEABLE IRON

ELSEA, A., and LORIG, C. H. "Effect of Copper Content and Low Temperature Pretreatment of Some White Irons on Malleablization," *Transactions*, American Foundrymen's Association, Vol. 50, No. 4 (June, 1943), 1032.

SCHWARTZ, H. A., FIORDALIS, V., FISHER, J. L., SHUMAR, J. F., and TRINTER, M. J. "Accelerating Effect of Certain Metallic Elements on Graphitization," *Transactions*, American Society for Metals, Vol. 28, No. 1 (March, 1940), 143.

AMERICAN FOUNDRYMEN'S ASSOCIATION. *Cast Metals Handbook*, "Alloy Malleable Iron," Chicago, 1940.

GNADE, R., PIWOWARSKY, E., and FELIX, W. "Short-Cycle Pearlitic Malleable Iron (Ueber Perlitischen Schnelltemperguss)," *Die Giesserei*, Vol. 25, No. 19 (Sept. 23, 1938), 469.

ROLL, F. "Effect of Copper on Malleable Iron (Der Einfluss von Kupfer auf Temperguss)," *Die Giesserei*, Vol. 25, No. 5 (Feb. 25, 1938), 80.

SALLITT, W. B. "Copper in Cast Iron and Malleable Iron," *Foundry Trade Journal*, Vol. 57, No. 1108 (Nov. 11, 1937), 379.

SCHWARTZ, H. A., JOHNSON, H. H., and JUNGE, C. H. "Retarding Effect of Certain Metallic Elements on Graphitization," *Transactions*, American Society for Metals, Vol. 25, No. 2 (June, 1937), 609.

RUSSELL, H. W. "Resistance to Damage by Overstress of Precipitation-Hardened Copper Steel and Copper Malleable," *Metals and Alloys*, Vol. 7 (1936), 321.

SMITH, C. S., and PALMER, E. W. "Some Effects of Copper in Malleable Iron," *Transactions*, American Institute of Mining and Metallurgical Engineers, Vol. 116 (1935), 363.

LORIG, C. H., and SMITH, C. S. "Effect of Copper in Malleable Iron," *Transactions*, American Foundrymen's Association, Vol. 43 (1934), 211.

HALL, R. "Alloys for Malleable Iron," *Iron Age*, Vol. 132 (1933), 8.

SCHWARTZ, H. A., and GUILER, G. M. "Chemical Elements Inhibiting Graphitization," *Transactions*, American Foundrymen's Association, Vol. 33 (1925), 639.

HALL, R. "High-Strength and Wear-Resistant Malleable Iron," *Transactions*, American Foundrymen's Association, Vol. 41 (1933), 112.

LYKKEN, L. "The Influence of Copper on the Graphitization Behavior of White Cast Iron," *Iowa State College Journal of Science*, Vol. 8, No. 1 (Oct., 1933), 207.

SOEHNCHEN, E. "Alloyed Malleable Iron (Legierter Temperguss)," *Zeitschrift fuer die Gesamte Giessereipraxis*, Vol. 54, Nos. 15–16 (April 16, 1933), 151.

COONAN, F. L. "Alloying Elements in Malleable Iron," *Foundry*, Vol. 60 (1932), 43.

JOSEPH, C. L. and BOEGEHOLD, A. L. "High-Silicon Pig Iron for Malleable Castings," *Transactions*, American Foundrymen's Association, Vol. 41 (1932), 241.

RIGGAN, F. B. "Forged and Alloy Malleable Iron for Special Uses," *Iron Age*, Vol. 129 (1932), 728.

JENNINGS, W. H., JR., and HENDERSON, E. L. "Effect of Molybdenum on Graphitization of White Cast Iron," *Metals and Alloys*, Vol. 2, No. 4 (Oct., 1931), 223.

SCHWARTZ, H. A. "Malleable Iron — Recent Progress," *Metals and Alloys*, Vol. 2, No. 3 (Sept., 1931), 143.

WOLF, F., and MEISSE, L. A. "Corrosion of Malleable Iron," *Symposium on Malleable Iron Castings*, American Foundrymen's Association and American Society for Testing Materials, 1931.

SHEPHERD, H. H. "Cupola Malleable Cast Iron," *Foundry Trade Journal*, Vol. 44 (1931), 83, 102, 125. See also *Iron and Steel Industry*, Vol. 4 (1931), 151, 199, 281.

THIERY, LÉON. "Influence of Nickel and Nickel-Chrome on the Properties of Malleable Iron (Étude de l'influence du nickel et du nickel-chrome sur les propriétés de la fonte malléable)," *Revue de Metallurgie*, Vol. 28 (1931), 1, 61.

WENTRUP, H., and STENGER, W. "Nickel and Chromium Alloyed Malleable Iron (Nickel und Chrom-legierter Temperguss)," *Die Giesserei*, Vol. 18, No. 1 (Jan. 2, 1931), 24.

PIWOWARSKY, E. "High Quality Malleable Iron (Ueber Hochwertiger Temperguss)," *Die Giesserei*, Vol. 18, No. 1 (Jan. 2, 1931), 19.

HRUSKA, J. H. "Small Quantity of Aluminum Improves Malleable Cast Iron Properties," *Foundry*, Vol. 59, No. 1 (Jan. 1, 1931), 70.

SCHUEZ, E., and STOTZ, R. *Malleable Iron (Der Temperguss)*, Berlin, Julius Springer, 1930.

STOTZ, R. "Influence of Chemical Composition of Pig Iron on Strength of Malleable Castings (Der Einfluss der chemischen Zusammensetzung des Rohgusses auf die Festigkeitseigenschaften des Tempergusses), *Zeitschrift fuer die Gesamte Giessereipraxis*, Vol. 51, No. 30 (July 27, 1930), 261.

SMITH, E. K., and AUFDERHAAR, H. C. "Molybdenum in Cast Iron," *Iron Age*, Vol. 124, No. 23 (Dec. 5, 1929), 1507.

COONAN, F. L. "Molybdenum in Malleable Cast Iron," *Heat Treating and Forging*, Vol. 15, No. 12 (Dec. 1929), 1561.

PLANT, C. H. "Malleable Cast Iron," *Iron and Steel Industry*, Vol. 2, Nos. 4, 5, 6, 7, 8, and 10 (Jan., Feb., Mar., Apr., May, and July, 1929), 117, 151, 175, 211, 253, and 333; Vol. 3, No. 1 (Oct., 1929), 25.

SCHWARTZ, H. A. "Graphitization in the Presence of Nickel," *Transactions*, American Society for Steel Treating, Vol. 15, No. 6 (June, 1929), 957.

SAWAMURA, H. "Influence of the Various Elements on the Graphitization in Cast Iron," *Memoirs*, College of Engineering, Kyoto Imperial University, Vol. 4, No. 4 (Sept., 1926), 159.

PIWOWARSKY, E. "Some Experiments as to the Effect of Titanium in Iron Castings (Einige Versuche Ueber den Einfluss eines Titanzusatze zum Rohguss auf den metallurgischen Verlauf des Temperprozesses)," *Stahl und Eisen*, Vol. 44, No. 26 (June 26, 1924), 745.

CONDITIONS OF SALE

THE CONDITIONS governing the quotation and sale of malleable iron castings are usually as follows:

QUOTATIONS

Quotations are generally made in price per pound. When the inquiry specifies a piece price, the quotation is made on the basis of an estimated unit weight, subject to modification because of any subsequent variation in unit weight. Prices will vary with quantity as well as with unit weight.

Changes in design after quotation has been made may lead to changes in cost and in quoted price.

Unless otherwise arranged, quotations are made for acceptance within 30 days and are effective only for the order in question and for the earliest possible continuous production and shipment.

Test bars if required are subject to a special charge.

Special testing, such as X-ray, gamma-ray, and magnetic, and similar tests, is subject to extra charges.

ORDERS

Cancellation of orders is handled by agreement of foundry and customer.

If alterations in pattern equipment or changes in the order cause the foundry to discard material after an order is in production, the customer reimburses the foundry for the cost thereof.

TERMS

Unless otherwise arranged, castings are sold f.o.b. the foundry for net cash 30 days from date of invoice.

PATTERNS

Pattern equipment, properly gated and of a type suitable for the economical production of castings of the required quality, quantity, and delivery schedule, is furnished by or at the expense of the customer, who pays transportation charges, including packing costs, to and from the foundry.

The patterns, core boxes, and loose pieces thereof should be properly marked for identification.

Alterations or repairs, such as those made necessary by change of design or by wear, are made at the expense of the customer.

The foundry reserves the right to mark patterns inconspicuously with its trade-mark in order that the origin of the castings may be known.

The foundry does not assume responsibility for loss or damage to pattern equipment through fire or other causes beyond its control.

CLAIMS

Claims of errors in weight or number of castings should be made by the customer within 10 days after the receipt of the castings.

Any castings which are claimed to be defective should be reported to the foundry immediately upon discovery, but not later than 60 days after receipt thereof.

The foundry assumes no responsibility for machine work or other expense incurred on castings which are rejected as defective, nor for any salvaging operations.

GLOSSARY

AIR FURNACE — A furnace of the reverberatory type, in which the metal is melted by the flame from fuel burning at one end of the hearth, which passes over the bath toward the stack at the other end of the hearth.

ALLOYING ELEMENTS — Elements which are added to iron or steel for the purpose of changing its properties.

ALLOYS — Metallic substances composed of two or more elements, and possessing properties different from those of their components.

ANNEAL — A heat-treatment which usually involves a slow cooling. As used with regard to malleable iron, it is a complete conversion, the hard brittle white iron being changed to tough ductile malleable iron by effecting malleabilization, or causing the carbon in the iron to precipitate in the free state as temper carbon.

ANNEALING POTS — Iron boxes or containers in which castings are packed for protection against the furnace atmosphere during the annealing operation.

ARBORS — Metal shapes embedded in and used to support either green or dry sand cores.

AUSTENITE — A solid solution of cementite, or iron carbide Fe_3C, in iron.

BLOWS — A term describing the trapping of gas in castings, causing voids in the metal.

BOTTOM BOARD — A wood board which acts as a base for the mold.

BOX, MOLD — See Jacket, Mold.

BRINELL HARDNESS — The value of hardness of a metal, tested by measuring the diameter of the impression made by a ball of given diameter applied under a known load. Values are expressed in Brinell hardness numbers.

BUILT-UP PLATE — A plate with the cope impressions of the pattern mounted or attached to one side, the drag impressions to the other.

CARBON STEEL (or straight carbon steel) — Steel which does not include substantial amounts of alloying elements and which therefore secures its properties principally from the amount of carbon present.

CASE HARDENING — A method of hardening the surface of a metal.

CAST PLATE — A plate of metal, usually aluminum, which has been cast with the cope part of a pattern on one side, the drag part on the other.

CEMENTITE — Iron carbide, a hard brittle crystalline compound observed in the microstructure of iron and steel.

CENTRIFUGAL CASTING — A process of filling molds by (1) pouring the metal into a sand or permanent mold that is revolving about either its horizontal or its vertical axis or (2) pouring the metal into a mold that is subsequently revolved before solidification of the metal is complete.

CHAPLET — Metal core support which is used in the mold cavity and which fuses into the casting.

CHEEK — The intermediate part of a flask or mold which has more than two parts.

CHILL — A formed piece of metal applied to the exterior or interior surface of a casting to hasten the solidification of heavy sections and cause the castings to cool at a uniform rate.

CHILLING — (1) A method of compensating for unevenness of section in a casting by the use of chills; (2) A method of chilling iron in the ladle by adding cold metal.

CHIPPING — Removing fins and gates from castings with a pneumatic or hand chisel.

COHESION — The force by which particles are held together. It varies with different metals, and depends upon hot or cold working as well as upon molecular arrangement due to heat-treatment.

COINING — A process of forming metals by pressing them to size and to very close tolerances.

COLD SHORTNESS — Brittleness when the metal is at low temperature.

COLD SHUT — An imperfect junction between two flows of metal in a mold.

COMBINED CARBON — The carbon in iron or steel which is combined with other elements and therefore is not in the free state as graphite or as temper carbon.

CONTINUOUS ANNEALING FURNACE — A furnace in which castings are annealed by passing through different zones which are kept at constant temperatures.

COPE — The upper or topmost section of a flask, mold, or pattern.

CORE — A separate part of the mold which forms cavities and openings in castings which are not possible with a pattern alone. Cores are usually made of a different sand from that used in the mold and are generally baked.

CORE DRIERS — Sand or metal supports used to keep cores in shape while being baked.

CORE OVENS — Low-temperature ovens used for baking cores.

CORE PLATES — Flat plates used to support cores while being baked.

CRACK, COLD — A crack which occurs in a casting after solidification and cooling due to excessive strain generally resulting from nonuniform cooling.

CRACK, HOT — Same as "Crack, cold" but developing before the casting has completely cooled.

CREEP — The gradual continuous distortion of metal under constant stress.

CRITICAL POINTS — The temperatures at which changes in the phase of a metal take place. They are determined by the liberation of heat when the metal is cooled and by the absorption of heat when the metal is heated, thus resulting in halts or arrests on the cooling or heating curves.

CUPOLA — A kind of blast furnace for melting metal, which consists of a vertical cylinder lined with refractory material and provided with openings for the entrance of a "blast," or air under pressure. In it metal is melted in direct contact with the fuel.

DAMPING — The property of resisting motion and absorbing energy.

DECARBURIZATION — The removal of carbon from a ferrous metal by the oxidizing action of media which may be gaseous, liquid or solid.

DENDRITE — A crystal characterized by a branching structure like that of a fir tree. Dendrites in metal occur with slow cooling during solidification.

DIE CASTING — Pouring metal into a metallic mold or die and holding it there until solidification takes place.

DRAFT, PATTERN — The taper on vertical elements in a pattern which allows it to be easily withdrawn from a sand mold.

DRAG — The lower or bottom section of a flask, mold, or pattern, also sometimes called a nowel.

DRAW BAR — A bar used for lifting the pattern from the sand of the mold.

DUCTILITY — The property permitting permanent deformation by stress in tension without rupture.

ELASTIC LIMIT — The greatest stress which a material can withstand without permanent deformation.

ELONGATION — The amount of permanent extension of the gauge length in tension tests; usually expressed as a percentage of the original gauge length, such as 20 per cent in two inches.

ENDURANCE LIMIT — A limiting stress, below which the metal will withstand, without rupture, an indefinitely large number of cycles of stress.

ENDURANCE RATIO — The ratio of the endurance limit to the ultimate tensile strength of the material.

EUTECTIC — The alloy which has the lowest melting point possible for the given composition.

EUTECTOID — A solid solution of any series which cools without change to its temperature of final composition.

FACING SAND — Specially prepared molding sand which is used in the mold adjacent to the pattern to produce a smooth casting surface.

FATIGUE LIMIT — Usually used as synonymous with endurance limit.

FEEDER, FEED HEAD — A reservoir of molten metal to make up for the contraction of metal as it solidifies. Molten metal flowing from the feed head, which is often also known as a riser, prevents voids in the casting.

FERRITE — Iron which is practically carbon-free. It may hold in solution considerable amounts of such elements as silicon, nickel, or phosphorus; so the term is also applied to solid solutions in which alpha iron or delta iron is the solvent.

FERRO-MANGANESE — An alloy of manganese and iron used to increase manganese content.

FERRO-SILICON — An alloy of iron and silicon used to increase silicon content.

FLAME HARDENING — Hardening the surface of a metal by heating with a flame and then quenching.

FLASK PINS — Pins to assure proper alignment of the cope and drag of the mold after the pattern is withdrawn.

FLASK, SNAP OR SLIP — As below but equipped with device permitting easy removal when mold is made.

FLASK, TIGHT — A metal or wood box without top and without fixed bottom, used to hold the sand in which a mold is formed; usually consists of two parts, cope and drag. Remains on mold during pouring.

GAGGERS — Irregular pieces of metal used to support sand in deep pockets of molds.

GALVANIZING EMBRITTLEMENT — Brittleness caused by cooling malleable iron quickly from a temperature of 800 to 900 degrees Fahrenheit.

GATE — The end of the runner where the molten metal enters the mold. The term is sometimes applied to the entire assembly of connected channels, to the pattern parts which form them, or to the metal which fills them, and also sometimes is restricted to mean the first, or main, channel.

GATED PATTERNS — One or more patterns with gates or channels attached.

GAUGING — Checking dimensional requirements by means of a gauge.

GRANULAR PEARLITE (or globular or divorced pearlite) — A structure formed from ordinary lamellar pearlite by long annealing at a temperature below but near to the critical point, causing the cementite to spheroidize in a ferrite matrix.

GRAPHITIZATION — The decomposition of carbide to give free carbon as graphite or as temper carbon.

GREEN SAND MOLD — A mold composed of prepared molding sand in the moist, or "as mixed," condition.

GRINDING — Removing gates and fins from castings by means of an abrasive grinding wheel.

HEAT-TREATMENT — The process of heating and cooling a metal or alloy in the solid state in order to obtain desirable qualities or properties.

HOT SPRUING — Removing castings from gates before the metal has completely solidified. Hot spruing is particularly necessary on light-section or intricate castings which might be cracked if cold sprued.

IMPACT TEST — A test to determine a metal's resistance to impact, by means of sudden blows applied to a specimen. The foot-pounds of energy absorbed, or the number of blows of a given intensity necessary to produce fracture are the usual values expressed.

INCLUSIONS — Particles of impurities, usually oxides, sulphides, silicates, and such, which are mechanically trapped during solidification or which are formed by subsequent reaction of the solid metal.

INTERNAL STRESSES — A system of balanced forces existing within a part which is not subjected to a working load.

IRON, MALLEABLE (măl'ē-à-b'l) — A mixture of iron and carbon, including smaller amounts of silicon, manganese, phosphorus, and sulphur, which after being cast is converted structurally by heat-treatment into a matrix of ferrite containing nodules of temper carbon.

IRON, WHITE OR HARD — The hard iron of suitable composition in which the castings, later to be malleableized, are originally cast. In it all carbon is in the combined form, hence its white fracture and name.

JACKET, MOLD — A wooden or metal form which is slipped over a mold made in a snap or slip flask, to support the four sides of the mold during pouring. Jackets are shifted, with the mold weights, from one row of molds to another during pouring.

LADLES — Metal receptacles, lined with refractories, used for transporting molten metal. Types include hand, bull, sulky, trolley, bottom pour, and teapot ladles.

LIQUID CONTRACTION — The shrinkage occurring in metal in the liquid state as it cools.

LUTE — To seal with clay or other plastic material.

MACROSTRUCTURE — The structure of metals as revealed by the eye or at a magnification of less than 10 diameters.

MALLEABILITY — The property of being permanently deformed by compression without rupture.

MALLEABILIZATION — The annealing operation performed on white iron castings to transform the combined carbon into temper carbon.

MALLEABLE IRON — See Iron, Malleable.

MARTENSITE — The hardest microconstituent in the structure of quenched metal, of an acicular or needlelike pattern.

MECHANICAL PROPERTIES — The properties of a metal determining its behavior under stress.

MICROSTRUCTURE — The structure of a metal as seen on a ground and polished, etched or unetched specimen at magnifications above 10 diameters.

MISRUN — A casting not fully formed.

MODULUS OF ELASTICITY — The ratio of stress to the corresponding strain, within the limit of elasticity of a material.

MOLD — The form, usually made of sand, which contains the cavity into which molten metal is poured in casting.

MOLD CLAMPS — Devices used to hold or lock cope and drag together.

MOLD WEIGHTS — Weights placed on top of molds while pouring, to offset internal pressure.

MOLDING, BENCH — Making sand molds from loose or production patterns at a bench.

MOLDING, FLOOR — Making sand molds from loose or production patterns of such size that they cannot be satisfactorily handled on a bench, the equipment being located on the floor during the entire operation of making the mold.

MOLDING, MACHINE — May refer to squeezer or jolt squeezer machines on which one operator makes the entire mold or to similar or larger machines including jolt-squeeze-strippers, and jolt and jolt-rollover pattern draw machines on which cope or drag halves of molds are made.

MULTIPLE MOLD — A composite mold made up of stacked sections, each of which produces a complete gate of castings and is poured from a central down-gate.

NITRIDING — A method of hardening ferrous alloys by adding nitrogen through heating the metal in contact with ammonia gas or other sources of atomic nitrogen.

NORMALIZING — A heat-treatment which involves heating to temperature, holding at temperature for a specific time, and cooling in still air.

PACKING OR PACKING MATERIAL — Sand, gravel, mill scale, or other similar material which is used to support castings packed in annealing pots, in order to prevent possible warpage.

PARTING COMPOUND — A material dusted or sprayed on patterns to prevent adherence of sand.

PARTING LINE — The line along which a pattern is divided for molding, or along which the sections of a mold separate.

PEARLITE — A microconstituent of iron and steel consisting of alternate layers of ferrite and iron carbide or cementite.

PERIODIC ANNEALING FURNACE — A furnace in which the castings go through a complete cycle of preheating, soaking, and cooling.

PERMEABILITY — As applied to sand molds, permeability means the property of the sand which permits passage of gases. The magnetic permeability of a substance is the ratio of the magnetic induction of the substance to the magnetizing field to which it is subjected.

PHASE — A constituent which is completely homogeneous both physically and chemically, which is separated from the rest of the alloy by definite bounding surfaces; for instance, austenite, ferrite, cementite. Not all constituents are phases, pearlite, for example.

PIG IRON — So called because as run from the blast furnace it resembles a sow with suckling pigs.

PROPORTIONAL LIMIT — The greatest stress which a material is capable of developing without deviation from the law of proportionality of stress to strain.

QUENCHING — Rapid cooling by immersion in air, gas, or liquids.

RAMMER, AIR — A pneumatic tool used in packing sand around a pattern.

RAMMER, HAND — A wooden tool with a round mallet-shaped head at one end and a wedge-shaped head at the other, used in packing sand around the pattern.

RAM OFF — A casting defect caused by improper ramming.

RECUPERATOR — A refractory checkerwork or other installation which is heated by the exhaust gases of a furnace and through sections or tubes of which air is drawn to provide preheated air for more efficient combustion of the furnace fuel.

RIDDLE — A sieve used to sift sand during molding, to eliminate large particles of sand or foreign material.

RISER — A reservoir of molten metal provided to compensate for the internal contraction of the casting as it solidifies.

ROCKWELL HARDNESS — The hardness value of a metal determined by measuring the depth of penetration of a 1/16 inch steel ball ("B" scale) or a diamond point ("C" scale).

RUNNER — The connection between the sprue and the gate.

SAND CUTTING — Preparing sand for molding, either by hand or by a machine, the operation also aerating the sand.

SAND TEMPERING — Adding sufficient moisture to molding sand to make it workable.

SCABS — Rough uneven areas on the surface of castings.

SELECTIVE HARDENING — The method of obtaining different degrees of hardness in different areas.

SHRINKAGE CAVITIES — Holes or cavities in solidified metal caused by contraction and insufficient feed metal, formed during the time the metal was changing from the liquid to the solid state.

SHRINKAGE, PATTERN MAKER'S — Shrinkage allowance on patterns to compensate for contraction as the solidified casting cools in the mold from the freezing temperature of the metal to room temperature.

SKIMMER — A tool used for removing slag from molten metal.

SLAG — A nonmetallic covering which forms on the molten metal as a result of the combining of impurities contained in the original charge, some ash from the fuel, and any silica and clay eroded from the refractory lining. It is skimmed off prior to tapping of the heat.

SOLID CONTRACTION — The shrinkage occurring in metal in the solid state as it cools from the solidifying temperature to room temperature.

SORBITE — A late stage in the tempering of martensite, when carbides have grown so that the structure is distinctly granular in appearance.

SPHEROIDIZED CEMENTITE — The globular condition of iron carbide after a spheroidizing treatment. (See granular pearlite.)

SPRUE — Gates and risers.

SPRUE BUTTON — A print attached to the top board of a mold, to make an impression in the cope indicating where the sprue should be cut.

SPRUE CUTTER — A metal tool used in cutting the pouring aperture.

Spruing — Removing gates from castings after the metal has solidified.

Stop-Off or Stop-Off Core — A core used to simplify the parting line of a pattern; that is, to make it unnecessary to carry the parting line above or below its normal position in order to provide for lugs or cored holes.

Strain — The change per unit of length in a linear dimension of a body, which change accompanies a stress measured in inches per inch of length.

Strained Castings — A phrase used to describe the result when molten metal is poured into the mold at too fast a rate, causing the cope to rise slightly from the drag and resulting in an oversize casting, with protruding fins.

Strains, Casting — Strains produced by internal stresses resulting from unequal contraction of the metal as a casting cools.

Stress — The intensity of the internal distributed forces or components of force which resist a change in the form of a body. Stress is measured in force per unit area.

Tap Hole Plug Stick — A wooden stick with a ball of clay on the end, used to close a tap hole.

Tap-out Bar — A bar used for opening tap-holes in furnaces.

Tapping — Reopening the aperture at the spout to permit the molten metal to run from the furnace.

Tear, Hot — Same as "Crack, hot" but developing before the casting has completely solidified.

Temper Carbon — Carbon in nodular form, characteristic of malleable iron.

Tempering (drawing) — Reheating ferrous alloys, after hardening, to some temperature below the critical range, followed by any desired rate of cooling.

Tensile Strength — The load per square inch of cross-sectional area at which fracture takes place under tension.

Top Board — A wood board which is used on the cope half of the mold to permit squeezing the mold.

Transformation Range — The range of temperatures at which changes in phase of iron-carbon alloys occur.

Trimming — Removing fins and gates from hard iron castings with hand hammers.

Tumbling Barrels — Rotating barrels in which castings are cleaned, also called rolling barrels and rattlers.

Vent Wire — A wire used to punch vents or small holes in the mold to allow gas to escape.

Weep Hole — A hole placed in a casting to allow drainage of moisture.

Yield Point — The load per unit of original cross section at which a marked increase in deformation occurs without increase in load.

BIBLIOGRAPHY OF SOURCES

1. SCHWARTZ, H. A. *American Malleable Cast Iron*, Cleveland, Penton Publishing Co., 1922.
2. AMERICAN SOCIETY FOR TESTING MATERIALS and AMERICAN FOUNDRYMEN'S ASSOCIATION. *Symposium on Malleable Iron Castings*, 1931.
3. BEAN, W. R. "Developments in Melting Malleable Cast Iron," *Transactions*, American Foundrymen's Association, Vol. 45 (1937), 334.
4. AMERICAN FOUNDRYMEN'S ASSOCIATION. *Cast Metals Handbook*, "Malleable Iron," Chicago, 1940.
5. LEROYER, M. *La Malléable*, Paris, Dunod, 1936.
6. SMITH, E. K. "Machinability of Ferrous Castings," *Machine Tool Blue Book*, June, 1938, 44.
7. SCHWARTZ, H. A. "Factors Affecting Machinability of Malleable Cast Iron," *Transactions*, American Foundrymen's Association, Vol. 38 (1930), 210.
8. SCHWARTZ, H. A., and JUNGE, C. H. "Young's Modulus of Elasticity and Some Related Properties of Graphitic Materials," *Proceedings*, American Society for Testing Materials, Vol. 41 (1941), 816.
9. BENEDICKS, C., ERICSSON, N., and ERICSSON, G. "Bestimmung des specifischen Volumes von Eisen, Nickel, und Eisenlegierungen im geschmolzenen Zustand," *Arch. f.d. Eisenhutten*, Jan., 1930, 473.
10. OBERG, E., and JONES, F. D. *Machinery's Handbook*, New York, The Industrial Press, 1940.
11. SCHUEZ, E., and STOTZ, R. *Malleable Iron (Der Temperguss)*, Berlin, Julius Springer, 1930.
12. DONALDSON, J. W. "Thermal Conductivity of Wrought Iron, Steel, Malleable Cast Iron, and Cast Iron," *Journal*, Iron and Steel Institute, Vol. 28, No. 2 (1933), 255.
13. BOLTON, J. W., and BORNSTEIN, H. "Effect of Elevated Temperatures on Certain Mechanical Properties of Gray Cast Iron and Malleable Iron," *Symposium on Effect of Temperature on Metals*, American Society of Mechanical Engineers and American Society for Testing Materials, 1931.

14. Touceda, E. "Malleable Iron Castings," *Product Engineering*, October, 1937.

15. Schwartz, H. A. "Effect of Machining and of Cross-Section on the Tensile Properties of Malleable Cast Iron," *Proceedings*, American Society for Testing Materials, Vol. 20, Part 2 (1920), 70.

16. Trotzky, G. N. "Factors Determining the Mechanical Properties of Russian Malleable Cast Iron," *Metallurg*, No. 12 (1938), 39.

17. Touceda, E. "Resistance of Malleable Iron to Repeated Impact Stresses and Comparison of Strength of Machined and Unmachined Malleable Castings," *Transactions*, American Foundrymen's Association, Vol. 34 (1920), 1072.

18. Touceda, E. "Remarks on the Strength and Ductility of Malleable Cast Iron after the Skin Has Been Removed," *Transactions*, American Foundrymen's Association, Vol. 24 (1916), 256.

19. Cornelius, H. "Behavior of Some Crankshaft Materials in Bending and Torsional Fatigue Tests (Verhalten einiger Kurbelwellen-Gusswerkstaffe bei Dauerbeanspruchung durch Beigung und Verdrehung)," *Die Giesserei*, Vol. 27, No. 25 (Dec. 13, 1940), 47.

20. Mailaender, R. "Endurance Strength of Gray Iron, Malleable Iron, and Cast Steel (Ueber die Dauerfestigkeit von Gusseisen, Temperguss, und Stahlguss)," *Tech. Mitt. Krupp.*, Vol. 4 (1936), 59.

21. Roll, F. "Cast Crankshafts (Gegossener Kurbelwellen)," *V.D.I. Zeitschrift*, Vol. 80 (1936), 1365.

22. Mahin, E. G., and Hamilton, J. W. "Endurance Limit of Blackheart Malleable Iron," *Transactions*, American Foundrymen's Association, Vol. 43 (1935), 41.

23. Marks, Lionel Simeon, ed. *Mechanical Engineer's Handbook*, New York, McGraw-Hill Book Company, 1941.

24. Roll, F. "The Transverse Strength of Malleable Iron and Cast Steel (Ueber die Biegifestigkeit von Temper- und Stahlguss)," *Die Giesserei*, Vol. 24, No. 23 (Nov. 5, 1937), 46.

25. Schuster, L. W. "Relation between Mechanical Properties of Ferrous Metals and Liability to Breakdown in Service," *Metallurgia*, Vol. 19, No. 109 (Nov., 1938), 25.

26. Marshall, L. H. "Embrittlement of Malleable Cast Iron Resulting from Heat Treatment," *Bureau of Standards Technologic Papers*, Vol. 17 (1923), 677.

27. Bean, W. R. "Deterioration of Malleable in the Hot-dip Galvanizing Process," *Transactions*, American Institute of Mining and Metallurgical Engineers, Vol. 49 (1923), 895.

28. Lansing, J. H. "Malleable Iron Castings, 1942," *Metals and Alloys*, Vol. 17 (1943), 63.

29. Schwartz, H. A. "Machinability of Iron and Steel," *Houghton's Black and White*, Sept., 1930.

30. *American Machinist.* "Malleable More Machinable," Vol. 82 (1938), 502.
31. MALLEABLE IRON RESEARCH INSTITUTE. *Bulletin,* No. 239.
32. WOLF, F. L., and MEISSE, L. A. "Corrosion of Malleable Iron," *Symposium on Malleable Iron Castings,* American Society for Testing Materials and American Foundrymen's Association, 1931.
33. WILDERMAN, M. "Theory and Practice of Blackheart Malleable Iron (Einiges aus Theorie und Praxis des Schwartzgusses)," *Die Giesserei,* Vol. 28, No. 11 (May 30, 1941), 252.
34. KRITZLER, G., ROLL, F., and DAUB. "Autogeneous Hardening of Cast Iron and Malleable Iron (Autogenes Haerten von Gusseisen und Tempcrguss)," *Die Giesserei,* Vol. 25, No. 24 (Dec. 2, 1938), 609.
35. SMITH, S. "Flame Hardening Malleable Iron," *Transactions,* American Foundrymen's Association, Vol. 49, No. 1 (Sept., 1941), 209.
36. DAY, R. O. "Some Metallurgical Phases of Flame Hardening," *Metals and Alloys,* Vol. 12, No. 2 (Aug., 1940), 167.
37. TIMKEN-DETROIT AXLE COMPANY. *Material Specification No. 103,* 1942.
38. AMERICAN WELDING SOCIETY. *Welding Handbook,* New York, 1942, 849.
39. LORIG, C. H. "Properties of Commercial Pearlitic Malleable Iron," *Bulletin,* American Society for Testing Materials, No. 105 (Aug., 1940), 29.
40. AMERICAN SOCIETY FOR TESTING MATERIALS. *Symposium on Pearlitic Malleable Cast Iron,* 1936.
41. BOYES, D. L. *The Commercial Market for Pearlitic Malleable Cast Iron,* Massachusetts Institute of Technology, 1941.
42. JOSEPH, C. F. "ArmaSteel," *Iron Age,* Vol. 143 (1939), 27.
43. *Iron Age.* "Belmalloy — Pearlitic Malleable Iron," Vol. 143 (1939), 33.
44. JOSEPH, C. F. "ArmaSteel," *American Foundryman,* Sept., Oct., Nov., 1942.
45. HATFIELD, W. H., STANFIELD, G., and ROTHERHAM, L. "Damping Capacity of Engineering Materials," *Engineering,* Vol. 153 (1942), 478.
46. MCMILLAN, W. D. "Production of Short Cycle Malleable Iron," *Transactions,* American Foundrymen's Association, Vol. 46 (1938), 697.
47. SCHWARTZ, H. A., JOHNSON, H. H., and JUNGE, C. H. "Retarding Effect of Certain Metallic Elements on Graphitization," *Transactions,* American Society for Metals, Vol. 25, No. 2 (June, 1937), 609.
48. HALL, R. "Alloys for Malleable Iron," *Iron Age,* Vol. 132 (1933), 8.
49. SOEHNCHEN, E. "Alloyed Malleable Iron (Legierter Temperguss)," *Z. f. d. Gesamte Giessereipraxis,* Vol. 54, Nos. 15–16 (Apr. 16, 1933), 151.
50. SCHWARTZ, H. A., FIORDALIS, V., FISHER, J. L., SHUMER, J. F., and TRINTER, M. J. "Accelerating Effect of Certain Metallic Elements on Graphitization," *Transactions,* American Society for Metals, Vol. 28, No. 1 (March, 1940), 143.
51. LORIG, C. H., and SMITH, C. S. "Effect of Copper in Malleable Iron," *Transactions,* American Foundrymen's Association, Vol. 43 (1934), 211.

52. LORIG, C. H. "Copper Additions to Malleable Cast Iron," *Foundry*, Vol. 62 (1934), 32.

53. AMERICAN FOUNDRYMEN'S ASSOCIATION. "Recommendations for Buyers of Castings," *Transactions*, Vol. 40 (1932), 515.

54. AMERICAN FOUNDRYMEN'S ASSOCIATION. *Cast Metals Handbook*, Chicago, 1940.

55. DAVIS, C. G. "Malleable Cast Iron—Its History in the United States," *Journal of the Franklin Institute*, Vol. 148 (1899), 134, 181.

56. KAYSER, J. A. "Some Observations on Malleable Furnace Refractories," *Transactions*, American Foundrymen's Association, Vol. 49, No. 4 (June, 1942), 874.

57. DIETERT, H. W., and VALTIER, F. "Molding Sand in the Malleable Foundry," *Transactions*, American Foundrymen's Association, Vol. 44 (1937), 337.

58. ZIRKOW, E. C. "Sand Control in a Malleable Foundry," *Transactions*, American Foundrymen's Association, Vol. 45 (1938), 134.

59. SAWTELLE, D. F. "Sand Control Program in a Malleable Foundry," *Transactions*, American Foundrymen's Association, Vol. 48 (1941), 723.

60. MALLEABLE FOUNDERS' SOCIETY. *Bulletin*, No. 218, July 12, 1938.

61. BEAN, W. R., and JAESCHKE, W. R. "Periodic Malleable Annealing Furnaces," *Transactions*, American Foundrymen's Association, Vol. 50, No. 1 (July, 1942), 39.

62. LANSING, J. H. "Temperature Control of Graphitizing Furnaces," *Transactions*, American Foundrymen's Association, Vol. 50, No. 1 (July, 1940), 126.

63. MALLEABLE FOUNDERS' SOCIETY. *Bulletin*, No. 219, July 18, 1938.

64. COX, R. E. "Annealing Malleable Castings in Elevator Furnace," *Foundry*, Vol. 69, No. 4 (April, 1941), 38.

65. ANDERSON, R. J. "Malleable Annealing in the Dressler or Tunnel-type Kiln," *Transactions*, American Foundrymen's Association, Vol. 50, No. 1 (July, 1942), 50.

66. CHERRY, R. M. "Electric Furnace Annealing of Malleable Iron," *Transactions*, American Foundrymen's Association, Vol. 50, No. 1 (July, 1942), 67.

67. CHERRY, R. M. "Short Cycle Annealing," *Iron Age*, Vol. 146, No. 13 (Sept. 26, 1940), 34.

68. MALLEABLE FOUNDERS' SOCIETY. *Bulletin*, No. 280, June 17, 1940.

69. WEEDFALL, C. W. "Design of Straightening Equipment for Malleable Iron Castings," *Transactions*, American Foundrymen's Association, Vol. 46 (1939), 713.

70. BRAUER, O. "Origin of Malleable Iron (Grundzuege der Geschichte des Temperguss)," *Z.f.d. Gesamte Giessereipraxis*, Vol. 58, Nos. 43–44 (Oct. 24, 1937), 431.

71. HALL, H. G. "Malleable Cast Iron," *Foundry Trade Journal*, Vol. 62, No. 1231 (March 21, 1940), 223.

72. BOYDEN, W. C., BOYDEN, M. N., and BOYDEN, A. J. *Thomas Boyden and his Descendants*, Boston, T. R. Marvin and Son, 1901.

73. *Dictionary of American Biography*. New York, Charles Scribner's Sons, 1928–1936, Vol. 2, 528.

74. FOXBOROUGH, MASSACHUSETTS. *Vital Records to the Year 1850*, Boston, The New England Historic Genealogical Society, 1911.

75. *Iron Age*. "The Records of Seth Boyden's Experiments on Malleable Cast Iron," Vol. 62 (1898), 15.

76. SIMONDS, H. R. "Marks Century in Producing Malleable Iron," *Foundry*, Vol. 57 (1929).

77. BELLE CITY MALLEABLE IRON COMPANY. *Catalogue No. 7*, Racine, Wisconsin.

78. MOLDENKE, R. *The Production of Malleable Castings*, Cleveland, Penton Publishing Company, 1910.

79. PARSON, S. J. *Malleable Cast Iron*, New York, D. Van Nostrand Company, 1909.

80. MALLEABLE IRON RESEARCH INSTITUTE. *Certified Malleable Iron*, Cleveland.

81. RICKETTS, P. C. "Physical Tests of Malleable Cast Iron," *Van Nostrand's Engineering Magazine*, April, 1885.

82. MOLDENKE, R. "Malleable Cast Iron," *Journal*, American Foundrymen's Association, Vol. 12, Part 1 (June, 1903), 1.

83. DILLER, H. E. "Malleable Cast Iron," *Journal*, American Foundrymen's Association, Vol. 11, Part 1 (Dec., 1902), 101.

84. GILDART, R. S. "How Malleables Came into Their Own," *Automobile Topics*, August 27, 1921.

85. MALLEABLE FOUNDERS' SOCIETY. *Industry Statistics*, Cleveland, June, 1942.

86. MALLEABLE FOUNDERS' SOCIETY. *Bulletin*, No. 195, Dec. 20, 1937.

87. SISCO, F. T. *The Constitution of Steel and Cast Iron*, Cleveland, American Society for Steel Treating, 1930.

88. SAUVEUR, A., and ANTHONY, H. L. "Malleable Castings," *Transactions*, American Society for Metals, Vol. 23 (1935), 409.

89. SCHNEIDEWIND, R. "Malleable Annealing Is Based on Composition," *Foundry*, Vol. 69 (1941), 103.

90. BOEGEHOLD, A. L. "Factors Influencing Annealing Malleable Iron," *Transactions*, American Foundrymen's Association, Vol. 46 (1938), 449.

91. SCHWARTZ, H. A., and JUNGE, C. H. "Metallographic Changes during Cooling between First and Second Stages of Graphitization," *Transactions*, American Foundrymen's Association, Vol. 44 (1937), 507.

92. McMILLAN, W. D. "The Effect of Composition on the Annealing of White Cast Iron," *Transactions*, American Foundrymen's Association, Vol. 50, No. 1 (July, 1942), 30.

Engineering Tables and Data

AMERICAN MALLEABLE IRON

FUNCTIONS OF NUMBERS

No.	Square	Cube	Square Root	Cube Root	Logarithm	1000 × Reciprocal	No. = Diameter	
							Circum.	Area
.01	.0001	.000001	0.1000	0.2154	2̄.00000	100000.000	.03142	.000079
.02	.0004	.000008	0.1414	0.2714	2̄.30103	50000.000	.06283	.000314
.03	.0009	.000027	0.1732	0.3107	2̄.47712	33333.333	.09425	.000707
.04	.0016	.000064	0.2000	0.3420	2̄.60206	25000.000	.12566	.001257
.05	.0025	.000125	0.2236	0.3684	2̄.69897	20000.000	.15708	.001964
.06	.0036	.000216	0.2449	0.3915	2̄.77815	16666.667	.18850	.002827
.07	.0049	.000343	0.2646	0.4121	2̄.84510	14285.714	.21991	.003849
.08	.0064	.000512	0.2828	0.4309	2̄.90309	12500.000	.25133	.005027
.09	.0081	.000729	0.3000	0.4481	2̄.95424	11111.111	.28274	.006362
.10	.0100	.001000	0.3162	0.4642	1̄.00000	10000.000	.31416	.007854
.11	.0121	.001331	0.3317	0.4791	1̄.04139	9090.909	.34558	.009503
.12	.0144	.001728	0.3464	0.4932	1̄.07918	8333.333	.37699	.011310
.13	.0169	.002197	0.3606	0.5066	1̄.11394	7692.308	.40841	.013273
.14	.0196	.002744	0.3742	0.5192	1̄.14613	7142.857	.43982	.015394
.15	.0225	.003375	0.3873	0.5313	1̄.17609	6666.667	.47124	.017672
.16	.0256	.004096	0.4000	0.5429	1̄.20412	6250.000	.50265	.020106
.17	.0289	.004913	0.4123	0.5540	1̄.23045	5882.353	.53407	.022698
.18	.0324	.005832	0.4243	0.5646	1̄.25527	5555.556	.56549	.025447
.19	.0361	.006859	0.4359	0.5749	1̄.27875	5263.158	.59690	.028353
.20	.0400	.008000	0.4472	0.5848	1̄.30103	5000.000	.62832	.031416
.21	.0441	.009261	0.4583	0.5944	1̄.32222	4761.905	.65973	.034636
.22	.0484	.010648	0.4690	0.6037	1̄.34242	4545.455	.69115	.038013
.23	.0529	.012167	0.4796	0.6127	1̄.36173	4347.826	.72257	.041548
.24	.0576	.013824	0.4899	0.6214	1̄.38021	4166.667	.75398	.045239
.25	.0625	.015625	0.5000	0.6300	1̄.39794	4000.000	.78540	.049087
.26	.0676	.017576	0.5099	0.6383	1̄.41497	3846.154	.81681	.053093
.27	.0729	.019683	0.5196	0.6463	1̄.43136	3703.704	.84823	.057256
.28	.0784	.021952	0.5292	0.6542	1̄.44716	3571.429	.87965	.061575
.29	.0841	.024389	0.5385	0.6619	1̄.46240	3448.276	.91106	.066052
.30	.0900	.027000	0.5477	0.6694	1̄.47712	3333.333	.94248	.070686
.31	.0961	.029791	0.5568	0.6768	1̄.49136	3225.807	.97389	.075477
.32	.1024	.032768	0.5657	0.6840	1̄.50515	3125.000	1.00531	.080425
.33	.1089	.035937	0.5745	0.6910	1̄.51851	3030.303	1.03673	.085530
.34	.1156	.039304	0.5831	0.6980	1̄.53148	2941.177	1.06814	.090792
.35	.1225	.042875	0.5916	0.7047	1̄.54407	2857.143	1.09956	.096211
.36	.1296	.046656	0.6000	0.7114	1̄.55630	2777.778	1.13097	.101788
.37	.1369	.050653	0.6083	0.7179	1̄.56820	2702.703	1.16239	.107521
.38	.1444	.054872	0.6164	0.7243	1̄.57978	2631.579	1.19381	.113411
.39	.1521	.059319	0.6245	0.7306	1̄.59106	2564.103	1.22522	.119459
.40	.1600	.064000	0.6325	0.7368	1̄.60206	2500.000	1.2566	.125664
.41	.1681	.068921	0.6403	0.7429	1̄.61278	2439.024	1.2881	.132025
.42	.1764	.074088	0.6481	0.7489	1̄.62325	2380.952	1.3195	.138544
.43	.1849	.079507	0.6557	0.7548	1̄.63347	2325.581	1.3509	.145220
.44	.1936	.085184	0.6633	0.7606	1̄.64345	2272.727	1.3823	.152053
.45	.2025	.091125	0.6708	0.7663	1̄.65321	2222.222	1.4137	.159043
.46	.2116	.097336	0.6782	0.7719	1̄.66276	2173.913	1.4451	.166190
.47	.2209	.103823	0.6856	0.7775	1̄.67210	2127.660	1.4765	.173494
.48	.2304	.110592	0.6928	0.7830	1̄.68124	2083.333	1.5080	.180956
.49	.2401	.117649	0.7000	0.7884	1̄.69020	2040.816	1.5394	.188574

FUNCTIONS OF NUMBERS

.50

.99

No.	Square	Cube	Square Root	Cube Root	Logarithm	1000 × Reciprocal	No. = Diameter	
							Circum.	Area
.50	.2500	.125000	0.7071	0.7937	1̄.69897	2000.000	1.5708	.19635
.51	.2601	.132651	0.7141	0.7990	1̄.70757	1960.784	1.6022	.20428
.52	.2704	.140608	0.7211	0.8041	1̄.71600	1923.077	1.6336	.21237
.53	.2809	.148877	0.7280	0.8093	1̄.72428	1886.793	1.6650	.22062·
.54	.2916	.157464	0.7348	0.8143	1̄.73239	1851.852	1.6965	.22902
.55	.3025	.166375	0.7416	0.8193	1̄.74036	1818.182	1.7279	.23758
.56	.3136	.175616	0.7483	0.8243	1̄.74819	1785.714	1.7593	.24630
.57	.3249	.185193	0.7550	0.8291	1̄.75587	1754.386	1.7907	.25518
.58	.3364	.195112	0.7616	0.8340	1̄.76343	1724.138	1.8221	.26401
.59	.3481	.205379	0.7681	0.8387	1̄.77085	1694.915	1.8535	.27340
.60	.3600	.216000	0.7746	0.8434	1̄.77815	1666.667	1.8850	.28274
.61	.3721	.226981	0.7810	0.8481	1̄.78533	1639.344	1.9164	.29225
.62	.3844	.238328	0.7874	0.8527	1̄.79239	1612.903	1.9478	.30191
.63	.3969	.250047	0.7937	0.8573	1̄.79934	1587.302	1.9792	.31173
.64	.4096	.262144	0.8000	0.8618	1̄.80618	1562.500	2.0106	.32170
.65	.4225	.274625	0.8062	0.8662	1̄.81291	1538.462	2.0420	.33183
.66	.4356	.287496	0.8124	0.8707	1̄.81954	1515.152	2.0735	.34212
.67	.4489	.300763	0.8185	0.8750	1̄.82607	1492.537	2.1049	.35257
.68	.4624	.314432	0.8246	0.8794	1̄.83251	1470.588	2.1363	.36317
.69	.4761	.328509	0.8307	0.8837	1̄.83885	1449.275	2.1677	.37393
.70	.4900	.343000	0.8367	0.8879	1̄.84510	1428.571	2.1991	.38485
.71	.5041	.357911	0.8426	0.8921	1̄.85126	1408.451	2.2305	.39592
.72	.5184	.373248	0.8485	0.8963	1̄.85733	1388.889	2.2620	.40715
.73	.5329	.389017	0.8544	0.9004	1̄.86332	1369.863	2.2934	.41854
.74	.5476	.405224	0.8602	0.9045	1̄.86923	1351.351	2.3248	.43008
.75	.5625	.421875	0.8660	0.9086	1̄.87506	1333.333	2.3562	.44179
.76	.5776	.438976	0.8718	0.9126	1̄.88081	1315.790	2.3876	.45365
.77	.5929	.456533	0.8775	0.9166	1̄.88649	1298.701	2.4190	.46566
.78	.6084	.474552	0.8832	0.9205	1̄.89209	1282.051	2.4504	.47784
.79	.6241	.493039	0.8888	0.9244	1̄.89763	1265.823	2.4819	.49017
.80	.6400	.512000	0.8944	0.9283	1̄.90309	1250.000	2.5133	.50266
.81	.6561	.531441	0.9000	0.9322	1̄.90849	1234.568	2.5447	.51530
.82	.6724	.551368	0.9055	0.9360	1̄.91381	1219.512	2.5761	.52810
.83	.6889	.571787	0.9110	0.9398	1̄.91908	1204.819	2.6075	.54106
.84	.7056	.592704	0.9165	0.9435	1̄.92428	1190.476	2.6389	.55418
.85	.7225	.614125	0.9220	0.9473	1̄.92942	1176.471	2.6704	.56745
.86	.7396	.636056	0.9274	0.9510	1̄.93450	1162.791	2.7018	.58088
.87	.7569	.658503	0.9327	0.9546	1̄.93952	1149.425	2.7332	.59447
.88	.7744	.681472	0.9381	0.9583	1̄.94448	1136.364	2.7646	.60821
.89	.7921	.704969	0.9434	0.9619	1̄.94939	1123.596	2.7960	.62211
.90	.8100	.729000	0.9487	0.9655	1̄.95424	1111.111	2.8274	.63617
.91	.8281	.753571	0.9539	0.9691	1̄.95904	1098.901	2.8589	.65039
.92	.8464	.778688	0.9592	0.9726	1̄.96379	1086.957	2.8903	.66476
.93	.8649	.804357	0.9644	0.9761	1̄.96848	1075.269	2.9217	.67929
.94	.8836	.830584	0.9695	0.9796	1̄.97313	1063.830	2.9531	.69398
.95	.9025	.857375	0.9747	0.9830	1̄.97772	1052.632	2.9845	.70882
.96	.9216	.884736	0.9798	0.9865	1̄.98227	1041.667	3.0159	.72382
.97	.9409	.912673	0.9849	0.9899	1̄.98677	1030.928	3.0473	.73898
.98	.9604	.941192	0.9899	0.9933	1̄.99123	1020.408	3.0788	.75430
.99	.9801	.970299	0.9950	0.9967	1̄.99564	1010.101	3.1102	.76977

FUNCTIONS OF NUMBERS

No.	Square	Cube	Square Root	Cube Root	Logarithm	1000 × Reciprocal	No. = Diameter	
							Circum.	Area
1	1	1	1.0000	1.0000	0.00000	1000.000	3.142	0.7854
2	4	8	1.4142	1.2599	0.30103	500.000	6.283	3.1416
3	9	27	1.7321	1.4422	0.47712	333.333	9.425	7.0686
4	16	64	2.0000	1.5874	0.60206	250.000	12.566	12.5664
5	25	125	2.2361	1.7100	0.69897	200.000	15.708	19.6350
6	36	216	2.4495	1.8171	0.77815	166.667	18.850	28.2743
7	49	343	2.6458	1.9129	0.84510	142.857	21.991	38.4845
8	64	512	2.8284	2.0000	0.90309	125.000	25.133	50.2655
9	81	729	3.0000	2.0801	0.95424	111.111	28.274	63.6173
10	100	1000	3.1623	2.1544	1.00000	100.000	31.416	78.5398
11	121	1331	3.3166	2.2240	1.04139	90.9091	34.558	95.0332
12	144	1728	3.4641	2.2894	1.07918	83.3333	37.699	113.097
13	169	2197	3.6056	2.3513	1.11394	76.9231	40.841	132.732
14	196	2744	3.7417	2.4101	1.14613	71.4286	43.982	153.938
15	225	3375	3.8730	2.4662	1.17609	66.6667	47.124	176.715
16	256	4096	4.0000	2.5198	1.20412	62.5000	50.265	201.062
17	289	4913	4.1231	2.5713	1.23045	58.8235	53.407	226.980
18	324	5832	4.2426	2.6207	1.25527	55.5556	56.549	254.469
19	361	6859	4.3589	2.6684	1.27875	52.6316	59.690	283.529
20	400	8000	4.4721	2.7144	1.30103	50.0000	62.832	314.159
21	441	9261	4.5826	2.7589	1.32222	47.6190	65.973	346.361
22	484	10648	4.6904	2.8020	1.34242	45.4545	69.115	380.133
23	529	12167	4.7958	2.8439	1.36173	43.4783	72.257	415.476
24	576	13824	4.8990	2.8845	1.38021	41.6667	75.398	452.389
25	625	15625	5.0000	2.9240	1.39794	40.0000	78.540	490.874
26	676	17576	5.0990	2.9625	1.41497	38.4615	81.681	530.929
27	729	19683	5.1962	3.0000	1.43136	37.0370	84.823	572.555
28	784	21952	5.2915	3.0366	1.44716	35.7143	87.965	615.752
29	841	24389	5.3852	3.0723	1.46240	34.4828	91.106	660.520
30	900	27000	5.4772	3.1072	1.47712	33.3333	94.248	706.858
31	961	29791	5.5678	3.1414	1.49136	32.2581	97.389	754.768
32	1024	32768	5.6569	3.1748	1.50515	31.2500	100.531	804.248
33	1089	35937	5.7446	3.2075	1.51851	30.3030	103.673	855.299
34	1156	39304	5.8310	3.2396	1.53148	29.4118	106.814	907.920
35	1225	42875	5.9161	3.2711	1.54407	28.5714	109.956	962.113
36	1296	46656	6.0000	3.3019	1.55630	27.7778	113.097	1017.88
37	1369	50653	6.0828	3.3322	1.56820	27.0270	116.239	1075.21
38	1444	54872	6.1644	3.3620	1.57978	26.3158	119.381	1134.11
39	1521	59319	6.2450	3.3912	1.59106	25.6410	122.522	1194.59
40	1600	64000	6.3246	3.4200	1.60206	25.0000	125.66	1256.64
41	1681	68921	6.4031	3.4482	1.61278	24.3902	128.81	1320.25
42	1764	74088	6.4807	3.4760	1.62325	23.8095	131.95	1385.44
43	1849	79507	6.5574	3.5034	1.63347	23.2558	135.09	1452.20
44	1936	85184	6.6332	3.5303	1.64345	22.7273	138.23	1520.53
45	2025	91125	6.7082	3.5569	1.65321	22.2222	141.37	1590.43
46	2116	97336	6.7823	3.5830	1.66276	21.7391	144.51	1661.90
47	2209	103823	6.8557	3.6088	1.67210	21.2766	147.65	1734.94
48	2304	110592	6.9282	3.6342	1.68124	20.8333	150.80	1809.56
49	2401	117649	7.0000	3.6593	1.69020	20.4082	153.94	1885.74

FUNCTIONS OF NUMBERS

No.	Square	Cube	Square Root	Cube Root	Logarithm	1000 × Reciprocal	No. = Diameter	
							Circum.	Area
50	2500	125000	7.0711	3.6840	1.69897	20.0000	157.08	1963.50
51	2601	132651	7.1414	3.7084	1.70757	19.6078	160.22	2042.82
52	2704	140608	7.2111	3.7325	1.71600	19.2308	163.36	2123.72
53	2809	148877	7.2801	3.7563	1.72428	18.8679	166.50	2206.18
54	2916	157464	7.3485	3.7798	1.73239	18.5185	169.65	2290.22
55	3025	166375	7.4162	3.8030	1.74036	18.1818	172.79	2375.83
56	3136	175616	7.4833	3.8259	1.74819	17.8571	175.93	2463.01
57	3249	185193	7.5498	3.8485	1.75587	17.5439	179.07	2551.76
58	3364	195112	7.6158	3.8709	1.76343	17.2414	182.21	2642.08
59	3481	205379	7.6811	3.8930	1.77085	16.9492	185.35	2733.97
60	3600	216000	7.7460	3.9149	1.77815	16.6667	188.50	2827.43
61	3721	226981	7.8102	3.9365	1.78533	16.3934	191.64	2922.47
62	3844	238328	7.8740	3.9579	1.79239	16.1290	194.78	3019.07
63	3969	250047	7.9373	3.9791	1.79934	15.8730	197.92	3117.25
64	4096	262144	8.0000	4.0000	1.80618	15.6250	201.06	3216.99
65	4225	274625	8.0623	4.0207	1.81291	15.3846	204.20	3318.31
66	4356	287496	8.1240	4.0412	1.81954	15.1515	207.35	3421.19
67	4489	300763	8.1854	4.0615	1.82607	14.9254	210.49	3525.65
68	4624	314432	8.2462	4.0817	1.83251	14.7059	213.63	3631.68
69	4761	328509	8.3066	4.1016	1.83885	14.4928	216.77	3739.28
70	4900	343000	8.3666	4.1213	1.84510	14.2857	219.91	3848.45
71	5041	357911	8.4261	4.1408	1.85126	14.0845	223.05	3959.19
72	5184	373248	8.4853	4.1602	1.85733	13.8889	226.19	4071.50
73	5329	389017	8.5440	4.1793	1.86332	13.6986	229.34	4185.39
74	5476	405224	8.6023	4.1983	1.86923	13.5135	232.48	4300.84
75	5625	421875	8.6603	4.2172	1.87506	13.3333	235.62	4417.86
76	5776	438976	8.7178	4.2358	1.88081	13.1579	238.76	4536.46
77	5929	456533	8.7750	4.2543	1.88649	12.9870	241.90	4656.63
78	6084	474552	8.8318	4.2727	1.89209	12.8205	245.04	4778.36
79	6241	493039	8.8882	4.2908	1.89763	12.6582	248.19	4901.67
80	6400	512000	8.9443	4.3089	1.90309	12.5000	251.33	5026.55
81	6561	531441	9.0000	4.3267	1.90849	12.3457	254.47	5153.00
82	6724	551368	9.0554	4.3445	1.91381	12.1951	257.61	5281.02
83	6889	571787	9.1104	4.3621	1.91908	12.0482	260.75	5410.61
84	7056	592704	9.1652	4.3795	1.92428	11.9048	263.89	5541.77
85	7225	614125	9.2195	4.3968	1.92942	11.7647	267.04	5674.50
86	7396	636056	9.2736	4.4140	1.93450	11.6279	270.18	5808.80
87	7569	658503	9.3274	4.4310	1.93952	11.4943	273.32	5944.68
88	7744	681472	9.3808	4.4480	1.94448	11.3636	276.46	6082.12
89	7921	704969	9.4340	4.4647	1.94939	11.2360	279.60	6221.14
90	8100	729000	9.4868	4.4814	1.95424	11.1111	282.74	6361.73
91	8281	753571	9.5394	4.4979	1.95904	10.9890	285.88	6503.88
92	8464	778688	9.5917	4.5144	1.96379	10.8696	289.03	6647.61
93	8649	804357	9.6437	4.5307	1.96848	10.7527	292.17	6792.91
94	8836	830584	9.6954	4.5468	1.97313	10.6383	295.31	6939.78
95	9025	857375	9.7468	4.5629	1.97772	10.5263	298.45	7088.22
96	9216	884736	9.7980	4.5789	1.98227	10.4167	301.59	7238.23
97	9409	912673	9.8489	4.5947	1.98677	10.3093	304.73	7389.81
98	9604	941192	9.8995	4.6104	1.99123	10.2041	307.88	7542.96
99	9801	970299	9.9499	4.6261	1.99564	10.1010	311.02	7697.69

FUNCTIONS OF NUMBERS

No.	Square	Cube	Square Root	Cube Root	Logarithm	1000 × Reciprocal	No. = Diameter	
							Circum.	Area
100	10000	1000000	10.0000	4.6416	2.00000	10.0000	314.16	7853.98
101	10201	1030301	10.0499	4.6570	2.00432	9.90099	317.30	8011.85
102	10404	1061208	10.0995	4.6723	2.00860	9.80392	320.44	8171.28
103	10609	1092727	10.1489	4.6875	2.01284	9.70874	323.58	8332.29
104	10816	1124864	10.1980	4.7027	2.01703	9.61538	326.73	8494.87
105	11025	1157625	10.2470	4.7177	2.02119	9.52381	329.87	8659.01
106	11236	1191016	10.2956	4.7326	2.02531	9.43396	333.01	8824.73
107	11449	1225043	10.3441	4.7475	2.02938	9.34579	336.15	8992.02
108	11664	1259712	10.3923	4.7622	2.03342	9.25926	339.29	9160.88
109	11881	1295029	10.4403	4.7769	2.03743	9.17431	342.43	9331.32
110	12100	1331000	10.4881	4.7914	2.04139	9.09091	345.58	9503.32
111	12321	1367631	10.5357	4.8059	2.04532	9.00901	348.72	9676.89
112	12544	1404928	10.5830	4.8203	2.04922	8.92857	351.86	9852.03
113	12769	1442897	10.6301	4.8346	2.05308	8.84956	355.00	10028.7
114	12996	1481544	10.6771	4.8488	2.05690	8.77193	358.14	10207.0
115	13225	1520875	10.7238	4.8629	2.06070	8.69565	361.28	10386.9
116	13456	1560896	10.7703	4.8770	2.06446	8.62069	364.42	10568.3
117	13689	1601613	10.8167	4.8910	2.06819	8.54701	367.57	10751.3
118	13924	1643032	10.8628	4.9049	2.07188	8.47458	370.71	10935.9
119	14161	1685159	10.9087	4.9187	2.07555	8.40336	373.85	11122.0
120	14400	1728000	10.9545	4.9324	2.07918	8.33333	376.99	11309.7
121	14641	1771561	11.0000	4.9461	2.08279	8.26446	380.13	11499.0
122	14884	1815848	11.0454	4.9597	2.08636	8.19672	383.27	11689.9
123	15129	1860867	11.0905	4.9732	2.08991	8.13008	386.42	11882.3
124	15376	1906624	11.1355	4.9866	2.09342	8.06452	389.56	12076.3
125	15625	1953125	11.1803	5.0000	2.09691	8.00000	392.70	12271.8
126	15876	2000376	11.2250	5.0133	2.10037	7.93651	395.84	12469.0
127	16129	2048383	11.2694	5.0265	2.10380	7.87402	398.98	12667.7
128	16384	2097152	11.3137	5.0397	2.10721	7.81250	402.12	12868.0
129	16641	2146689	11.3578	5.0528	2.11059	7.75194	405.27	13069.8
130	16900	2197000	11.4018	5.0658	2.11394	7.69231	408.41	13273.2
131	17161	2248091	11.4455	5.0788	2.11727	7.63359	411.55	13478.2
132	17424	2299968	11.4891	5.0916	2.12057	7.57576	414.69	13684.8
133	17689	2352637	11.5326	5.1045	2.12385	7.51880	417.83	13892.9
134	17956	2406104	11.5758	5.1172	2.12710	7.46269	420.97	14102.6
135	18225	2460375	11.6190	5.1299	2.13033	7.40741	424.12	14313.9
136	18496	2515456	11.6619	5.1426	2.13354	7.35294	427.26	14526.7
137	18769	2571353	11.7047	5.1551	2.13672	7.29927	430.40	14741.1
138	19044	2628072	11.7473	5.1676	2.13988	7.24638	433.54	14957.1
139	19321	2685619	11.7898	5.1801	2.14301	7.19424	436.68	15174.7
140	19600	2744000	11.8322	5.1925	2.14613	7.14286	439.82	15393.8
141	19881	2803221	11.8743	5.2048	2.14922	7.09220	442.96	15614.5
142	20164	2863288	11.9164	5.2171	2.15229	7.04225	446.11	15836.8
143	20449	2924207	11.9583	5.2293	2.15534	6.99301	449.25	16060.6
144	20736	2985984	12.0000	5.2415	2.15836	6.94444	452.39	16286.0
145	21025	3048625	12.0416	5.2536	2.16137	6.89655	455.53	16513.0
146	21316	3112136	12.0830	5.2656	2.16435	6.84932	458.67	16741.5
147	21609	3176523	12.1244	5.2776	2.16732	6.80272	461.81	16971.7
148	21904	3241792	12.1655	5.2896	2.17026	6.75676	464.96	17203.4
149	22201	3307949	12.2066	5.3015	2.17319	6.71141	468.10	17436.6

FUNCTIONS OF NUMBERS

No.	Square	Cube	Square Root	Cube Root	Logarithm	1000 × Reciprocal	No. = Diameter	
							Circum.	Area
150	22500	3375000	12.2474	5.3133	2.17609	6.66667	471.24	17671.5
151	22801	3442951	12.2882	5.3251	2.17898	6.62252	474.38	17907.9
152	23104	3511808	12.3288	5.3368	2.18184	6.57895	477.52	18145.8
153	23409	3581577	12.3693	5.3485	2.18469	6.53595	480.66	18385.4
154	23716	3652264	12.4097	5.3601	2.18752	6.49351	483.81	18626.5
155	24025	3723875	12.4499	5.3717	2.19033	6.45161	486.95	18869.2
156	24336	3796416	12.4900	5.3832	2.19312	6.41026	490.09	19113.4
157	24649	3869893	12.5300	5.3947	2.19590	6.36943	493.23	19359.3
158	24964	3944312	12.5698	5.4061	2.19866	6.32911	496.37	19606.7
159	25281	4019679	12.6095	5.4175	2.20140	6.28931	499.51	19855.7
160	25600	4096000	12.6491	5.4288	2.20412	6.25000	502.65	20106.2
161	25921	4173281	12.6886	5.4401	2.20683	6.21118	505.80	20358.3
162	26244	4251528	12.7279	5.4514	2.20952	6.17284	508.94	20612.0
163	26569	4330747	12.7671	5.4626	2.21219	6.13497	512.08	20867.2
164	26896	4410944	12.8062	5.4737	2.2148	6.09756	515.22	21124.1
165	27225	4492125	12.8452	5.4848	2.21748	6.06061	518.36	21382.5
166	27556	4574296	12.8841	5.4959	2.22011	6.02410	521.50	21642.4
167	27889	4657463	12.9228	5.5069	2.22272	5.98802	524.65	21904.0
168	28224	4741632	12.9615	5.5178	2.22531	5.95238	527.79	22167.1
169	28561	4826809	13.0000	5.5288	2.22789	5.91716	530.93	22431.8
170	28900	4913000	13.0384	5.5397	2.23045	5.88235	534.07	22698.0
171	29241	5000211	13.0767	5.5505	2.23300	5.84795	537.21	22965.8
172	29584	5088448	13.1149	5.5613	2.23553	5.81395	540.35	23235.2
173	29929	5177717	13.1529	5.5721	2.23805	5.78035	543.50	23506.2
174	30276	5268024	13.1909	5.5828	2.24055	5.74713	546.64	23778.7
175	30625	5359375	13.2288	5.5934	2.24304	5.71429	549.78	24052.8
176	30976	5451776	13.2665	5.6041	2.24551	5.68182	552.92	24328.5
177	31329	5545233	13.3041	5.6147	2.24797	5.64972	556.06	24605.7
178	31684	5639752	13.3417	5.6252	2.25042	5.61798	559.20	24884.6
179	32041	5735339	13.3791	5.6357	2.25285	5.58659	562.35	25164.9
180	32400	5832000	13.4164	5.6462	2.25527	5.55556	565.49	25446.9
181	32761	5929741	13.4536	5.6567	2.25768	5.52486	568.63	25730.4
182	33124	6028568	13.4907	5.6671	2.26007	5.49451	571.77	26015.5
183	33489	6128487	13.5277	5.6774	2.26245	5.46448	574.91	26302.2
184	33856	6229504	13.5647	5.6877	2.26482	5.43478	578.05	26590.4
185	34225	6331625	13.6015	5.6980	2.26717	5.40541	581.19	26880.3
186	34596	6434856	13.6382	5.7083	2.26951	5.37634	584.34	27171.6
187	34969	6539203	13.6748	5.7185	2.27184	5.34759	587.48	27464.6
188	35344	6644672	13.7113	5.7287	2.27416	5.31915	590.62	27759.1
189	35721	6751269	13.7477	5.7388	2.27646	5.29101	593.76	28055.2
190	36100	6859000	13.7840	5.7489	2.27875	5.26316	596.90	28352.9
191	36481	6967871	13.8203	5.7590	2.28103	5.23560	600.04	28652.1
192	36864	7077888	13.8564	5.7690	2.28330	5.20833	603.19	28952.9
193	37249	7189057	13.8924	5.7790	2.28556	5.18135	606.33	29255.3
194	37636	7301384	13.9284	5.7890	2.28780	5.15464	609.47	29559.2
195	38025	7414875	13.9642	5.7989	2.29003	5.12821	612.61	29864.8
196	38416	7529536	14.0000	5.8088	2.29226	5.10204	615.75	30171.9
197	38809	7645373	14.0357	5.8186	2.29447	5.07614	618.89	30480.5
198	39204	7762392	14.0712	5.8285	2.29667	5.05051	622.04	30790.7
199	39601	7880599	14.1067	5.8383	2.29885	5.02513	625.18	31102.6

FUNCTIONS OF NUMBERS

No.	Square	Cube	Square Root	Cube Root	Logarithm	1000 × Reciprocal	No. = Diameter	
							Circum.	Area
200	40000	8000000	14.1421	5.8480	2.30103	5.00000	628.32	31415.9
201	40401	8120601	14.1774	5.8578	2.30320	4.97512	631.46	31730.9
202	40804	8242408	14.2127	5.8675	2.30535	4.95050	634.60	32047.4
203	41209	8365427	14.2478	5.8771	2.30750	4.92611	637.74	32365.5
204	41616	8489664	14.2829	5.8868	2.30963	4.90196	640.88	32685.1
205	42025	8615125	14.3178	5.8964	2.31175	4.87805	644.03	33006.4
206	42436	8741816	14.3527	5.9059	2.31387	4.85437	647.17	33329.2
207	42849	8869743	14.3875	5.9155	2.31597	4.83092	650.31	33653.5
208	43264	8998912	14.4222	5.9250	2.31806	4.80769	653.45	33979.5
209	43681	9129329	14.4568	5.9345	2.32015	4.78469	656.59	34307.0
210	44100	9261000	14.4914	5.9439	2.32222	4.76190	659.73	34636.1
211	44521	9393931	14.5258	5.9533	2.32428	4.73934	662.88	34966.7
212	44944	9528128	14.5602	5.9627	2.32634	4.71698	666.02	35298.9
213	45369	9663597	14.5945	5.9721	2.32838	4.69484	669.16	35632.7
214	45796	9800344	14.6287	5.9814	2.33041	4.67290	672.30	35968.1
215	46225	9938375	14.6629	5.9907	2.33244	4.65116	675.44	36305.0
216	46656	10077696	14.6969	6.0000	2.33445	4.62963	678.58	36643.5
217	47089	10218313	14.7309	6.0092	2.33646	4.60829	681.73	36983.6
218	47524	10360232	14.7648	6.0185	2.33846	4.58716	684.87	37325.3
219	47961	10503459	14.7986	6.0277	2.34044	4.56621	688.01	37668.5
220	48400	10648000	14.8324	6.0368	2.34242	4.54545	691.15	38013.3
221	48841	10793861	14.8661	6.0459	2.34439	4.52489	694.29	38359.6
222	49284	10941048	14.8997	6.0550	2.34635	4.50450	697.43	38707.6
223	49729	11089567	14.9332	6.0641	2.34830	4.48430	700.58	39057.1
224	50176	11239424	14.9666	6.0732	2.35025	4.46429	703.72	39408.1
225	50625	11390625	15.0000	6.0822	2.35218	4.44444	706.86	39760.8
226	51076	11543176	15.0333	6.0912	2.35411	4.42478	710.00	40115.0
227	51529	11697083	15.0665	6.1002	2.35603	4.40529	713.14	40470.8
228	51984	11852352	15.0997	6.1091	2.35793	4.38596	716.28	40828.1
229	52441	12008989	15.1327	6.1180	2.35984	4.36681	719.42	41187.1
230	52900	12167000	15.1658	6.1269	2.36173	4.34783	722.57	41547.6
231	53361	12326391	15.1987	6.1358	2.36361	4.32900	725.71	41909.6
232	53824	12487168	15.2315	6.1446	2.36549	4.31034	728.85	42273.3
233	54289	12649337	15.2643	6.1534	2.36736	4.29185	731.99	42638.5
234	54756	12812904	15.2971	6.1622	2.36922	4.27350	735.13	43005.3
235	55225	12977875	15.3297	6.1710	2.37107	4.25532	738.27	43373.6
236	55696	13144256	15.3623	6.1797	2.37291	4.23729	741.42	43743.5
237	56169	13312053	15.3948	6.1885	2.37475	4.21941	744.56	44115.0
238	56644	13481272	15.4272	6.1972	2.37658	4.20168	747.70	44488.1
239	57121	13651919	15.4596	6.2058	2.37840	4.18410	750.84	44862.7
240	57600	13824000	15.4919	6.2145	2.38021	4.16667	753.98	45238.9
241	58081	13997521	15.5242	6.2231	2.38202	4.14938	757.12	45616.7
242	58564	14172488	15.5563	6.2317	2.38382	4.13223	760.27	45996.1
243	59049	14348907	15.5885	6.2403	2.38561	4.11523	763.41	46377.0
244	59536	14526784	15.6205	6.2488	2.38739	4.09836	766.55	46759.5
245	60025	14706125	15.6525	6.2573	2.38917	4.08163	769.69	47143.5
246	60516	14886936	15.6844	6.2658	2.39094	4.06504	772.83	47529.2
247	61009	15069223	15.7162	6.2743	2.39270	4.04858	775.97	47916.4
248	61504	15252992	15.7480	6.2828	2.39445	4.03226	779.12	48305.1
249	62001	15438249	15.7797	6.2912	2.39620	4.01606	782.26	48695.5

FUNCTIONS OF NUMBERS

No.	Square	Cube	Square Root	Cube Root	Logarithm	1000 × Reciprocal	No. = Diameter	
							Circum.	Area
250	62500	15625000	15.8114	6.2996	2.39794	4.00000	785.40	49087.4
251	63001	15813251	15.8430	6.3080	2.39967	3.98406	788.54	49480.9
252	63504	16003008	15.8745	6.3164	2.40140	3.96825	791.68	49875.9
253	64009	16194277	15.9060	6.3247	2.40312	3.95257	794.82	50272.6
254	64516	16387064	15.9374	6.3330	2.40483	3.93701	797.96	50670.7
255	65025	16581375	15.9687	6.3413	2.40654	3.92157	801.11	51070.5
256	65536	16777216	16.0000	6.3496	2.40824	3.90625	804.25	51471.9
257	66049	16974593	16.0312	6.3579	2.40993	3.89105	807.39	51874.8
258	66564	17173512	16.0624	6.3661	2.41162	3.87597	810.53	52279.2
259	67081	17373979	16.0935	6.3743	2.41330	3.86100	813.67	52685.3
260	67600	17576000	16.1245	6.3825	2.41497	3.84615	816.81	53092.9
261	68121	17779581	16.1555	6.3907	2.41664	3.83142	819.96	53502.1
262	68644	17984728	16.1864	6.3988	2.41830	3.81679	823.10	53912.9
263	69169	18191447	16.2173	6.4070	2.41996	3.80228	826.24	54325.2
264	69696	18399744	16.2481	6.4151	2.42160	3.78788	829.38	54739.1
265	70225	18609625	16.2788	6.4232	2.42325	3.77358	832.52	55154.6
266	70756	18821096	16.3095	6.4312	2.42488	3.75940	835.66	55571.6
267	71289	19034163	16.3401	6.4393	2.42651	3.74532	838.81	55990.2
268	71824	19248832	16.3707	6.4473	2.42813	3.73134	841.95	56410.4
269	72361	19465109	16.4012	6.4553	2.42975	3.71747	845.09	56832.2
270	72900	19683000	16.4317	6.4633	2.43136	3.70370	848.23	57255.5
271	73441	19902511	16.4621	6.4713	2.43297	3.69004	851.37	57680.4
272	73984	20123648	16.4924	6.4792	2.43457	3.67647	854.51	58106.9
273	74529	20346417	16.5227	6.4872	2.43616	3.66300	857.65	58534.9
274	75076	20570824	16.5529	6.4951	2.43775	3.64964	860.80	58964.6
275	75625	20796875	16.5831	6.5030	2.43933	3.63636	863.94	59395.7
276	76176	21024576	16.6132	6.5108	2.44091	3.62319	867.08	59828.5
277	76729	21253933	16.6433	6.5187	2.44248	3.61011	870.22	60262.8
278	77284	21484952	16.6733	6.5265	2.44404	3.59712	873.36	60698.7
279	77841	21717639	16.7033	6.5343	2.44560	3.58423	876.50	61136.2
280	78400	21952000	16.7332	6.5421	2.44716	3.57143	879.65	61575.2
281	78961	22188041	16.7631	6.5499	2.44871	3.55872	882.79	62015.8
282	79524	22425768	16.7929	6.5577	2.45025	3.54610	885.93	62458.0
283	80089	22665187	16.8226	6.5654	2.45179	3.53357	889.07	62901.8
284	80656	22906304	16.8523	6.5731	2.45332	3.52113	892.21	63347.1
285	81225	23149125	16.8819	6.5808	2.45484	3.50877	895.35	63794.0
286	81796	23393656	16.9115	6.5885	2.45637	3.49650	898.50	64242.4
287	82369	23639903	16.9411	6.5962	2.45788	3.48432	901.64	64692.5
288	82944	23887872	16.9706	6.6039	2.45939	3.47222	904.78	65144.1
289	83521	24137569	17.0000	6.6115	2.46090	3.46021	907.92	65597.2
290	84100	24389000	17.0294	6.6191	2.46240	3.44828	911.06	66052.0
291	84681	24642171	17.0587	6.6267	2.46389	3.43643	914.20	66508.3
292	85264	24897088	17.0880	6.6343	2.46538	3.42466	917.35	66966.2
293	85849	25153757	17.1172	6.6419	2.46687	3.41297	920.49	67425.6
294	86436	25412184	17.1464	6.6494	2.46835	3.40136	923.63	67886.7
295	87025	25672375	17.1756	6.6569	2.46982	3.38983	926.77	68349.3
296	87616	25934336	17.2047	6.6644	2.47129	3.37838	929.91	68813.4
297	88209	26198073	17.2337	6.6719	2.47276	3.36700	933.05	69279.2
298	88804	26463592	17.2627	6.6794	2.47422	3.35570	936.19	69746.5
299	89401	26730899	17.2916	6.6869	2.47567	3.34448	939.34	70215.4

FUNCTIONS OF NUMBERS

No.	Square	Cube	Square Root	Cube Root	Logarithm	1000 × Reciprocal	No. = Diameter	
							Circum.	Area
300	90000	27000000	17.3205	6.6943	2.47712	3.33333	942.48	70685.8
301	90601	27270901	17.3494	6.7018	2.47857	3.32226	945.62	71157.9
302	91204	27543608	17.3781	6.7092	2.48001	3.31126	948.76	71631.5
303	91809	27818127	17.4069	6.7166	2.48144	3.30033	951.90	72106.6
304	92416	28094464	17.4356	6.7240	2.48287	3.28947	955.04	72583.4
305	93025	28372625	17.4642	6.7313	2.48430	3.27869	958.19	73061.7
306	93636	28652616	17.4929	6.7387	2.48572	3.26797	961.33	73541.5
307	94249	28934443	17.5214	6.7460	2.48714	3.25733	964.47	74023.0
308	94864	29218112	17.5499	6.7533	2.48855	3.24675	967.61	74506.0
309	95481	29503629	17.5784	6.7606	2.48996	3.23625	970.75	74990.6
310	96100	29791000	17.6068	6.7679	2.49136	3.22581	973.89	75476.8
311	96721	30080231	17.6352	6.7752	2.49276	3.21543	977.04	75964.5
312	97344	30371328	17.6635	6.7824	2.49415	3.20513	980.18	76453.8
313	97969	30664297	17.6918	6.7897	2.49554	3.19489	983.32	76944.7
314	98596	30959144	17.7200	6.7969	2.49693	3.18471	986.46	77437.1
315	99225	31255875	17.7482	6.8041	2.49831	3.17460	989.60	77931.1
316	99856	31554496	17.7764	6.8113	2.49969	3.16456	992.74	78426.7
317	100489	31855013	17.8045	6.8185	2.50106	3.15457	995.88	78923.9
318	101124	32157432	17.8326	6.8256	2.50243	3.14465	999.03	79422.6
319	101761	32461759	17.8606	6.8328	2.50379	3.13480	1002.2	79922.9
320	102400	32768000	17.8885	6.8399	2.50515	3.12500	1005.3	80424.8
321	103041	33076161	17.9165	6.8470	2.50651	3.11526	1008.5	80928.2
322	103684	33386248	17.9444	6.8541	2.50786	3.10559	1011.6	81433.2
323	104329	33698267	17.9722	6.8612	2.50920	3.09598	1014.7	81939.8
324	104976	34012224	18.0000	6.8683	2.51055	3.08642	1017.9	82448.0
325	105625	34328125	18.0278	6.8753	2.51188	3.07692	1021.0	82957.7
326	106276	34645976	18.0555	6.8824	2.51322	3.06749	1024.2	83469.0
327	106929	34965783	18.0831	6.8894	2.51455	3.05810	1027.3	83981.8
328	107584	35287552	18.1108	6.8964	2.51587	3.04878	1030.4	84496.3
329	108241	35611289	18.1384	6.9034	2.51720	3.03951	1033.6	85012.3
330	108900	35937000	18.1659	6.9104	2.51851	3.03030	1036.7	85529.9
331	109561	36264691	18.1934	6.9174	2.51983	3.02115	1039.9	86049.0
332	110224	36594368	18.2209	6.9244	2.52114	3.01205	1043.0	86569.7
333	110889	36926037	18.2483	6.9313	2.52244	3.00300	1046.2	87092.0
334	111556	37259704	18.2757	6.9382	2.52375	2.99401	1049.3	87615.9
335	112225	37595375	18.3030	6.9451	2.52504	2.98507	1052.4	88141.3
336	112896	37933056	18.3303	6.9521	2.52634	2.97619	1055.6	88668.3
337	113569	38272753	18.3576	6.9589	2.52763	2.96736	1058.7	89196.9
338	114244	38614472	18.3848	6.9658	2.52892	2.95858	1061.9	89727.0
339	114921	38958219	18.4120	6.9727	2.53020	2.94985	1065.0	90258.7
340	115600	39304000	18.4391	6.9795	2.53148	2.94118	1068.1	90792.0
341	116281	39651821	18.4662	6.9864	2.53275	2.93255	1071.3	91326.9
342	116964	40001688	18.4932	6.9932	2.53403	2.92398	1074.4	91863.3
343	117649	40353607	18.5203	7.0000	2.53529	2.91545	1077.6	92401.3
344	118336	40707584	18.5472	7.0068	2.53656	2.90698	1080.7	92940.9
345	119025	41063625	18.5742	7.0136	2.53782	2.89855	1083.8	93482.0
346	119716	41421736	18.6011	7.0203	2.53908	2.89017	1087.0	94024.7
347	120409	41781923	18.6279	7.0271	2.54033	2.88184	1090.1	94569.0
348	121104	42144192	18.6548	7.0338	2.54158	2.87356	1093.3	95114.9
349	121801	42508549	18.6815	7.0406	2.54283	2.86533	1096.4	95662.3

FUNCTIONS OF NUMBERS

No.	Square	Cube	Square Root	Cube Root	Logarithm	1000 × Reciprocal	No. = Diameter	
							Circum.	Area
350	122500	42875000	18.7083	7.0473	2.54407	2.85714	1099.6	96211.3
351	123201	43243551	18.7350	7.0540	2.54531	2.84900	1102.7	96761.8
352	123904	43614208	18.7617	7.0607	2.54654	2.84091	1105.8	97314.0
353	124609	43986977	18.7883	7.0674	2.54777	2.83286	1109.0	97867.7
354	125316	44361864	18.8149	7.0740	2.54900	2.82486	1112.1	98423.0
355	126025	44738875	18.8414	7.0807	2.55023	2.81690	1115.3	98979.8
356	126736	45118016	18.8680	7.0873	2.55145	2.80899	1118.4	99538.2
357	127449	45499293	18.8944	7.0940	2.55267	2.80112	1121.5	100098
358	128164	45882712	18.9209	7.1006	2.55388	2.79330	1124.7	100660
359	128881	46268279	18.9473	7.1072	2.55509	2.78552	1127.8	101223
360	129600	46656000	18.9737	7.1138	2.55630	2.77778	1131.0	101788
361	130321	47045881	19.0000	7.1204	2.55751	2.77008	1134.1	102354
362	131044	47437928	19.0263	7.1269	2.55871	2.76243	1137.3	102922
363	131769	47832147	19.0526	7.1335	2.55991	2.75482	1140.4	103491
364	132496	48228544	19.0788	7.1400	2.56110	2.74725	1143.5	104062
365	133225	48627125	19.1050	7.1466	2.56229	2.73973	1146.7	104635
366	133956	49027896	19.1311	7.1531	2.56348	2.73224	1149.8	105209
367	134689	49430863	19.1572	7.1596	2.56467	2.72480	1153.0	105785
368	135424	49836032	19.1833	7.1661	2.56585	2.71739	1156.1	106362
369	136161	50243409	19.2094	7.1726	2.56703	2.71003	1159.2	106941
370	136900	50653000	19.2354	7.1791	2.56820	2.70270	1162.4	107521
371	137641	51064811	19.2614	7.1855	2.56937	2.69542	1165.5	108103
372	138384	51478848	19.2873	7.1920	2.57054	2.68817	1168.7	108687
373	139129	51895117	19.3132	7.1984	2.57171	2.68097	1171.8	109272
374	139876	52313624	19.3391	7.2048	2.57287	2.67380	1175.0	109858
375	140625	52734375	19.3649	7.2112	2.57403	2.66667	1178.1	110447
376	141376	53157376	19.3907	7.2177	2.57519	2.65957	1181.2	111036
377	142129	53582633	19.4165	7.2240	2.57634	2.65252	1184.4	111628
378	142884	54010152	19.4422	7.2304	2.57749	2.64550	1187.5	112221
379	143641	54439939	19.4679	7.2368	2.57864	2.63852	1190.7	112815
380	144400	54872000	19.4936	7.2432	2.57978	2.63158	1193.8	113411
381	145161	55306341	19.5192	7.2495	2.58093	2.62467	1196.9	114009
382	145924	55742968	19.5448	7.2558	2.58206	2.61780	1200.1	114608
383	146689	56181887	19.5704	7.2622	2.58320	2.61097	1203.2	115209
384	147456	56623104	19.5959	7.2685	2.58433	2.60417	1206.4	115812
385	148225	57066625	19.6214	7.2748	2.58546	2.59740	1209.5	116416
386	148996	57512456	19.6469	7.2811	2.58659	2.59067	1212.7	117021
387	149769	57960603	19.6723	7.2874	2.58771	2.58398	1215.8	117628
388	150544	58411072	19.6977	7.2936	2.58883	2.57732	1218.9	118237
389	151321	58863869	19.7231	7.2999	2.58995	2.57069	1222.1	118847
390	152100	59319000	19.7484	7.3061	2.59106	2.56410	1225.2	119459
391	152881	59776471	19.7737	7.3124	2.59218	2.55754	1228.4	120072
392	153664	60236288	19.7990	7.3186	2.59329	2.55102	1231.5	120687
393	154449	60698457	19.8242	7.3248	2.59439	2.54453	1234.6	121304
394	155236	61162984	19.8494	7.3310	2.59550	2.53807	1237.8	121922
395	156025	61629875	19.8746	7.3372	2.59660	2.53165	1240.9	122542
396	156816	62099136	19.8997	7.3434	2.59770	2.52525	1244.1	123163
397	157609	62570773	19.9249	7.3496	2.59879	2.51889	1247.2	123786
398	158404	63044792	19.9499	7.3558	2.59988	2.51256	1250.4	124410
399	159201	63521199	19.9750	7.3619	2.60097	2.50627	1253.5	125036

400

FUNCTIONS OF NUMBERS

449

No.	Square	Cube	Square Root	Cube Root	Logarithm	1000 × Reciprocal	No. = Diameter Circum.	No. = Diameter Area
400	160000	64000000	20.0000	7.3681	2.60206	2.50000	1256.6	125664
401	160801	64481201	20.0250	7.3742	2.60314	2.49377	1259.8	126293
402	161604	64964808	20.0499	7.3803	2.60423	2.48756	1262.9	126923
403	162409	65450827	20.0749	7.3864	2.60531	2.48139	1266.1	127556
404	163216	65939264	20.0998	7.3925	2.60638	2.47525	1269.2	128190
405	164025	66430125	20.1246	7.3986	2.60746	2.46914	1272.3	128825
406	164836	66923416	20.1494	7.4047	2.60853	2.46305	1275.5	129462
407	165649	67419143	20.1742	7.4108	2.60959	2.45700	1278.6	130100
408	166464	67917312	20.1990	7.4169	2.61066	2.45098	1281.8	130741
409	167281	68417929	20.2237	7.4229	2.61172	2.44499	1284.9	131382
410	168100	68921000	20.2485	7.4290	2.61278	2.43902	1288.1	132025
411	168921	69426531	20.2731	7.4350	2.61384	2.43309	1291.2	132670
412	169744	69934528	20.2978	7.4410	2.61490	2.42718	1294.3	133317
413	170569	70444997	20.3224	7.4470	2.61595	2.42131	1297.5	133965
414	171396	70957944	20.3470	7.4530	2.61700	2.41546	1300.6	134614
415	172225	71473375	20.3715	7.4590	2.61805	2.40964	1303.8	135265
416	173056	71991296	20.3961	7.4650	2.61909	2.40385	1306.9	135918
417	173889	72511713	20.4206	7.4710	2.62014	2.39808	1310.0	136572
418	174724	73034632	20.4450	7.4770	2.62118	2.39234	1313.2	137228
419	175561	73560059	20.4695	7.4829	2.62221	2.38663	1316.3	137885
420	176400	74088000	20.4939	7.4889	2.62325	2.38095	1319.5	138544
421	177241	74618461	20.5183	7.4948	2.62428	2.37530	1322.6	139205
422	178084	75151448	20.5426	7.5007	2.62531	2.36967	1325.8	139867
423	178929	75686967	20.5670	7.5067	2.62634	2.36407	1328.9	140531
424	179776	76225024	20.5913	7.5126	2.62737	2.35849	1332.0	141196
425	180625	76765625	20.6155	7.5185	2.62839	2.35294	1335.2	141863
426	181476	77308776	20.6398	7.5244	2.62941	2.34742	1338.3	142531
427	182329	77854483	20.6640	7.5302	2.63043	2.34192	1341.5	143201
428	183184	78402752	20.6882	7.5361	2.63144	2.33645	1344.6	143872
429	184041	78953589	20.7123	7.5420	2.63246	2.33100	1347.7	144545
430	184900	79507000	20.7364	7.5478	2.63347	2.32558	1350.9	145220
431	185761	80062991	20.7605	7.5537	2.63448	2.32019	1354.0	145896
432	186624	80621568	20.7846	7.5595	2.63548	2.31481	1357.2	146574
433	187489	81182737	20.8087	7.5654	2.63649	2.30947	1360.3	147254
434	188356	81746504	20.8327	7.5712	2.63749	2.30415	1363.5	147934
435	189225	82312875	20.8567	7.5770	2.63849	2.29885	1366.6	148617
436	190096	82881856	20.8806	7.5828	2.63949	2.29358	1369.7	149301
437	190969	83453453	20.9045	7.5886	2.64048	2.28833	1372.9	149987
438	191844	84027672	20.9284	7.5944	2.64147	2.28311	1376.0	150674
439	192721	84604519	20.9523	7.6001	2.64246	2.27790	1379.2	151363
440	193600	85184000	20.9762	7.6059	2.64345	2.27273	1382.3	152053
441	194481	85766121	21.0000	7.6117	2.64444	2.26757	1385.4	152745
442	195364	86350888	21.0238	7.6174	2.64542	2.26244	1388.6	153439
443	196249	86938307	21.0476	7.6232	2.64640	2.25734	1391.7	154134
444	197136	87528384	21.0713	7.6289	2.64738	2.25225	1394.9	154830
445	198025	88121125	21.0950	7.6346	2.64836	2.24719	1398.0	155528
446	198916	88716536	21.1187	7.6403	2.64933	2.24215	1401.2	156228
447	199809	89314623	21.1424	7.6460	2.65031	2.23714	1404.3	156930
448	200704	89915392	21.1660	7.6517	2.65128	2.23214	1407.4	157633
449	201601	90518849	21.1896	7.6574	2.65225	2.22717	1410.6	158337

FUNCTIONS OF NUMBERS

No.	Square	Cube	Square Root	Cube Root	Logarithm	1000 × Reciprocal	No. = Diameter	
							Circum.	Area
450	202500	91125000	21.2132	7.6631	2.65321	2.22222	1413.7	159043
451	203401	91733851	21.2368	7.6688	2.65418	2.21729	1416.9	159751
452	204304	92345408	21.2603	7.6744	2.65514	2.21239	1420.0	160460
453	205209	92959677	21.2838	7.6801	2.65610	2.20751	1423.1	161171
454	206116	93576664	21.3073	7.6857	2.65706	2.20264	1426.3	161883
455	207025	94196375	21.3307	7.6914	2.65801	2.19780	1429.4	162597
456	207936	94818816	21.3542	7.6970	2.65896	2.19298	1432.6	163313
457	208849	95443993	21.3776	7.7026	2.65992	2.18818	1435.7	164030
458	209764	96071912	21.4009	7.7082	2.66087	2.18341	1438.8	164748
459	210681	96702579	21.4243	7.7138	2.66181	2.17865	1442.0	165468
460	211600	97336000	21.4476	7.7194	2.66276	2.17391	1445.1	166190
461	212521	97972181	21.4709	7.7250	2.66370	2.16920	1448.3	166914
462	213444	98611128	21.4942	7.7306	2.66464	2.16450	1451.4	167639
463	214369	99252847	21.5174	7.7362	2.66558	2.15983	1454.6	168365
464	215296	99897344	21.5407	7.7418	2.66652	2.15517	1457.7	169093
465	216225	100544625	21.5639	7.7473	2.66745	2.15054	1460.8	169823
466	217156	101194696	21.5870	7.7529	2.66839	2.14592	1464.0	170554
467	218089	101847563	21.6102	7.7584	2.66932	2.14133	1467.1	171287
468	219024	102503232	21.6333	7.7639	2.67025	2.13675	1470.3	172021
469	219961	103161709	21.6564	7.7695	2.67117	2.13220	1473.4	172757
470	220900	103823000	21.6795	7.7750	2.67210	2.12766	1476.5	173494
471	221841	104487111	21.7025	7.7805	2.67302	2.12314	1479.7	174234
472	222784	105154048	21.7256	7.7860	2.67394	2.11864	1482.8	174974
473	223729	105823817	21.7486	7.7915	2.67486	2.11416	1486.0	175716
474	224676	106496424	21.7715	7.7970	2.67578	2.10970	1489.1	176460
475	225625	107171875	21.7945	7.8025	2.67669	2.10526	1492.3	177205
476	226576	107850176	21.8174	7.8079	2.67761	2.10084	1495.4	177952
477	227529	108531333	21.8403	7.8134	2.67852	2.09644	1498.5	178701
478	228484	109215352	21.8632	7.8188	2.67943	2.09205	1501.7	179451
479	229441	109902239	21.8861	7.8243	2.68034	2.08768	1504.8	180203
480	230400	110592000	21.9089	7.8297	2.68124	2.08333	1508.0	180956
481	231361	111284641	21.9317	7.8352	2.68215	2.07900	1511.1	181711
482	232324	111980168	21.9545	7.8406	2.68305	2.07469	1514.2	182467
483	233289	112678587	21.9773	7.8460	2.68395	2.07039	1517.4	183225
484	234256	113379904	22.0000	7.8514	2.68485	2.06612	1520.5	183984
485	235225	114084125	22.0227	7.8568	2.68574	2.06186	1523.7	184745
486	236196	114791256	22.0454	7.8622	2.68664	2.05761	1526.8	185508
487	237169	115501303	22.0681	7.8676	2.68753	2.05339	1530.0	186272
488	238144	116214272	22.0907	7.8730	2.68842	2.04918	1533.1	187038
489	239121	116930169	22.1133	7.8784	2.68931	2.04499	1536.2	187805
490	240100	117649000	22.1359	7.8837	2.69020	2.04082	1539.4	188574
491	241081	118370771	22.1585	7.8891	2.69108	2.03666	1542.5	189345
492	242064	119095488	22.1811	7.8944	2.69197	2.03252	1545.7	190117
493	243049	119823157	22.2036	7.8998	2.69285	2.02840	1548.8	190890
494	244036	120553784	22.2261	7.9051	2.69373	2.02429	1551.9	191665
495	245025	121287375	22.2486	7.9105	2.69461	2.02020	1555.1	192442
496	246016	122023936	22.2711	7.9158	2.69548	2.01613	1558.2	193221
497	247009	122763473	22.2935	7.9211	2.69636	2.01207	1561.4	194000
498	248004	123505992	22.3159	7.9264	2.69723	2.00803	1564.5	194782
499	249001	124251499	22.3383	7.9317	2.69810	2.00401	1567.7	195565

AMERICAN MALLEABLE IRON

500

FUNCTIONS OF NUMBERS

549

No.	Square	Cube	Square Root	Cube Root	Logarithm	1000 × Reciprocal	No. = Diameter	
							Circum.	Area
500	250000	125000000	22.3607	7.9370	2.69897	2.00000	1570.8	196350
501	251001	125751501	22.3830	7.9423	2.69984	1.99601	1573.9	197136
502	252004	126506008	22.4054	7.9476	2.70070	1.99203	1577.1	197923
503	253009	127263527	22.4277	7.9528	2.70157	1.98807	1580.2	198713
504	254016	128024064	22.4499	7.9581	2.70243	1.98413	1583.4	199504
505	255025	128787625	22.4722	7.9634	2.70329	1.98020	1586.5	200296
506	256036	129554216	22.4944	7.9686	2.70415	1.97628	1589.6	201090
507	257049	130323843	22.5167	7.9739	2.70501	1.97239	1592.8	201886
508	258064	131096512	22.5389	7.9791	2.70586	1.96850	1595.9	202683
509	259081	131872229	22.5610	7.9843	2.70672	1.96464	1599.1	203482
510	260100	132651000	22.5832	7.9896	2.70757	1.96078	1602.2	204282
511	261121	133432831	22.6053	7.9948	2.70842	1.95695	1605.4	205084
512	262144	134217728	22.6274	8.0000	2.70927	1.95312	1608.5	205887
513	263169	135005697	22.6495	8.0052	2.71012	1.94932	1611.6	206692
514	264196	135796744	22.6716	8.0104	2.71096	1.94553	1614.8	207499
515	265225	136590875	22.6936	8.0156	2.71181	1.94175	1617.9	208307
516	266256	137388096	22.7156	8.0208	2.71265	1.93798	1621.1	209117
517	267289	138188413	22.7376	8.0260	2.71349	1.93424	1624.2	209928
518	268324	138991832	22.7596	8.0311	2.71433	1.93050	1627.3	210741
519	269361	139798359	22.7816	8.0363	2.71517	1.92678	1630.5	211556
520	270400	140608000	22.8035	8.0415	2.71600	1.92308	1633.6	212372
521	271441	141420761	22.8254	8.0466	2.71684	1.91939	1636.8	213189
522	272484	142236648	22.8473	8.0517	2.71767	1.91571	1639.9	214008
523	273529	143055667	22.8692	8.0569	2.71850	1.91205	1643.1	214829
524	274576	143877824	22.8910	8.0620	2.71933	1.90840	1646.2	215651
525	275625	144703125	22.9129	8.0671	2.72016	1.90476	1649.3	216475
526	276676	145531576	22.9347	8.0723	2.72099	1.90114	1652.5	217301
527	277729	146363183	22.9565	8.0774	2.72181	1.89753	1655.6	218128
528	278784	147197952	22.9783	8.0825	2.72263	1.89394	1658.8	218956
529	279841	148035889	23.0000	8.0876	2.72346	1.89036	1661.9	219787
530	280900	148877000	23.0217	8.0927	2.72428	1.88679	1665.0	220618
531	281961	149721291	23.0434	8.0978	2.72509	1.88324	1668.2	221452
532	283024	150568768	23.0651	8.1028	2.72591	1.87970	1671.3	222287
533	284089	151419437	23.0868	8.1079	2.72673	1.87617	1674.5	223123
534	285156	152273304	23.1084	8.1130	2.72754	1.87266	1677.6	223961
535	286225	153130375	23.1301	8.1180	2.72835	1.86916	1680.8	224801
536	287296	153990656	23.1517	8.1231	2.72916	1.86567	1683.9	225642
537	288369	154854153	23.1733	8.1281	2.72997	1.86220	1687.0	226484
538	289444	155720872	23.1948	8.1332	2.73078	1.85874	1690.2	227329
539	290521	156590819	23.2164	8.1382	2.73159	1.85529	1693.3	228175
540	291600	157464000	23.2379	8.1433	2.73239	1.85185	1696.5	229022
541	292681	158340421	23.2594	8.1483	2.73320	1.84843	1699.6	229871
542	293764	159220088	23.2809	8.1533	2.73400	1.84502	1702.7	230722
543	294849	160103007	23.3024	8.1583	2.73480	1.84162	1705.9	231574
544	295936	160989184	23.3238	8.1633	2.73560	1.83824	1709.0	232428
545	297025	161878625	23.3452	8.1683	2.73640	1.83486	1712.2	233283
546	298116	162771336	23.3666	8.1733	2.73719	1.83150	1715.3	234140
547	299209	163667323	23.3880	8.1783	2.73799	1.82815	1718.5	234998
548	300304	164566592	23.4094	8.1833	2.73878	1.82482	1721.6	235858
549	301401	165469149	23.4307	8.1882	2.73957	1.82149	1724.7	236720

FUNCTIONS OF NUMBERS

No.	Square	Cube	Square Root	Cube Root	Logarithm	1000 × Reciprocal	No. = Diameter	
							Circum.	Area
550	302500	166375000	23.4521	8.1932	2.74036	1.81818	1727.9	237583
551	303601	167284151	23.4734	8.1982	2.74115	1.81488	1731.0	238448
552	304704	168196608	23.4947	8.2031	2.74194	1.81159	1734.2	239314
553	305809	169112377	23.5160	8.2081	2.74273	1.80832	1737.3	240182
554	306916	170031464	23.5372	8.2130	2.74351	1.80505	1740.4	241051
555	308025	170953875	23.5584	8.2180	2.74429	1.80180	1743.6	241922
556	309136	171879616	23.5797	8.2229	2.74507	1.79856	1746.7	242795
557	310249	172808693	23.6008	8.2278	2.74586	1.79533	1749.9	243669
558	311364	173741112	23.6220	8.2327	2.74663	1.79211	1753.0	244545
559	312481	174676879	23.6432	8.2377	2.74741	1.78891	1756.2	245422
560	313600	175616000	23.6643	8.2426	2.74819	1.78571	1759.3	246301
561	314721	176558481	23.6854	8.2475	2.74896	1.78253	1762.4	247181
562	315844	177504328	23.7065	8.2524	2.74974	1.77936	1765.6	248063
563	316969	178453547	23.7276	8.2573	2.75051	1.77620	1768.7	248947
564	318096	179406144	23.7487	8.2621	2.75128	1.77305	1771.9	249832
565	319225	180362125	23.7697	8.2670	2.75205	1.76991	1775.0	250719
566	320356	181321496	23.7908	8.2719	2.75282	1.76678	1778.1	251607
567	321489	182284263	23.8118	8.2768	2.75358	1.76367	1781.3	252497
568	322624	183250432	23.8328	8.2816	2.75435	1.76056	1784.4	253388
569	323761	184220009	23.8537	8.2865	2.75511	1.75747	1787.6	254281
570	324900	185193000	23.8747	8.2913	2.75587	1.75439	1790.7	255176
571	326041	186169411	23.8956	8.2962	2.75664	1.75131	1793.8	256072
572	327184	187149248	23.9165	8.3010	2.75740	1.74825	1797.0	256970
573	328329	188132517	23.9374	8.3059	2.75815	1.74520	1800.1	257869
574	329476	189119224	23.9583	8.3107	2.75891	1.74216	1803.3	258770
575	330625	190109375	23.9792	8.3155	2.75967	1.73913	1806.4	259672
576	331776	191102976	24.0000	8.3203	2.76042	1.73611	1809.6	260576
577	332929	192100033	24.0208	8.3251	2.76118	1.73310	1812.7	261482
578	334084	193100552	24.0416	8.3300	2.76193	1.73010	1815.8	262389
579	335241	194104539	24.0624	8.3348	2.76268	1.72712	1819.0	263298
580	336400	195112000	24.0832	8.3396	2.76343	1.72414	1822.1	264208
581	337561	196122941	24.1039	8.3443	2.76418	1.72117	1825.3	265120
582	338724	197137368	24.1247	8.3491	2.76492	1.71821	1828.4	266033
583	339889	198155287	24.1454	8.3539	2.76567	1.71527	1831.6	266948
584	341056	199176704	24.1661	8.3587	2.76641	1.71233	1834.7	267865
585	342225	200201625	24.1868	8.3634	2.76716	1.70940	1837.8	268783
586	343396	201230056	24.2074	8.3682	2.76790	1.70648	1841.0	269703
587	344569	202262003	24.2281	8.3730	2.76864	1.70358	1844.1	270624
588	345744	203297472	24.2487	8.3777	2.76938	1.70068	1847.3	271547
589	346921	204336469	24.2693	8.3825	2.77012	1.69779	1850.4	272471
590	348100	205379000	24.2899	8.3872	2.77085	1.69492	1853.5	273397
591	349281	206425071	24.3105	8.3919	2.77159	1.69205	1856.7	274325
592	350464	207474688	24.3311	8.3967	2.77232	1.68919	1859.8	275254
593	351649	208527857	24.3516	8.4014	2.77305	1.68634	1863.0	276184
594	352836	209584584	24.3721	8.4061	2.77379	1.68350	1866.1	277117
595	354025	210644875	24.3926	8.4108	2.77452	1.68067	1869.2	278051
596	355216	211708736	24.4131	8.4155	2.77525	1.67785	1872.4	278986
597	356409	212776173	24.4336	8.4202	2.77597	1.67504	1875.5	279923
598	357604	213847192	24.4540	8.4249	2.77670	1.67224	1878.7	280862
599	358801	214921799	24.4745	8.4296	2.77743	1.66945	1881.8	281802

AMERICAN MALLEABLE IRON

FUNCTIONS OF NUMBERS

| No. | Square | Cube | Square Root | Cube Root | Logarithm | 1000 × Reciprocal | No. = Diameter | |
							Circum.	Area
600	360000	216000000	24.4949	8.4343	2.77815	1.66667	1885.0	282743
601	361201	217081801	24.5153	8.4390	2.77887	1.66389	1888.1	283687
602	362404	218167208	24.5357	8.4437	2.77960	1.66113	1891.2	284631
603	363609	219256227	24.5561	8.4484	2.78032	1.65837	1894.4	285578
604	364816	220348864	24.5764	8.4530	2.78104	1.65563	1897.5	286526
605	366025	221445125	24.5967	8.4577	2.78176	1.65289	1900.7	287475
606	367236	222545016	24.6171	8.4623	2.78247	1.65017	1903.8	288426
607	368449	223648543	24.6374	8.4670	2.78319	1.64745	1906.9	289379
608	369664	224755712	24.6577	8.4716	2.78390	1.64474	1910.1	290333
609	370881	225866529	24.6779	8.4763	2.78462	1.64204	1913.2	291289
610	372100	226981000	24.6982	8.4809	2.78533	1.63934	1916.4	292247
611	373321	228099131	24.7184	8.4856	2.78604	1.63666	1919.5	293206
612	374544	229220928	24.7386	8.4902	2.78675	1.63399	1922.7	294166
613	375769	230346397	24.7588	8.4948	2.78746	1.63132	1925.8	295128
614	376996	231475544	24.7790	8.4994	2.78817	1.62866	1928.9	296092
615	378225	232608375	24.7992	8.5040	2.78888	1.62602	1932.1	297057
616	379456	233744896	24.8193	8.5086	2.78958	1.62338	1935.2	298024
617	380689	234885113	24.8395	8.5132	2.79029	1.62075	1938.4	298992
618	381924	236029032	24.8596	8.5178	2.79099	1.61812	1941.5	299962
619	383161	237176659	24.8797	8.5224	2.79169	1.61551	1944.6	300934
620	384400	238328000	24.8998	8.5270	2.79239	1.61290	1947.8	301907
621	385641	239483061	24.9199	8.5316	2.79309	1.61031	1950.9	302882
622	386884	240641848	24.9399	8.5362	2.79379	1.60772	1954.1	303858
623	388129	241804367	24.9600	8.5408	2.79449	1.60514	1957.2	304836
624	389376	242970624	24.9800	8.5453	2.79518	1.60256	1960.4	305815
625	390625	244140625	25.0000	8.5499	2.79588	1.60000	1963.5	306796
626	391876	245314376	25.0200	8.5544	2.79657	1.59744	1966.6	307779
627	393129	246491883	25.0400	8.5590	2.79727	1.59490	1969.8	308763
628	394384	247673152	25.0599	8.5635	2.79796	1.59236	1972.9	309748
629	395641	248858189	25.0799	8.5681	2.79865	1.58983	1976.1	310736
630	396900	250047000	25.0998	8.5726	2.79934	1.58730	1979.2	311725
631	398161	251239591	25.1197	8.5772	2.80003	1.58479	1982.3	312715
632	399424	252435968	25.1396	8.5817	2.80072	1.58228	1985.5	313707
633	400689	253636137	25.1595	8.5862	2.80140	1.57978	1988.6	314700
634	401956	254840104	25.1794	8.5907	2.80209	1.57729	1991.8	315696
635	403225	256047875	25.1992	8.5952	2.80277	1.57480	1994.9	316692
636	404496	257259456	25.2190	8.5997	2.80346	1.57233	1998.1	317690
637	405769	258474853	25.2389	8.6043	2.80414	1.56986	2001.2	318690
638	407044	259694072	25.2587	8.6088	2.80482	1.56740	2004.3	319692
639	408321	260917119	25.2784	8.6132	2.80550	1.56495	2007.5	320695
640	409600	262144000	25.2982	8.6177	2.80618	1.56250	2010.6	321699
641	410881	263374721	25.3180	8.6222	2.80686	1.56006	2013.8	322705
642	412164	264609288	25.3377	8.6267	2.80754	1.55763	2016.9	323713
643	413449	265847707	25.3574	8.6312	2.80821	1.55521	2020.0	324722
644	414736	267089984	25.3772	8.6357	2.80889	1.55280	2023.2	325733
645	416025	268336125	25.3969	8.6401	2.80956	1.55039	2026.3	326745
646	417316	269586136	25.4165	8.6446	2.81023	1.54799	2029.5	327759
647	418609	270840023	25.4362	8.6490	2.81090	1.54560	2032.6	328775
648	419904	272097792	25.4558	8.6535	2.81158	1.54321	2035.8	329792
649	421201	273359449	25.4755	8.6579	2.81224	1.54083	2038.9	330810

FUNCTIONS OF NUMBERS

No.	Square	Cube	Square Root	Cube Root	Logarithm	1000 × Reciprocal	No. = Diameter	
							Circum.	Area
650	422500	274625000	25.4951	8.6624	2.81291	1.53846	2042.0	331831
651	423801	275894451	25.5147	8.6668	2.81358	1.53610	2045.2	332853
652	425104	277167808	25.5343	8.6713	2.81425	1.53374	2048.3	333876
653	426409	278445077	25.5539	8.6757	2.81491	1.53139	2051.5	334901
654	427716	279726264	25.5734	8.6801	2.81558	1.52905	2054.6	335927
655	429025	281011375	25.5930	8.6845	2.81624	1.52672	2057.7	336955
656	430336	282300416	25.6125	8.6890	2.81690	1.52439	2060.9	337985
657	431649	283593393	25.6320	8.6934	2.81757	1.52207	2064.0	339016
658	432964	284890312	25.6515	8.6978	2.81823	1.51976	2067.2	340049
659	434281	286191179	25.6710	8.7022	2.81889	1.51745	2070.3	341084
660	435600	287496000	25.6905	8.7066	2.81954	1.51515	2073.5	342119
661	436921	288804781	25.7099	8.7110	2.82020	1.51286	2076.6	343157
662	438244	290117528	25.7294	8.7154	2.82086	1.51057	2079.7	344196
663	439569	291434247	25.7488	8.7198	2.82151	1.50830	2082.9	345237
664	440896	292754944	25.7682	8.7241	2.82217	1.50602	2086.0	346279
665	442225	294079625	25.7876	8.7285	2.82282	1.50376	2089.2	347323
666	443556	295408296	25.8070	8.7329	2.82347	1.50150	2092.3	348368
667	444889	296740963	25.8263	8.7373	2.82413	1.49925	2095.4	349415
668	446224	298077632	25.8457	8.7416	2.82478	1.49701	2098.6	350464
669	447561	299418309	25.8650	8.7460	2.82543	1.49477	2101.7	351514
670	448900	300763000	25.8844	8.7503	2.82607	1.49254	2104.9	352565
671	450241	302111711	25.9037	8.7547	2.82672	1.49031	2108.0	353618
672	451584	303464448	25.9230	8.7590	2.82737	1.48810	2111.2	354673
673	452929	304821217	25.9422	8.7634	2.82082	1.48588	2114.3	355730
674	454276	306182024	25.9615	8.7677	2.82866	1.48368	2117.4	356788
675	455625	307546875	25.9808	8.7721	2.82930	1.48148	2120.6	357847
676	456976	308915776	26.0000	8.7764	2.82995	1.47929	2123.7	358908
677	458329	310288733	26.0192	8.7807	2.83059	1.47710	2126.9	359971
678	459684	311665752	26.0384	8.7850	2.83123	1.47493	2130.0	361035
679	461041	313046839	26.0576	8.7893	2.83187	1.47275	2133.1	362101
680	462400	314432000	26.0768	8.7937	2.83251	1.47059	2136.3	363168
681	463761	315821241	26.0960	8.7980	2.83315	1.46843	2139.4	364237
682	465124	317214568	26.1151	8.8023	2.83378	1.46628	2142.6	365308
683	466489	318611987	26.1343	8.8066	2.83442	1.46413	2145.7	366380
684	467856	320013504	26.1534	8.8109	2.83506	1.46199	2148.8	367453
685	469225	321419125	26.1725	8.8152	2.83569	1.45985	2152.0	368528
686	470596	322828856	26.1916	8.8194	2.83632	1.45773	2155.1	369605
687	471969	324242703	26.2107	8.8237	2.83696	1.45560	2158.3	370684
688	473344	325660672	26.2298	8.8280	2.83759	1.45349	2161.4	371764
689	474721	327082769	26.2488	8.8323	2.83822	1.45138	2164.6	372845
690	476100	328509000	26.2679	8.8366	2.83885	1.44928	2167.7	373928
691	477481	329939371	26.2869	8.8408	2.83948	1.44718	2170.8	375013
692	478864	331373888	26.3059	8.8451	2.84011	1.44509	2174.0	376099
693	480249	332812557	26.3249	8.8493	2.84073	1.44300	2177.1	377187
694	481636	334255384	26.3439	8.8536	2.84136	1.44092	2180.3	378276
695	483025	335702375	26.3629	8.8578	2.84198	1.43885	2183.4	379367
696	484416	337153536	26.3818	8.8621	2.84261	1.43678	2186.5	380459
697	485809	338608873	26.4008	8.8663	2.84323	1.43472	2189.7	381553
698	487204	340068392	26.4197	8.8706	2.84386	1.43266	2192.8	382649
699	488601	341532099	26.4386	8.8748	2.84448	1.43062	2196.0	383746

FUNCTIONS OF NUMBERS

No.	Square	Cube	Square Root	Cube Root	Logarithm	1000 × Reciprocal	No. = Diameter	
							Circum.	Area
700	490000	343000000	26.4575	8.8790	2.84510	1.42857	2199.1	384845
701	491401	344472101	26.4764	8.8833	2.84572	1.42653	2202.3	385945
702	492804	345948408	26.4953	8.8875	2.84634	1.42450	2205.4	387047
703	494209	347428927	26.5141	8.8917	2.84696	1.42248	2208.5	388151
704	495616	348913664	26.5330	8.8959	2.84757	1.42045	2211.7	389256
705	497025	350402625	26.5518	8.9001	2.84819	1.41844	.2214.8	390363
706	498436	351895816	26.5707	8.9043	2.84880	1.41643	2218.0	391471
707	499849	353393243	26.5895	8.9085	2.84942	1.41443	2221.1	392580
708	501264	354894912	26.6083	8.9127	2.85003	1.41243	2224.2	393692
709	502681	356400829	26.6271	8.9169	2.85065	1.41044	2227.4	394805
710	504100	357911000	26.6458	8.9211	2.85126	1.40845	2230.5	395919
711	505521	359425431	26.6646	8.9253	2.85187	1.40647	2233.7	397035
712	506944	360944128	26.6833	8.9295	2.85248	1.40449	2236.8	398153
713	508369	362467097	26.7021	8.9337	2.85309	1.40252	2240.0	399272
714	509796	363994344	26.7208	8.9378	2.85370	1.40056	2243.1	400393
715	511225	365525875	26.7395	8.9420	2.85431	1.39860	2246.2	401515
716	512656	367061696	26.7582	8.9462	2.85491	1.39665	2249.4	402639
717	514089	368601813	26.7769	8.9503	2.85552	1.39470	2252.5	403765
718	515524	370146232	26.7955	8.9545	2.85612	1.39276	2255.7	404892
719	516961	371694959	26.8142	8.9587	2.85673	1.39082	2258.8	406020
720	518400	373248000	26.8328	8.9628	2.85733	1.38889	2261.9	407150
721	519841	374805361	26.8514	8.9670	2.85794	1.38696	2265.1	408282
722	521284	376367048	26.8701	8.9711	2.85854	1.38504	2268.2	409415
723	522729	377933067	26.8887	8.9752	2.85914	1.38313	2271.4	410550
724	524176	379503424	26.9072	8.9794	2.85974	1.38122	2274.5	411687
725	525625	381078125	26.9258	8.9835	2.86034	1.37931	2277.7	412825
726	527076	382657176	26.9444	8.9876	2.86094	1.37741	2280.8	413965
727	528529	384240583	26.9629	8.9918	2.86153	1.37552	2283.9	415106
728	529984	385828352	26.9815	8.9959	2.86213	1.37363	2287.1	416248
729	531441	387420489	27.0000	9.0000	2.86273	1.37174	2290.2	417393
730	532900	389017000	27.0185	9.0041	2.86332	1.36986	2293.4	418539
731	534361	390617891	27.0370	9.0082	2.86392	1.36799	2296.5	419686
732	535824	392223168	27.0555	9.0123	2.86451	1.36612	2299.6	420835
733	537289	393832837	27.0740	9.0164	2.86510	1.36426	2302.8	421986
734	538756	395446904	27.0924	9.0205	2.86570	1.36240	2305.9	423138
735	540225	397065375	27.1109	9.0246	2.86629	1.36054	2309.1	424293
736	541696	398688256	27.1293	9.0287	2.86688	1.35870	2312.2	425447
737	543169	400315553	27.1477	9.0328	2.86747	1.35685	2315.4	426604
738	544644	401947272	27.1662	9.0369	2.86806	1.35501	2318.5	427762
739	546121	403583419	27.1846	9.0410	2.86864	1.35318	2321.6	428922
740	547600	405224000	27.2029	9.0450	2.86923	1.35135	2324.8	430084
741	549081	406869021	27.2213	9.0491	2.86982	1.34953	2327.9	431247
742	550564	408518488	27.2397	9.0532	2.87040	1.34771	2331.1	432412
743	552049	410172407	27.2580	9.0572	2.87099	1.34590	2334.2	433578
744	553536	411830784	27.2764	9.0613	2.87157	1.34409	2337.3	434746
745	555025	413493625	27.2947	9.0654	2.87216	1.34228	2340.5	435916
746	556516	415160936	27.3130	9.0694	2.87274	1.34048	2343.6	437087
747	558009	416832723	27.3313	9.0735	2.87332	1.33869	2346.8	438259
748	559504	418508992	27.3496	9.0775	2.87390	1.33690	2349.9	439433
749	561001	420189749	27.3679	9.0816	2.87448	1.33511	2353.1	440609

FUNCTIONS OF NUMBERS

No.	Square	Cube	Square Root	Cube Root	Logarithm	1000 × Reciprocal	No. = Diameter	
							Circum.	Area
750	562500	421875000	27.3861	9.0856	2.87506	1.33333	2356.2	441786
751	564001	423564751	27.4044	9.0896	2.87564	1.33156	2359.3	442965
752	565504	425259008	27.4226	9.0937	2.87622	1.32979	2362.5	444146
753	567009	426957777	27.4408	9.0977	2.87680	1.32802	2365.6	445328
754	568516	428661064	27.4591	9.1017	2.87737	1.32626	2368.8	446511
755	570025	430368875	27.4773	9.1057	2.87795	1.32450	2371.9	447697
756	571536	432081216	27.4955	9.1098	2.87852	1.32275	2375.0	448883
757	573049	433798093	27.5136	9.1138	2.87910	1.32100	2378.2	450072
758	574564	435519512	27.5318	9.1178	2.87967	1.31926	2381.3	451262
759	576081	437245479	27.5500	9.1218	2.88024	1.31752	2384.5	452453
760	577600	438976000	27.5681	9.1258	2.88081	1.31579	2387.6	453646
761	579121	440711081	27.5862	9.1298	2.88138	1.31406	2390.8	454841
762	580644	442450728	27.6043	9.1338	2.88196	1.31234	2393.9	456037
763	582169	444194947	27.6225	9.1378	2.88252	1.31062	2397.0	457234
764	583696	445943744	27.6405	9.1418	2.88309	1.30890	2400.2	458434
765	585225	447697125	27.6586	9.1458	2.88366	1.30719	2403.3	459635
766	586756	449455096	27.6767	9.1498	2.88423	1.30548	2406.5	460837
767	588289	451217663	27.6948	9.1537	2.88480	1.30378	2409.6	462041
768	589824	452984832	27.7128	9.1577	2.88536	1.30208	2412.7	463247
769	591361	454756609	27.7308	9.1617	2.88593	1.30039	2415.9	464454
770	592900	456533000	27.7489	9.1657	2.88649	1.29870	2419.0	465663
771	594441	458314011	27.7669	9.1696	2.88705	1.29702	2422.2	466873
772	595984	460099648	27.7849	9.1736	2.88762	1.29534	2425.3	468085
773	597529	461889917	27.8029	9.1775	2.88818	1.29366	2428.5	469298
774	599076	463684824	27.8209	9.1815	2.88874	1.29199	2431.6	470513
775	600625	465484375	27.8388	9.1855	2.88930	1.29032	2434.7	471730
776	602176	467288576	27.8568	9.1894	2.88986	1.28866	2437.9	472948
777	603729	469097433	27.8747	9.1933	2.89042	1.28700	2441.0	474168
778	605284	470910952	27.8927	9.1973	2.89098	1.28535	2444.2	475389
779	606841	472729139	27.9106	9.2012	2.89154	1.28370	2447.3	476612
780	608400	474552000	27.9285	9.2052	2.89209	1.28205	2450.4	477836
781	609961	476379541	27.9464	9.2091	2.89265	1.28041	2453.6	479062
782	611524	478211768	27.9643	9.2130	2.89321	1.27877	2456.7	480290
783	613089	480048687	27.9821	9.2170	2.89376	1.27714	2459.9	481519
784	614656	481890304	28.0000	9.2209	2.89432	1.27551	2463.0	482750
785	616225	483736625	28.0179	9.2248	2.89487	1.27389	2466.2	483982
786	617796	485587656	28.0357	9.2287	2.89542	1.27226	2469.3	485216
787	619369	487443403	28.0535	9.2326	2.89597	1.27065	2472.4	486451
788	620944	489303872	28.0713	9.2365	2.89653	1.26904	2475.6	487688
789	622521	491169069	28.0891	9.2404	2.89708	1.26743	2478.7	488927
790	624100	493039000	28.1069	9.2443	2.89763	1.26582	2481.9	490167
791	625681	494913671	28.1247	9.2482	2.89818	1.26422	2485.0	491409
792	627264	496793088	28.1425	9.2521	2.89873	1.26263	2488.1	492652
793	628849	498677257	28.1603	9.2560	2.89927	1.26103	2491.3	493897
794	630436	500566184	28.1780	9.2599	2.89982	1.25945	2494.4	495143
795	632025	502459875	28.1957	9.2638	2.90037	1.25786	2497.6	496391
796	633616	504358336	28.2135	9.2677	2.90091	1.25628	2500.7	497641
797	635209	506261573	28.2312	9.2716	2.90146	1.25471	2503.8	498892
798	636804	508169592	28.2489	9.2754	2.90200	1.25313	2507.0	500145
799	638401	510082399	28.2666	9.2793	2.90255	1.25156	2510.1	501399

800

FUNCTIONS OF NUMBERS

849

No.	Square	Cube	Square Root	Cube Root	Logarithm	1000 × Reciprocal	No. = Diameter	
							Circum.	Area
800	640000	512000000	28.2843	9.2832	2.90309	1.25000	2513.3	502655
801	641601	513922401	28.3019	9.2870	2.90363	1.24844	2516.4	503912
802	643204	515849608	28.3196	9.2909	2.90417	1.24688	2519.6	505171
803	644809	517781627	28.3373	9.2948	2.90472	1.24533	2522.7	506432
804	646416	519718464	28.3549	9.2986	2.90526	1.24378	2525.8	507694
805	648025	521660125	28.3725	9.3025	2.90580	1.24224	2529.0	508958
806	649636	523606616	28.3901	9.3063	2.90634	1.24069	2532.1	510223
807	651249	525557943	28.4077	9.3102	2.90687	1.23916	2535.3	411490
808	652864	527514112	28.4253	9.3140	2.90741	1.23762	2538.4	512758
809	654481	529475129	28.4429	9.3179	2.90795	1.23609	2541.5	514028
810	656100	531441000	28.4605	9.3217	2.90849	1.23457	2544.7	515300
811	657721	533411731	28.4781	9.3255	2.90902	1.23305	2547.8	516573
812	659344	535387328	28.4956	9.3294	2.90956	1.23153	2551.0	517848
813	660969	537367797	28.5132	9.3332	2.91009	1.23001	2554.1	519124
814	662596	539353144	28.5307	9.3370	2.91062	1.22850	2557.3	520402
815	664225	541343375	28.5482	9.3408	2.91116	1.22699	2560.4	521681
816	665856	543338496	28.5657	9.3447	2.91169	1.22549	2563.5	522962
817	667489	545338513	28.5832	9.3485	2.91222	1.22399	2566.7	524245
818	669124	547343432	28.6007	9.3523	2.91275	1.22249	2569.8	525529
819	670761	549353259	28.6182	9.3561	2.91328	1.22100	2573.0	526814
820	672400	551368000	28.6356	9.3599	2.91381	1.21951	2576.1	528102
821	674041	553387661	28.6531	9.3637	2.91434	1.21803	2579.2	529391
822	675684	555412248	28.6705	9.3675	2.91487	1.21655	2582.4	530681
823	677329	557441767	28.6880	9.3713	2.91540	1.21507	2585.5	531973
824	678976	559476224	28.7054	9.3751	2.91593	1.21359	2588.7	533267
825	680625	561515625	28.7228	9.3789	2.91645	1.21212	2591.8	534562
826	682276	563559976	28.7402	9.3827	2.91698	1.21065	2595.0	535858
827	683929	565609283	28.7576	9.3865	2.91751	1.20919	2598.1	537157
828	685584	567663552	28.7750	9.3902	2.91803	1.20773	2601.2	538456
829	687241	569722789	28.7924	9.3940	2.91855	1.20627	2604.4	539758
830	688900	571787000	28.8097	9.3978	2.91908	1.20482	2607.5	541061
831	690561	573856191	28.8271	9.4016	2.91960	1.20337	2610.7	542365
832	692224	575930368	28.8444	9.4053	2.92012	1.20192	2613.8	543671
833	693889	578009537	28.8617	9.4091	2.92065	1.20048	2616.9	544979
834	695556	580093704	28.8791	9.4129	2.92117	1.19904	2620.1	546288
835	697225	582182875	28.8964	9.4166	2.92169	1.19760	2623.2	547599
836	698896	584277056	28.9137	9.4204	2.92221	1.19617	2626.4	548912
837	700569	586376253	28.9310	9.4241	2.92273	1.19474	2629.5	550226
838	702244	588480472	28.9482	9.4279	2.92324	1.19332	2632.7	551541
839	703921	590589719	28.9655	9.4316	2.92376	1.19190	2635.8	552858
840	705600	592704000	28.9828	9.4354	2.92428	1.19048	2638.9	554177
841	707281	594823321	29.0000	9.4391	2.92480	1.18906	2642.1	555497
842	708964	596947688	29.0172	9.4429	2.92531	1.18765	2645.2	556819
843	710649	599077107	29.0345	9.4466	2.92583	1.18624	2648.4	558142
844	712336	601211584	29.0517	9.4503	2.92634	1.18483	2651.5	559467
845	714025	603351125	29.0689	9.4541	2.92686	1.18343	2654.6	560794
846	715716	605495736	29.0861	9.4578	2.92737	1.18203	2657.8	562122
847	717409	607645423	29.1033	9.4615	2.92788	1.18064	2660.9	563452
848	719104	609800192	29.1204	9.4652	2.92840	1.17925	2664.1	564783
849	720801	611960049	29.1376	9.4690	2.92891	1.17786	2667.2	566116

FUNCTIONS OF NUMBERS

No.	Square	Cube	Square Root	Cube Root	Logarithm	1000 × Reciprocal	No. = Diameter	
							Circum.	Area
850	722500	614125000	29.1548	9.4727	2.92942	1.17647	2670.4	567450
851	724201	616295051	29.1719	9.4764	2.92993	1.17509	2673.5	568786
852	725904	618470208	29.1890	9.4801	2.93044	1.17371	2676.6	570124
853	727609	620650477	29.2062	9.4838	2.93095	1.17233	2679.8	571463
854	729316	622835864	29.2233	9.4875	2.93146	1.17096	2682.9	572803
855	731025	625026375	29.2404	9.4912	2.93197	1.16959	2686.1	574146
856	732736	627222016	29.2575	9.4949	2.93247	1.16822	2689.2	575490
857	734449	629422793	29.2746	9.4986	2.93298	1.16686	2692.3	576835
858	736164	631628712	29.2916	9.5023	2.93349	1.16550	2695.5	578182
859	737881	633839779	29.3087	9.5060	2.93399	1.16414	2698.6	579530
860	739600	636056000	29.3258	9.5097	2.93450	1.16279	2701.8	580880
861	741321	638277381	29.3428	9.5134	2.93500	1.16144	2704.9	582232
862	743044	640503928	29.3598	9.5171	2.93551	1.16009	2708.1	583585
863	744769	642735647	29.3769	9.5207	2.93601	1.15875	2711.2	584940
864	746496	644972544	29.3939	9.5244	2.93651	1.15741	2714.3	586297
865	748225	647214625	29.4109	9.5281	2.93702	1.15607	2717.5	587655
866	749956	649461896	29.4279	9.5317	2.93752	1.15473	2720.6	589014
867	751689	651714363	29.4449	9.5354	2.93802	1.15340	2723.8	590375
868	753424	653972032	29.4618	9.5391	2.93852	1.15207	2726.9	591738
869	755161	656234909	29.4788	9.5427	2.93902	1.15075	2730.0	593102
870	756900	658503000	29.4958	9.5464	2.93952	1.14943	2733.2	594468
871	758641	660776311	29.5127	9.5501	2.94002	1.14811	2736.3	595835
872	760384	663054848	29.5296	9.5537	2.94052	1.14679	2739.5	597204
873	762129	665338617	29.5466	9.5574	2.94101	1.14548	2742.6	598575
874	763876	667627624	29.5635	9.5610	2.94151	1.14416	2745.8	599947
875	765625	669921875	29.5804	9.5647	2.94201	1.14286	2748.9	601320
876	767376	672221376	29.5973	9.5683	2.94250	1.14155	2752.0	602696
877	769129	674526133	29.6142	9.5719	2.94300	1.14025	2755.2	604073
878	770884	676836152	29.6311	9.5756	2.94349	1.13895	2758.3	605451
879	772641	679151439	29.6479	9.5792	2.94399	1.13766	2761.5	606831
880	774400	681472000	29.6648	9.5828	2.94448	1.13636	2764.6	608212
881	776161	683797841	29.6816	9.5865	2.94498	1.13507	2767.7	609595
882	777924	686128968	29.6985	9.5901	2.94547	1.13379	2770.9	610980
883	779689	688465387	29.7153	9.5937	2.94596	1.13250	2774.0	612366
884	781456	690807104	29.7321	9.5973	2.94645	1.13122	2777.2	613754
885	783225	693154125	29.7489	9.6010	2.94694	1.12994	2780.3	615143
886	784996	695506456	29.7658	9.6046	2.94743	1.12867	2783.5	616534
887	786769	697864103	29.7825	9.6082	2.94792	1.12740	2786.6	617927
888	788544	700227072	29.7993	9.6118	2.94841	1.12613	2789.7	619321
889	790321	702595369	29.8161	9.6154	2.94890	1.12486	2792.9	620717
890	792100	704969000	29.8329	9.6190	2.94939	1.12360	2796.0	622114
891	793881	707347971	29.8496	9.6226	2.94988	1.12233	2799.2	623513
892	795664	709732288	29.8664	9.6262	2.95036	1.12108	2802.3	624913
893	797449	712121957	29.8831	9.6298	2.95085	1.11982	2805.4	626315
894	799236	714516984	29.8998	9.6334	2.95134	1.11857	2808.6	627718
895	801025	716917375	29.9166	9.6370	2.95182	1.11732	2811.7	629124
896	802816	719323136	29.9333	9.6406	2.95231	1.11607	2814.9	630530
897	804609	721734273	29.9500	9.6442	2.95279	1.11483	2818.0	631938
898	806404	724150792	29.9666	9.6477	2.95328	1.11359	2821.2	633348
899	808201	726572699	29.9833	9.6513	2.95376	1.11235	2824.3	634760

AMERICAN MALLEABLE IRON

900

949

FUNCTIONS OF NUMBERS

No.	Square	Cube	Square Root	Cube Root	Logarithm	1000 × Reciprocal	No. = Diameter	
							Circum.	Area
900	810000	729000000	30.0000	9.6549	2.95424	1.11111	2827.4	636173
901	811801	731432701	30.0167	9.6585	2.95472	1.10988	2830.6	637587
902	813604	733870808	30.0333	9.6620	2.95521	1.10865	2833.7	639003
903	815409	736314327	30.0500	9.6656	2.95569	1.10742	2836.9	640421
904	817216	738763264	30.0666	9.6692	2.95617	1.10619	2840.0	641840
905	819025	741217625	30.0832	9.6727	2.95665	1.10497	2843.1	643261
906	820836	743677416	30.0998	9.6763	2.95713	1.10375	2846.3	644683
907	822649	746142643	30.1164	9.6799	2.95761	1.10254	2849.4	646107
908	824464	748613312	30.1330	9.6834	2.95809	1.10132	2852.6	647533
909	826281	751089429	30.1496	9.6870	2.95856	1.10011	2855.7	648960
910	828100	753571000	30.1662	9.6905	2.95904	1.09890	2858.8	650388
911	829921	756058031	30.1828	9.6941	2.95952	1.09769	2862.0	651818
912	831744	758550528	30.1993	9.6976	2.95999	1.09649	2865.1	653250
913	833569	761048497	30.2159	9.7012	2.96047	1.09529	2868.3	654684
914	835396	763551944	30.2324	9.7047	2.96095	1.09409	2871.4	656118
915	837225	766060875	30.2490	9.7082	2.96142	1.09290	2874.6	657555
916	839056	768575296	30.2655	9.7118	2.96190	1.09170	2877.7	658993
917	840889	771095213	30.2820	9.7153	2.96237	1.09051	2880.8	660433
918	842724	773620632	30.2985	9.7188	2.96284	1.08932	2884.0	661874
919	844561	776151559	30.3150	9.7224	2.96332	1.08814	2887.1	663317
920	846400	778688000	30.3315	9.7259	2.96379	1.08696	2890.3	664761
921	848241	781229961	30.3480	9.7294	2.96426	1.08578	2893.4	666207
922	850084	783777448	30.3645	9.7329	2.96473	1.08460	2896.5	667654
923	851929	786330467	30.3809	9.7364	2.96520	1.08342	2899.7	669103
924	853776	788889024	30.3974	9.7400	2.96567	1.08225	2902.8	670554
925	855625	791453125	30.4138	9.7435	2.96614	1.08108	2906.0	672006
926	857476	794022776	30.4302	9.7470	2.96661	1.07991	2909.1	673460
927	859329	796597983	30.4467	9.7505	2.96708	1.07875	2912.3	674915
928	861184	799178752	30.4631	9.7540	2.96755	1.07759	2915.4	676372
929	863041	801765089	30.4795	9.7575	2.96802	1.07643	2918.5	677831
930	864900	804357000	30.4959	9.7610	2.96848	1.07527	2921.7	679291
931	866761	806954491	30.5123	9.7645	2.96895	1.07411	2924.8	680752
932	868624	809557568	30.5287	9.7680	2.96942	1.07296	2928.0	682216
933	870489	812166237	30.5450	9.7715	2.96988	1.07181	2931.1	683680
934	872356	814780504	30.5614	9.7750	2.97035	1.07066	2934.2	685147
935	874225	817400375	30.5778	9.7785	2.97081	1.06952	2937.4	686615
936	876096	820025856	30.5941	9.7819	2.97128	1.06838	2940.5	688084
937	877969	822656953	30.6105	9.7854	2.97174	1.06724	2943.7	689555
938	879844	825293672	30.6268	9.7889	2.97220	1.06610	2946.8	691028
939	881721	827936019	30.6431	9.7924	2.97267	1.06496	2950.0	692502
940	883600	830584000	30.6594	9.7959	2.97313	1.06383	2953.1	693978
941	885481	833237621	30.6757	9.7993	2.97359	1.06270	2956.2	695455
942	887364	835896888	30.6920	9.8028	2.97405	1.06157	2959.4	696934
943	889249	838561807	30.7083	9.8063	2.97451	1.06045	2962.5	698415
944	891136	841232384	30.7246	9.8097	2.97497	1.05932	2965.7	699897
945	893025	843908625	30.7409	9.8132	2.97543	1.05820	2968.8	701380
946	894916	846590536	30.7571	9.8167	2.97589	1.05708	2971.9	702865
947	896809	849278123	30.7734	9.8201	2.97635	1.05597	2975.1	704352
948	898704	851971392	30.7896	9.8236	2.97681	1.05485	2978.2	705840
949	900601	854670349	30.8058	9.8270	2.97727	1.05374	2981.4	707330

FUNCTIONS OF NUMBERS

No.	Square	Cube	Square Root	Cube Root	Logarithm	1000 × Reciprocal	No. = Diameter	
							Circum.	Area
950	902500	857375000	30.8221	9.8305	2.97772	1.05263	2984.5	708822
951	904401	860085351	30.8383	9.8339	2.97818	1.05152	2987.7	710315
952	906304	862801408	30.8545	9.8374	2.97864	1.05042	2990.8	711809
953	908209	865523177	30.8707	9.8408	2.97909	1.04932	2993.9	713306
954	910116	868250664	30.8869	9.8443	2.97955	1.04822	2997.1	714803
955	912025	870983875	30.9031	9.8477	2.98000	1.04712	3000.2	716303
956	913936	873722816	30.9192	9.8511	2.98046	1.04603	3003.4	717804
957	915849	876467493	30.9354	9.8546	2.98091	1.04493	3006.5	719306
958	917764	879217912	30.9516	9.8580	2.98137	1.04384	3009.6	720810
959	919681	881974079	30.9677	9.8614	2.98182	1.04275	3012.8	722316
960	921600	884736000	30.9839	9.8648	2.98227	1.04167	3015.9	723823
961	923521	887503681	31.0000	9.8683	2.98272	1.04058	3019.1	725332
962	925444	890277128	31.0161	9.8717	2.98318	1.03950	3022.2	726842
963	927369	893056347	31.0322	9.8751	2.98363	1.03842	3025.4	728354
964	929296	895841344	31.0483	9.8785	2.98408	1.03734	3028.5	729867
965	931225	898632125	31.0644	9.8819	2.98453	1.03627	3031.6	731382
966	933156	901428696	31.0805	9.8854	2.98498	1.03520	3034.8	732899
967	935089	904231063	31.0966	9.8888	2.98543	1.03413	3037.9	734417
968	937024	907039232	31.1127	9.8922	2.98588	1.03306	3041.1	735937
969	938961	909853209	31.1288	9.8956	2.98632	1.03199	3044.2	737458
970	940900	912673000	31.1448	9.8990	2.98677	1.03093	3047.3	738981
971	942841	915498611	31.1609	9.9024	2.98722	1.02987	3050.5	740506
972	944784	918330048	31.1769	9.9058	2.98767	1.02881	3053.6	742032
973	946729	921167317	31.1929	9.9092	2.98811	1.02775	3056.8	743559
974	948676	924010424	31.2090	9.9126	2.98856	1.02669	3059.9	745088
975	950625	926859375	31.2250	9.9160	2.98900	1.02564	3063.1	746619
976	952576	929714176	31.2410	9.9194	2.98945	1.02459	3066.2	748151
977	954529	932574833	31.2570	9.9227	2.98989	1.02354	3069.3	749685
978	956484	935441352	31.2730	9.9261	2.99034	1.02249	3072.5	751221
979	958441	938313739	31.2890	9.9295	2.99078	1.02145	3075.6	752758
980	960400	941192000	31.3050	9.9329	2.99123	1.02041	3078.8	754296
981	962361	944076141	31.3209	9.9363	2.99167	1.01937	3081.9	755837
982	964324	946966168	31.3369	9.9396	2.99211	1.01833	3085.0	757378
983	966289	949862087	31.3528	9.9430	2.99255	1.01729	3088.2	758922
984	968256	952763904	31.3688	9.9464	2.99300	1.01626	3091.3	760466
985	970225	955671625	31.3847	9.9497	2.99344	1.01523	3094.5	762013
986	972196	958585256	31.4006	9.9531	2.99388	1.01420	3097.6	763561
987	974169	961504803	31.4166	9.9565	2.99432	1.01317	3100.8	765111
988	976144	964430272	31.4325	9.9598	2.99476	1.01215	3103.9	766662
989	978121	967361669	31.4484	9.9632	2.99520	1.01112	3107.0	768214
990	980100	970299000	31.4643	9.9666	2.99564	1.01010	3110.2	769769
991	982081	973242271	31.4802	9.9699	2.99607	1.00908	3113.3	771325
992	984064	976191488	31.4960	9.9733	2.99651	1.00806	3116.5	772882
993	986049	979146657	31.5119	9.9766	2.99695	1.00705	3119.6	774441
994	988036	982107784	31.5278	9.9800	2.99739	1.00604	3122.7	776002
995	990025	985074875	31.5436	9.9833	2.99782	1.00503	3125.9	777564
996	992016	988047936	31.5595	9.9866	2.99826	1.00402	3129.0	779128
997	994009	991026973	31.5753	9.9900	2.99870	1.00301	3132.2	780693
998	996004	994011992	31.5911	9.9933	2.99913	1.00200	3135.3	782260
999	998001	997002999	31.6070	9.9967	2.99957	1.00100	3138.5	783828

PROPERTIES OF THE CIRCLE

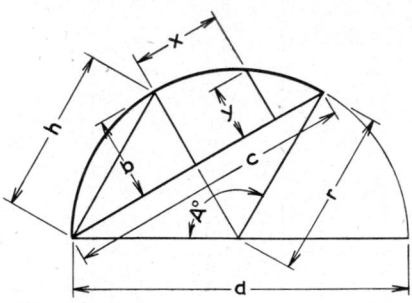

Circumference = 6.28318 r = 3.14159 d
Diameter = 0.31831 circumference
Area = 3.14159 r²

Arc
$$a = \frac{\pi r\,A°}{180°} = 0.017453\ r\,A° = \frac{8\,h - c}{3}\ \text{(approximately)}$$

Angle
$$A° = \frac{180°\,a}{\pi r} = 57.29578\,\frac{a}{r}$$

Radius
$$r = \frac{4\,b^2 + c^2}{8\,b}$$

Diameter
$$d = \frac{h^2}{b} = \frac{c^2}{4\,b} + b$$

Chord
$$c = 2\,\sqrt{2\,br - b^2} = 2\,r\,\sin\frac{A}{2}$$
$$= 2\,\sqrt{h^2 - b^2} = 2\,\sqrt{(d - b) \times b}$$

Chord of ½ the arc $\quad h = \sqrt{d \times b} = \dfrac{3\,a + c}{8}$ (approximately)

Rise
$$b = r - \tfrac{1}{2}\,\sqrt{4\,r^2 - c^2} = \frac{c}{2}\,\tan\frac{A}{4}$$
$$= 2\,r\,\sin^2\frac{A}{4} = r + y - \sqrt{r^2 - x^2} = \frac{h^2}{d}$$
$$y = b - r + \sqrt{r^2 - x^2}$$
$$x = \sqrt{r^2 - (r + y - b)^2}$$

Diameter of circle of equal periphery as square = 1.27324 side of square
Side of square of equal periphery as circle = 0.78540 diameter of circle
Diameter of circle circumscribed about square = 1.41421 side of square
Side of square inscribed in circle = 0.70711 diameter of circle
Side of square of equal area = 0.8862 diameter of circle

PROPERTIES OF THE CIRCLE

CIRCULAR SECTOR

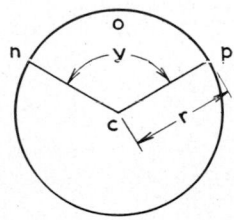

r — radius of circle   y = angle ncp in degrees

Area of Sector ncpo = ½ (length of arc nop × r)

$$= \text{Area of Circle} \times \frac{y}{360}$$

$$= 0.0087266 \times r^2 \times y$$

CIRCULAR SEGMENT

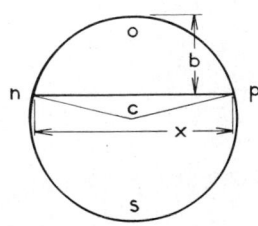

r = radius of circle   x = chord   b = rise

Area of Segment nop = Area of Sector ncpo — Area of triangle ncp

$$= \frac{(\text{Length of arc nop} \times r) - x\,(r - b)}{2}$$

Area of Segment nsp = Area of Circle — Area of Segment nop

VALUES FOR FUNCTIONS OF π

$\pi = 3.14159265359,$ $\quad \log = 0.4971499$ $\qquad \dfrac{1}{\pi^2} = 0.1013212,$ $\quad \log = \overline{1}.0057003$

$\pi^2 = 9.8696044,$ $\qquad \log = 0.9942997$ $\qquad \dfrac{1}{\pi^3} = 0.0322515,$ $\quad \log = \overline{2}.5085500$

$\pi^3 = 31.0062767,$ $\qquad \log = 1.4914496$ $\qquad \sqrt{\dfrac{1}{\pi}} = 0.5641896,$ $\quad \log = \overline{1}.7514251$

$\sqrt{\pi} = 1.7724539,$ $\qquad \log = 0.2485749$ $\qquad \dfrac{\pi}{180} = 0.0174533,$ $\quad \log = \overline{2}.2418774$

$\dfrac{1}{\pi} = 0.3183099,$ $\qquad \log = \overline{1}.5028501$ $\qquad \dfrac{180}{\pi} = 57.2957795,$ $\quad \log = 1.7581226$

LENGTH OF CIRCULAR ARCS
FOR UNIT RADIUS

DEGREES

1°	.017 4533	46°	.802 8515	91°	1.588 2496	136°	2.373 6478
2	.034 9066	47	.820 3047	92	1.605 7029	137	2.391 1011
3	.052 3599	48	.837 7580	93	1.623 1562	138	2.408 5544
4	.069 8132	49	.855 2113	94	1.640 6095	139	2.426 0077
5	.087 2665	50	.872 6646	95	1.658 0628	140	2.443 4610
6	.104 7198	51	.890 1179	96	1.675 5161	141	2.460 9142
7	.122 1730	52	.907 5712	97	1.692 9694	142	2.478 3675
8	.139 6263	53	.925 0245	98	1.710 4227	143	2.495 8208
9	157 0796	54	.942 4778	99	1.727 8760	144	2.513 2741
10	.174 5329	55	.959 9311	100	1.745 3293	145	2.530 7274
11	.191 9862	56	.977 3844	101	1.762 7825	146	2.548 1807
12	.209 4395	57	.994 8377	102	1.780 2358	147	2.565 6340
13	.226 8928	58	1.012 2910	103	1.797 6891	148	2.583 0873
14	.244 3461	59	1.029 7443	104	1.815 1424	149	2.600 5406
15	.261 7994	60	1.047 1976	105	1.832 5957	150	2.617 9939
16	.279 2527	61	1.064 6508	106	1.850 0490	151	2.635 4472
17	.296 7060	62	1.082 1041	107	1.867 5023	152	2.652 9005
18	.314 1593	63	1.099 5574	108	1.884 9556	153	2.670 3538
19	.331 6126	64	1.117 0107	109	1.902 4089	154	2.687 8070
20	.349 0659	65	1.134 4640	110	1.919 8622	155	2.705 2603
21	.366 5191	66	1.151 9173	111	1.937 3155	156	2.722 7136
22	.383 9724	67	1.169 3706	112	1.954 7688	157	2.740 1669
23	.401 4257	68	1.186 8239	113	1.972 2221	158	2.757 6202
24	.418 8790	69	1.204 2772	114	1.989 6753	159	2.775 0735
25	.436 3323	70	1.221 7305	115	2.007 1286	160	2.792 5268
26	.453 7856	71	1.239 1838	116	2.024 5819	161	2.809 9801
27	.471 2389	72	1.256 6371	117	2.042 0352	162	2.827 4334
28	.488 6922	73	1.274 0904	118	2.059 4885	163	2.844 8867
29	.506 1455	74	1.291 5436	119	2.076 9418	164	2.862 3400
30	.523 5988	75	1.308 9969	120	2.094 3951	165	2.879 7933
31	.541 0521	76	1.326 4502	121	2.111 8484	166	2.897 2466
32	.558 5054	77	1.343 9035	122	2.129 3017	167	2.914 6999
33	.575 9587	78	1.361 3568	123	2.146 7550	168	2.932 1531
34	.593 4119	79	1.378 8101	124	2.164 2083	169	2.949 6064
35	.610 8652	80	1.396 2634	125	2.181 6616	170	2.967 0597
36	.628 3185	81	1.413 7167	126	2.199 1149	171	2.984 5130
37	.645 7718	82	1.431 1700	127	2.216 5682	172	3.001 9663
38	.663 2251	83	1.448 6233	128	2.234 0214	173	3.019 4196
39	.680 6784	84	1.466 0766	129	2.251 4747	174	3.036 8729
40	.698 1317	85	1.483 5299	130	2.268 9280	175	3.054 3262
41	.715 5850	86	1.500 9832	131	2.286 3813	176	3.071 7795
42	.733 0383	87	1.518 4364	132	2.303 8346	177	3.089 2328
43	.750 4916	88	1.535 8897	133	2.321 2879	178	3.106 6861
44	.767 9449	89	1.553 3430	134	2.338 7412	179	3.124 1394
45	.785 3982	90	1.570 7963	135	2.356 1945	180	3.141 5927

LENGTH OF CIRCULAR ARCS
FOR UNIT RADIUS
(CONTINUED)

MINUTES				SECONDS			
1'	.000 2909	31'	.009 0175	1"	.000 0048	31"	.000 1503
2	.000 5818	32	.009 3084	2	.000 0097	32	.000 1551
3	.000 8727	33	.009 5993	3	.000 0145	33	.000 1600
4	.001 1636	34	.009 8902	4	.000 0194	34	.000 1648
5	.001 4544	35	.010 1811	5	.000 0242	35	.000 1697
6	.001 7453	36	.010 4720	6	000 0291	36	.000 1745
7	.002 0362	37	.010 7629	7	.000 0339	37	.000 1794
8	.002 3271	38	.011 0538	8	.000 0388	38	.000 1842
9	.002 6180	39	.011 3446	9	.000 0436	39	.000 1891
10	.002 9089	40	.011 6355	10	.000 0485	40	.000 1939
11	.003 1998	41	.011 9264	11	.000 0533	41	.000 1988
12	.003 4907	42	.012 2173	12	.000 0582	42	.000 2036
13	.003 7815	43	.012 5082	13	.000 0630	43	.000 2085
14	.004 0724	44	.012 7991	14	.000 0679	44	.000 2133
15	.004 3633	45	.013 0900	15	.000 0727	45	.000 2182
16	.004 6542	46	.013 3809	16	.000 0776	46	.000 2230
17	.004 9451	47	.013 6717	17	.000 0824	47	.000 2279
18	.005 2360	48	.013 9626	18	.000 0873	48	.000 2327
19	.005 5269	49	.014 2535	19	.000 0921	49	.000 2376
20	.005 8178	50	.014 5444	20	.000 0970	50	.000 2424
21	.006 1087	51	.014 8353	21	.000 1018	51	.000 2473
22	.006 3995	52	.015 1262	22	.000 1067	52	.000 2521
23	.006 6904	53	.015 4171	23	.000 1115	53	.000 2570
24	.006 9813	54	.015 7080	24	.000 1164	54	.000 2618
25	.007 2722	55	.015 9989	25	.000 1212	55	.000 2666
26	.007 5631	56	.016 2897	26	.000 1261	56	.000 2715
27	.007 8540	57	.016 5806	27	.000 1309	57	.000 2763
28	.008 1449	58	.016 8715	28	.000 1357	58	.000 2812
29	.008 4358	59	.017 1624	29	.000 1406	59	.000 2860
30	.008 7266	60	.017 4533	30	.000 1454	60	.000 2909

By the use of the tables on these two pages, the length of any arc may be found if the length of the radius and the angle of the segment are known.

Example:— Required the length of arc of segment of 32° 15' 27'' with radius of 24 feet 3 inches.

From table: Length of arc (Radius 1) for 32° = .5585054
15' = .0043633
27'' = .0001309
.5629996

.5629996 × 24.25 (length of radius) = 13.65 feet.

AREAS AND VOLUMES
PLANE SURFACES

Ellipse

Area = $\frac{1}{4}\pi AB$, A and B being length and breadth (major and minor axes) respectively.

Triangle

Area = $\frac{1}{2}$ base $\times$ altitude
= $\sqrt{S\,(S-A)\,(S-B)\,(S-C)}$, S = $\frac{1}{2}$ sum of 3 sides, A, B, and C.

Trapezium

Area = sum of area of its 2 triangles.

Trapezoid

Area = $\frac{1}{2}$ sum of parallel sides $\times$ perpendicular height.

Parallelogram

Area = base $\times$ perpendicular height.

Regular Polygon

Area = $\frac{1}{2}$ sum of sides $\times$ inside radius.
Distance across corners of hexagon = 1.155 $\times$ distance across flats.

LATERAL SURFACES (S) AND VOLUMES (V) OF VARIOUS GEOMETRIC SOLIDS

Parallelopiped

S = perimeter, P, perpendicular to sides $\times$ lateral length, L = PL
V = area of base, B, $\times$ perpendicular height, H = BH
V = area of section, A, perpendicular to sides $\times$ lateral length, L = AL

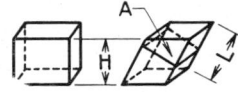

Prism, Right or Oblique, Regular or Irregular

S = perimeter, P, perpendicular to sides $\times$ lateral length, L = PL
V = area of base, B, $\times$ perpendicular height, H = BH
V = area of section, A, perpendicular to sides $\times$ lateral length, L = AL

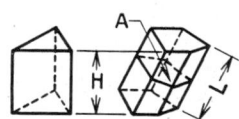

Cylinder, Right or Oblique, Circular or Elliptical

S = perimeter of base, P, $\times$ perpendicular height, H = PH
S = perimeter, P_1, perpendicular to sides $\times$ lateral length, L = P_1L
V = area of base, B, $\times$ perpendicular height, H = BH
V = area of section, A, perpendicular to sides $\times$ lateral length, L = AL

Frustum of Any Prism or Cylinder

V = area of base, B, $\times$ perpendicular distance, H, from base to center of gravity of opposite face = BH
For cylinder: V = $\frac{1}{2}$ A $(L_1 + L_2)$

("KENT" AND "CARNEGIE")

AREAS AND VOLUMES
(CONTINUED)

LATERAL SURFACES (S) AND VOLUMES (V) OF VARIOUS GEOMETRIC SOLIDS
(CONTINUED)

Pyramid or Cone, Right and Regular

S = perimeter of base, P, $\times$ ½ slant height,
   L = ½ PL
V = area of base, B, $\times$ ⅓ perpendicular height,
   H = ⅓ BH

Pyramid or Cone, Right or Oblique, Regular or Irregular

V = area of base, B $\times$ ⅓ perpendicular height,
   H = ⅓ BH
V = ⅓ volume of prism or cylinder of same base and
   perpendicular height

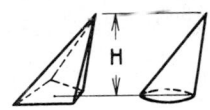

Frustum of Pyramid or Cone, Right and Regular, Parallel Ends

S = (sum of perimeter of base, P, and top, p) $\times$ ½
   slant height, L = ½ L (P + p)
V = (sum of areas of base, B, and top, b, plus square
   root of their products) $\times$ ⅓ perpendicular
   height, H = ⅓ H (B + b + $\sqrt{B\,b}$)

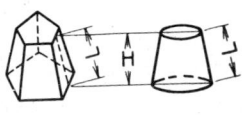

Frustum of Any Pyramid or Cone, Parallel Ends

V = (sum of areas of base, B, and top, b, plus square
   root of their products) $\times$ ⅓ perpendicular
   height, H = ⅓ H (B + b + $\sqrt{B\,b}$)

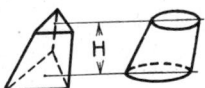

Wedge. Parallelogram Face

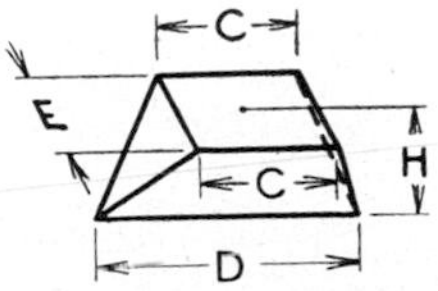

V = ⅙ (sum of three edges, C D C, $\times$ perpendicular
   height, H, $\times$ perpendicular width, E) =
   ⅙ E H (2 C + D)

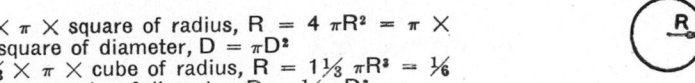

Sphere

S = 4 $\times$ π $\times$ square of radius, R = 4 πR^2 = π $\times$
   square of diameter, D = πD^2
V = 1⅓ $\times$ π $\times$ cube of radius, R = 1⅓ πR^3 = ⅙
   $\times$ π $\times$ cube of diameter, D = ⅙ πD^3

TRIGONOMETRIC FORMULAS

TRIGONOMETRIC FUNCTIONS

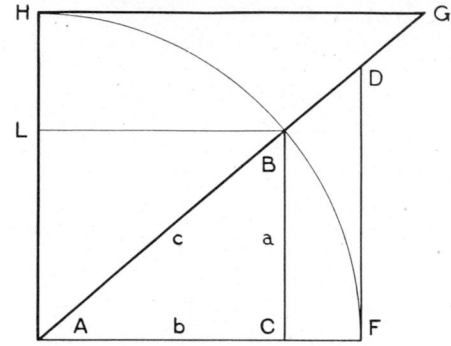

Radius AF   = 1

$$= \sin^2 A = \cos^2 A = \sin A \operatorname{cosec} A$$

$$= \cos A \sec A = \tan A \cot A$$

Sine A $= \dfrac{\cos A}{\cot A} = \dfrac{1}{\operatorname{cosec} A} = \cos A \tan A = \sqrt{1 - \cos^2 A} = BC$

Cosine A $= \dfrac{\sin A}{\tan A} = \dfrac{1}{\sec A} = \sin A \cot A = \sqrt{1 - \sin^2 A} = AC$

Tangent A $= \dfrac{\sin A}{\cos A} = \dfrac{1}{\cot A} = \sin A \sec A \qquad\qquad = FD$

Cotangent A $= \dfrac{\cos A}{\sin A} = \dfrac{1}{\tan A} = \cos A \operatorname{cosec} A \qquad\quad = HG$

Secant A $= \dfrac{\tan A}{\sin A} = \dfrac{1}{\cos A} \qquad\qquad\qquad\qquad = AD$

Cosecant A $= \dfrac{\cot A}{\cos A} = \dfrac{1}{\sin A} \qquad\qquad\qquad\qquad = AG$

TRIGONOMETRIC FORMULAS

RIGHT-ANGLED TRIANGLES

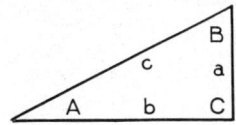

$$a^2 = c^2 - b^2$$
$$b^2 = c^2 - a^2$$
$$c^2 = a^2 + b^2$$

Known	Required					
	A	B	a	b	c	Area
a, b	$\tan A = \dfrac{a}{b}$	$\tan B = \dfrac{b}{a}$			$\sqrt{a^2 + b^2}$	$\dfrac{ab}{2}$
a, c	$\sin A = \dfrac{a}{c}$	$\cos B = \dfrac{a}{c}$		$\sqrt{c^2 - a^2}$		$\dfrac{a\sqrt{c^2 - a^2}}{2}$
A, a		$90° - A$		$a \cot A$	$\dfrac{a}{\sin A}$	$\dfrac{a^2 \cot A}{2}$
A, b		$90° - A$	$b \tan A$		$\dfrac{b}{\cos A}$	$\dfrac{b^2 \tan A}{2}$
A, c		$90° - A$	$c \sin A$	$c \cos A$		$\dfrac{c^2 \sin 2A}{4}$

OBLIQUE-ANGLED TRIANGLES

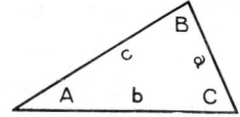

$$s = \frac{a + b + c}{2}$$

$$a^2 = b^2 + c^2 - 2bc \cos A$$
$$b^2 = a^2 + c^2 - 2ac \cos B$$
$$c^2 = a^2 + b^2 - 2ab \cos C$$

Known	Required		
	A	B	C
a, b, c	$\cos \dfrac{1}{2} A = \sqrt{\dfrac{s(s - a)}{bc}}$	$\cos \dfrac{1}{2} B = \sqrt{\dfrac{s(s - b)}{ac}}$	$\cos \dfrac{1}{2} C = \sqrt{\dfrac{s(s - c)}{ab}}$
a, A, B			$180° - (A + B)$
a, b, A		$\sin B = \dfrac{b \sin A}{a}$	
a, b, C	$\tan A = \dfrac{a \sin C}{b - a \cos C}$		

Known	Required		
	b	c	Area
a, b, c			$\sqrt{s(s - a)(s - b)(s - c)}$
a, A, B	$\dfrac{a \sin B}{\sin A}$	$\dfrac{a \sin C}{\sin A}$	
a, b, A		$\dfrac{b \sin C}{\sin B}$	
a, b, C		$\sqrt{a^2 + b^2 - 2ab \cos C}$	$\dfrac{ab \sin C}{2}$

NATURAL TRIGONOMETRIC FUNCTIONS

Deg.	Sin	Cos	Tan	Ctn	Sec	Csc	
0	0.0000	1.0000	0.0000	. . . . . .	1.0000	. . . . . .	90
1	0.0175	0.9998	0.0175	57.290	1.0002	57.299	89
2	0.0349	0.9994	0.0349	28.636	1.0006	28.654	88
3	0.0523	0.9986	0.0524	19.081	1.0014	19.107	87
4	0.0698	0.9976	0.0699	14.301	1.0024	14.336	86
5	0.0872	0.9962	0.0875	11.430	1.0038	11.474	85
6	0.1045	0.9945	0.1051	9.5144	1.0055	9.5668	84
7	0.1219	0.9925	0.1228	8.1443	1.0075	8.2055	83
8	0.1392	0.9903	0.1405	7.1154	1.0098	7.1853	82
9	0.1564	0.9877	0.1584	6.3138	1.0125	6.3925	81
10	0.1736	0.9848	0.1763	6.6713	1.0154	5.7588	80
11	0.1908	0.9816	0.1944	5.1446	1.0187	5.2408	79
12	0.2079	0.9781	0.2126	4.7046	1.0223	4.8097	78
13	0.2250	0.9744	0.2309	4.3315	1.0263	4.4454	77
14	0.2419	0.9703	0 2493	4.0108	1.0306	4.1336	76
15	0.2588	0.9659	0.2679	3.7321	1.0353	3.8637	75
16	0.2756	0.9613	0.2867	3.4874	1.0403	3.6280	74
17	0.2924	0.9563	0.3057	3.2709	1.0457	3.4203	73
18	0.3090	0.9511	0.3249	3.0777	1.0515	3.2361	72
19	0.3256	0.9455	0.3443	2.9042	1.0576	3.0716	71
20	0.3420	0.9397	0.3640	2.7475	1.0642	2.9238	70
21	0.3584	0.9336	0.3839	2.6051	1.0711	2.7904	69
22	0.3746	0.9272	0.4040	2.4751	1.0785	2.6695	68
23	0.3907	0.9205	0.4245	2.3559	1.0864	2.5593	67
24	0.4067	0.9135	0.4452	2.2460	1.0946	2.4586	66
25	0.4226	0.9063	0.4663	2.1445	1.1034	2.3662	65
26	0.4384	0.8988	0.4877	2.0503	1.1126	2.2812	64
27	0.4540	0.8910	0.5095	1.9626	1.1223	2.2027	63
28	0.4695	0.8829	0.5317	1.8807	1.1326	2.1301	62
29	0.4848	0.8746	0.5543	1.8040	1.1434	2.0627	61
30	0.5000	0.8660	0.5774	1.7321	1.1547	2.0000	60
31	0.5150	0.8572	0.6009	1.6643	1.1666	1.9416	59
32	0.5299	0.8480	0.6249	1.6003	1.1792	1.8871	58
33	0.5446	0.8387	0.6494	1.5399	1.1924	1.8361	57
34	0.5592	0.8290	0.6745	1.4826	1.2062	1.7883	56
35	0.5736	0.8192	0.7002	1.4281	1.2208	1.7434	55
36	0.5878	0.8090	0.7265	1.3764	1.2361	1.7013	54
37	0.6018	0.7986	0.7536	1.3270	1.2521	1.6616	53
38	0.6157	0.7880	0.7813	1.2799	1.2690	1.6243	52
39	0.6293	0.7771	0.8098	1.2349	1.2868	1.5890	51
40	0.6428	0.7660	0.8391	1.1918	1.3054	1.5557	50
41	0.6561	0.7547	0.8693	1.1504	1.3250	1.5243	49
42	0.6691	0.7431	0.9004	1.1106	1.3456	1.4945	48
43	0.6820	0.7314	0.9325	1.0724	1.3673	1.4663	47
44	0.6947	0.7193	0.9657	1.0355	1.3902	1.4396	46
45	0.7071	0.7071	1.0000	1.0000	1.4142	1.4142	45
	Cos	Sin	Ctn	Tan	Csc	Sec	Deg.

BEVELS

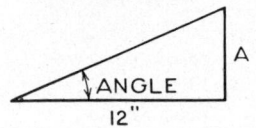

Rise A, Inches	RISE A — INCHES											
	0		1		2		3		4		5	
	Angle		Angle		Angle		Angle		Angle		Angle	
	Deg.	Min.	Deg.	Min.	Deg.	Min.	Deg.	Min.	Deg.	Min.	Deg.	Min.
0	....	....	4	46	9	28	14	02	18	26	22	37
1/16	0	18	5	04	9	45	14	19	18	42	22	52
1/8	0	36	5	21	10	03	14	36	18	58	23	08
3/16	0	54	5	39	10	20	14	53	19	14	23	23
1/4	1	12	5	57	10	37	15˚	09	19	30	23	38
5/16	1	30	6	15	10	54	15	26	19	46	23	53
3/8	1	47	6	32	11	12	15	43	20	02	24	08
7/16	2	05	6	50	11	29	15	59	20	18	24	23
1/2	2	23	7	08	11	46	16	16	20	33	24	37
9/16	2	41	7	25	12	03	16	32	20	49	24	52
5/8	2	59	7	43	12	20	16	49	21	05	25	07
11/16	3	17	8	00	12	37	17	05	21	20	25	22
3/4	3	35	8	18	12	54	17	21	21	36	25	36
13/16	3	52	8	35	13	11	17	38	21	51	25	51
7/8	4	10	8	53	13	28	17	54	22	07	26	05
15/16	4	28	9	10	13	45	18	10	22	22	26	20

Rise A, Inches	RISE A — INCHES											
	6		7		8		9		10		11	
	Angle		Angle		Angle		Angle		Angle		Angle	
	Deg.	Min.	Deg.	Min.	Deg.	Min.	Deg.	Min.	Deg.	Min.	Deg.	Min.
0	26	34	30	15	33	41	36	52	39	48	42	31
1/16	26	48	30	29	33	54	37	04	39	59	42	40
1/8	27	02	30	42	34	06	37	15	40	09	42	50
3/16	27	17	30	55	34	18	37	26	40	20	43	00
1/4	27	31	31	08	34	31	37	38	40	30	43	09
5/16	27	45	31	21	34	43	37	49	40	41	43	19
3/8	27	59	31	34	34	55	38	00	40	51	43	28
7/16	28	13	31	47	35	07	38	11	41	01	43	38
1/2	28	27	32	00	35	19	38	22	41	11	43	47
9/16	28	40	32	13	35	31	38	33	41	21	43	56
5/8	28	54	32	26	35	42	38	44	41	31	44	05
11/16	29	08	32	39	35	54	38	55	41	41	44	15
3/4	29	21	32	51	36	06	39	06	41	51	44	24
13/16	29	35	33	04	36	18	39	16	42	01	44	33
7/8	29	49	33	17	36	29	39	27	42	11	44	42
15/16	30	02	33	29	36	41	39	38	42	21	44	51

(SMOLEY)

BEAM FORMULAS

$W = W_1 + W_2 =$ **Total load,** in pounds, uniformly distributed, including weight of beam.
$W_1 =$ Total **superimposed** or **live load,** in pounds, uniformly distributed.
$W_2 =$ Total **weight** of beam or **dead load,** in pounds, uniformly distributed.
$M =$ Maximum bending moment, inch-pounds.
$R =$ Maximum shear at point or points of support, in pounds.
$P =$ **Load** in pounds, concentrated at any points.
$L =$ **Length** of span, in inches.
$I =$ **Moment of inertia,** in inches.[4]
$E =$ **Modulus of elasticity,** in pounds per square inch (steel $= 29,000,000$).
$D =$ Maximum deflection of beam in inches.

(1) Beam Supported at Both Ends and Uniformly Loaded.

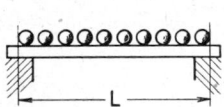

$$M = \frac{WL}{8}$$

$$R = \frac{W}{2}$$

$$D = \frac{5\,WL^3}{384\,EI}$$

(2) Beam Supported at Both Ends with Load Concentrated at the Middle.

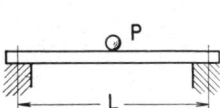

$$M = \frac{PL}{4} + \frac{W_2L}{8}$$

$$R = \frac{P + W_2}{2}$$

$$D = \frac{PL^3}{48\,EI} + \frac{5\,W_2L^3}{384\,EI}$$

(3) Beam Supported at Both Ends with Two Symmetrical Loads.

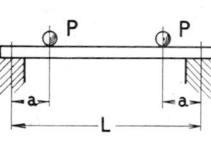

$$M = Pa + \frac{W_2L}{8}$$

$$R = \frac{2P + W_2}{2}$$

$$D = \frac{Pa(3L^2 - 4a^2)}{24\,EI} + \frac{5\,W_2L^3}{384\,EI}$$

BEAM FORMULAS
(CONTINUED)

(FOR NOTATIONS, SEE OPPOSITE PAGE)

(4) Beam Fixed at One End, Unsupported at the Other, and Uniformly Loaded.

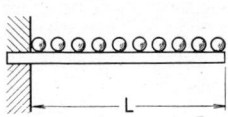

$$M = \frac{WL}{2}$$

$$R = W$$

$$D = \frac{WL^3}{8\,EI}$$

(5) Beam Fixed at One End, Unsupported at the Other, with Load Concentrated at the Free End.

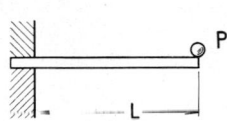

$$M = PL + \frac{W}{2}$$

$$R = P + W_2$$

$$D = \frac{PL^3}{3\,EI} + \frac{W_2 L^3}{8\,EI}$$

(6) Beam Supported at Both Ends with Load Concentrated at Any Point.

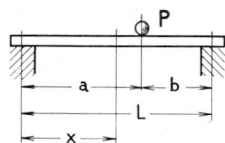

$$M = \frac{a(2\,Pb + W_2 L - W_2 a)}{2\,L}$$

Max. shear at nearest support

$$R = \frac{Pa}{L} + \frac{W_2}{2}$$

$$D = \frac{1}{3\,EIL}\left[\frac{2\,aL - a^2}{3}\right]^{\frac{3}{2}}\left[Pb + \frac{W_2}{8}\left(\sqrt{\frac{2\,aL - a^2}{3}} + \frac{3\,L^3}{2\,aL - a^2} - 2\,L\right)\right]$$

Distance "x", from left support to point of maximum deflection for superimposed load

$$= \sqrt{\frac{2\,aL - a^2}{3}}$$

SECTION ELEMENTS

A = area. I = moment of inertia about axis shown. c = distance from axis to remotest point of the section. I/c = section modulus. r = radius of gyration.

Rectangle
Axis through center.

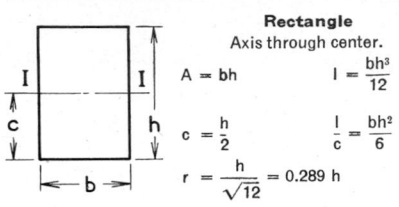

$$A = bh \qquad I = \frac{bh^3}{12}$$

$$c = \frac{h}{2} \qquad \frac{I}{c} = \frac{bh^2}{6}$$

$$r = \frac{h}{\sqrt{12}} = 0.289\,h$$

Triangle
Axis through center of gravity.

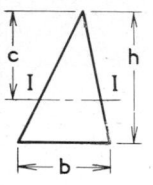

$$A = \frac{bh}{2} \qquad I = \frac{bh^3}{36}$$

$$c = \tfrac{2}{3}\,h \qquad \frac{I}{c} = \frac{bh^2}{24}$$

$$r = \frac{h}{\sqrt{18}} = 0.236\,h$$

Hollow Rectangle
Axis through center.

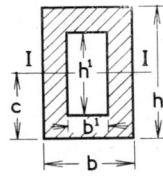

$$A = bh - b_1 h_1$$

$$I = \frac{bh^3 - b_1 h_1^3}{12} \qquad c = \frac{h}{2}$$

$$\frac{I}{c} = \frac{bh^3 - b_1 h_1^3}{6h}$$

$$r = \sqrt{\frac{bh^3 - b_1 h_1^3}{12(bh - b_1 h_1)}}$$

Trapezoid
Axis through center of gravity.

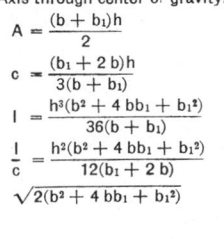

$$A = \frac{(b + b_1)h}{2}$$

$$c = \frac{(b_1 + 2b)h}{3(b + b_1)}$$

$$I = \frac{h^3(b^2 + 4bb_1 + b_1^2)}{36(b + b_1)}$$

$$\frac{I}{c} = \frac{h^2(b^2 + 4bb_1 + b_1^2)}{12(b_1 + 2b)}$$

$$\frac{\sqrt{2(b^2 + 4bb_1 + b_1^2)}}{6(b + b_1)}\,h$$

$$r = \frac{h}{6(b + b_1)}$$

Regular Polygon
Axis through center normal to side. n = even number of sides.
$$A = nR_1^2 \tan \phi$$

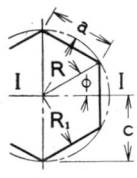

$$c = R = \frac{a}{2 \sin \phi}$$

$$I = \frac{A(6R^2 - a^2)}{24}$$

$$\frac{I}{c} = \frac{A(6R^2 - a^2)}{24R}$$

$$r = \sqrt{\frac{6R^2 - a^2}{24}}$$

Circle
Axis through center.

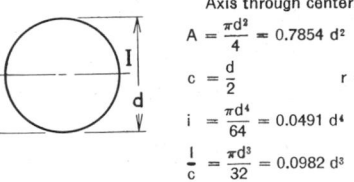

$$A = \frac{\pi d^2}{4} = 0.7854\,d^2$$

$$c = \frac{d}{2} \qquad r = \frac{d}{4}$$

$$i = \frac{\pi d^4}{64} = 0.0491\,d^4$$

$$\frac{I}{c} = \frac{\pi d^3}{32} = 0.0982\,d^3$$

Regular Polygon
Axis through center parallel to one side.
n = even number of sides.
$$A = nR_1^2 \tan \phi$$

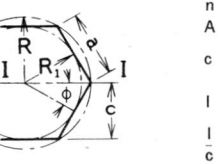

$$c = R_1 = \frac{a}{2 \tan \phi}$$

$$I = \frac{A(12R_1^2 + a^2)}{48}$$

$$\frac{I}{c} = \frac{A(12R_1^2 + a^2)}{48R_1}$$

$$r = \sqrt{\frac{12R_1^2 + a^2}{48}}$$

Hollow Circle
Axis through center.

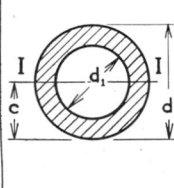

$$A = \frac{\pi(d^2 - d_1^2)}{4}$$

$$= 0.7854(d^2 - d_1^2)$$

$$c = \frac{d}{2}$$

$$I = \frac{\pi(d^4 - d_1^4)}{64}$$

$$r = \frac{\sqrt{d^2 + d_1^2}}{4}$$

$$\frac{I}{c} = \frac{\pi(d^4 - d_1^4)}{32\,d}$$

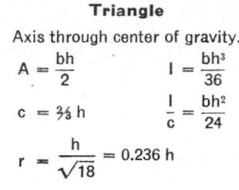

ENGINEERING CONSTANTS

Existing engineering handbooks are remarkably complete in the matter of engineering constants; this table does not pretend to compete with them in their natural field. It frequently happens, however, that the reader of technical journals and books runs across a constant, the meaning of which is not clear to him. Often there is no clue to aid him in locating it in the engineering handbooks. On this page and the following two pages a large number of the more important constants are arranged numerically (regardless of the position of the decimal point) so that a given constant may be located almost instantly. An asterisk (*) means that the constant is exact as far as given, being generally either a mathematical constant or one fixed by definition. Where the first constant given is followed by another in parenthesis, the first is the round number ordinarily used and the second the more exact value.

(Note list of special abbreviations on page 293)

0* deg. C. = freezing point of water

1 = atomic wgt. hydrogen

100* deg. C. = boiling point of water at atm. press.

10.764* sq. ft. = 1 sq. meter

0.1134 hp. = available water power from 1 cu. ft.-sec. falling 1 ft.

1.134 ft. water at 62 deg. F. = 1 in. Hg at 62 deg. F.

1,150.4 B. t. u. = Total heat sat. steam at atm. press.

11.52 lb. = theoret. air to burn 1 lb. carbon

12 = atomic wgt. carbon (C)

12.387 cu. ft. = vol. 1 lb. air at 32 deg. F. and 14.7 lb. per sq. in.

12.52 lb. = wgt. theoret. combustion products from 1 lb. C.

1,273,239* circular mils = 1 sq. in.

13.144 cu. ft. = vol. 1 lb. air at 62 deg. F. and 14.7 lb. per sq. in.

1.3410 hp. = 1 kw.

14 = atomic wgt. nitrogen (N)

1.406 = γ = ratio of C_p to C_v for air

1.4142* = square root of 2

14.223* lb. per sq. in. = 1 kg. per sq. cm. = 1 "metric atmosphere"

144* sq. in. = 1 sq. ft.

144 (143.15) B. t. u. = latent heat of fusion of ice.

14,600 B. t. u. per lb. = Cal. val. of carbon (C)

14.7 (14.696*) lb. per sq. in. = atm. press.

16* ounces = 1 lb.

16 = atomic wgt. oxygen (O)

0.1689 = C_v for air

0.017138* grams per liter = 1 grain per gal.

17.138* ppm. = 1 grain per gal.

1,728* cu. in. = 1 cu. ft.

1.7321* = square root of 3

1.8* B. t. u. per lb. = 1 kg. calorie per kg.

1.8* Fahrenheit degrees = 1 Centigrade degree

18 = mol. wgt. water (H_2O)

2,000* lb. = 1 short ton

2.0355 in. Hg at 32 deg. F. = 1 lb. per sq. in.

2.0416 in. Hg at 62 deg. F. = 1 lb. per sq. in.

2,116.3* lb. per sq. ft. = atm. press.

212* deg. F. = boiling point water at atm. press.

2.2046 lb.* = 1 kg.

223.8* × sq. root adiabatic heat drop = theoret. vel., ft. per sec., of steam expanding through nozzle.

2,240* lb. = long ton

2.3026* × $\log_{10} a$ = $\log_e a$

2.309 ft. water at 62 deg. F. = 1 lb. per sq. in.

231* cu. in. = 1 gal.

0.2375 = C_p for air

(Continued on next page)

ENGINEERING CONSTANTS

(Continued from preceding page)

2.54* cm. = 1 in.

2,545 (2,547) B. t. u. per hr. = 1 hp.

2.666 lb. = wgt. oxygen required to burn 1 lb. carbon

27* cu. ft. = 1 cubic yard

−270 deg. C. = absolute zero

2.7183* = e = base hyperbolic logs.

27.71 in. water at 62 deg. F. = 1 lb. per sq. in.

277.274 cu. in. = 1 British gal.

28 = mol. wgt. nitrogen gas (N_2)

28 = mol. wgt. carbon monoxide (CO)

28.8 = equivalent mol. wgt. of air

288,000* B. t. u. per 24 hr. = 1 ton of refrigeration

29.921* in. Hg at 32 deg. F. = atm. press.

.3* ft. = 1 yard

30 in. Hg at 62 deg. = atm. press. (very closely)

3.1416* = π (Greek letter "pi") = ratio circumference of circle to diameter = ratio area of circle to square of radius

32* deg. F. = freezing point of water = 0 deg. C.

32 = atomic wgt. sulphur (S)

32 = mol. wgt. oxygen gas (O_2)

32.5* gal. = 1 barrel

3.2808* ft. = 1 meter

33,000* ft.-lb. per min. = 1 hp.

33.947 ft. water at 62 deg. F. = atm. press.

3,415 B. t. u. = 1 kw.-hr.

3.45* lb. steam "f. & a. 212" per sq. ft. of heating surface per hr. = rated boiler evaporation.

34.56 lb. = wgt. air to burn 1 lb. hydrogen (H)

35.314* cu. ft. = 1 cu. meter

3.785* liters = 1 gal.

39.37* in. = 1 meter = 100 cm.

3.9683* B. t. u. = 1 kg. calorie

4,000 B. t. u. (4,050) = cal. val. of sulphur (S)

4.32 lb. = wgt. air req. to burn 1 lb. sulphur (S)

0.433 lb. per sq. in. = 1 ft. of water at 62 deg. F.

44 = mol. wgt. carbon dioxide (CO_2)

0.45359* kg. = 1 lb.

−460 (459.6) deg. F. = absolute zero.

0.47 B. t. u. per pound per deg. F. = approx. specific heat of super-heated steam at atm. press.

0.491 lb. per sq. in. = 1 in. Hg at 62 deg. F.

5.196 lb. per sq. ft. = 1 in. water at 62 deg. F.

5,280* ft. = 1 mile

53.32 = R, a constant for air, in expansion equation: PV = MRT

550* ft.-lb. per sec. = 1 hp.

57.296* deg. = 1 radian (angle)

58.349* grains per gal. = 1 gram per liter

59.76 lb. = wgt. 1 cu. ft. water at 212 deg. F.

61.023* cu. in. = 1 liter

62,000 B. t. u. = cal. val. (higher) hydrogen (H)

0.62137* miles = 1 kilometer

0.062428* lb. per cu. ft. = 1 kg. per cu. meter

62.5 (62.355) lb. = wgt. 1 cu. ft. water at 62 deg. F.

7,000* grains = 1 lb.

0.0735 in. Hg at 62 deg. F. = 1 in. water at 62 deg. F.

746 (745.7) watts = 1 hp.

7.5 (7.4805*) gal. = 1 cu. ft.

760* millimeters Hg = atm. press. at 0 deg. C.

0.07608 lb. = wgt. 1 cu. ft. air at 62 deg. F. and 14.7 lb. per sq. in.

778 (777.5) ft.-lb. = 1 B. t. u.

0.7854* (=3.1416 ÷ 4) × diameter squared = area circle

8 = lb. oxygen required to burn 1 lb. hydrogen (H)

(POWER)

ENGINEERING CONSTANTS

8.025* (= square root of 2 g) × square root of head (ft.) = theoretical velocity of fluids in ft. per sec.

0.08073 lb. = wgt. 1 cu. ft. air at 32 deg. and 14.7 lb. per sq. in.

8⅓ (8.3356) lb. = wgt. 1 gal. water at 62 deg. F.

8,760* hr. = 1 year of 365 days

88* ft. per sec. (min.) = 1 mile per min. (hr.)

9* sq. ft. = 1 sq. yard.

0.0929* sq. meters = 1 sq. ft.

970.4 B. t. u. = Latent heat of evap. of water at 212 deg. F.

SPECIAL ABBREVIATIONS

approx....................approximate
atm. pres. standard atmospheric pressure
av............................average
cal. val..................calorific value
B. t. u.............British thermal unit
C_p.....specific heat at constant pressure
C_v......specific heat at constant volume
cm........................centimeters
diam........................diameter
evap......................evaporation
g..............gravity acceleration
gal.......gallons (U. S. unless otherwise specified)
Hg ....mercury

in. Hg .....inches of mercury (pressure)
kg...........................kilograms
$\log_{10}$..........logarithm to the base 10
$\log_e$..........logarithm to the base "e"
min,.........................minute
mol. wgt..............molecular weight
pres........................pressure
req.........................required
sat..............dry saturated (steam)
sec...........................second
sup......................superheated
vel...........................velocity
vol..........................volume
wgt.........................weight

WEIGHTS AND MEASURES

Linear Measure

12 inches	= 1 foot
3 feet	= 1 yard
1760 yards or 5280 feet	= 1 mile
1000 mils	= 1 inch
16½ feet or 5½ yards	= 1 rod

(Sometimes called pole or perch.)

Square Measure

100 square feet	= 1 square

(Used for roofing, etc.)

30¼ square yards	= 1 square rod
160 square rods	= 1 acre
640 acres	= 1 square mile

Liquid Measure

4 gills	= 1 pint
2 pints	= 1 quart
4 quarts	= 1 gallon
1 U. S. gallon	= 231 cubic inches, 3.785 liters
1 British Imperial gallon	= 277.41 cubic inches
	= 1.2 U. S. gallons
7.48 U. S. gallons	= 1 cubic foot

Dry Measure — U. S.

2 pints	= 1 quart
8 quarts	= 1 peck
4 pecks	= 1 bushel

1 Standard U. S. bushel = 2,150.42 cubic inches = 1.2445 cubic feet
1 British Imperial bushel = 2,218.19 cubic inches = 1.2837 cubic feet

Board Measure

One board foot is a piece of wood 12 inches square by 1 inch thick, or 144 cubic inches. 1 cubic foot, therefore, equals 12 board feet.

Shipping Measure

Register ton is used to measure internal capacity of ships. 100 cubic feet = 1 register ton.

Shipping ton, for measurement of cargo:

40 cubic feet = { 1 U. S. shipping ton / 32.143 U. S. bushels / 31.16 Imperial bushels

42 cubic feet = { 1 British shipping ton / 33.75 U. S. bushels / 32.718 Imperial bushels

Measures of Weight — Avoirdupois

16 drachms or 437.5 grains = 1 ounce (oz.)
16 ounces or 7000 grains = 1 pound (lb.)

2000 pounds	= 1 net or short ton
2240 pounds	= 1 gross or long ton
2204.6 pounds	= 1 metric ton

Specific Gravity

The specific gravity of a substance is its weight as compared with the weight of an equal bulk of pure water.

For making specific gravity determinations the temperature of the water is usually taken at 62 degrees Fahrenheit when 1 cubic foot of water weighs 62.355 pounds. Water is at its greatest density at 39.2 degrees Fahrenheit or 4 degrees Centigrade.

Temperature

The following equation will be found convenient for transforming temperature from one system to another:

Let F = degrees Fahrenheit; C = degrees Centigrade; R = degrees Réaumur.

$$\frac{F - 32}{180} = \frac{C}{100} = \frac{R}{80}$$

WEIGHTS AND MEASURES

Linear Measure

French	U. S. and British
1 meter	= 39.37 inches or 3.28083 feet or 1.09361 yards
0.3048 meter	= 1 foot
1 centimeter	= 0.3937 inch
2.54 centimeters	= 1 inch
25.4 millimeters	= 1 inch
1 kilometer	= 1093.61 yards or 0.62137 mile

Square Measure

French	U. S. and British
1 square meter	= 10.764 square feet or 1.196 square yards
0.836 square meter	= 1 square yard
6.452 square centimeters	= 1 square inch
1 square millimeter	= 0.00155 square inch = 1973.5 circular mils
645.2 square millimeters	= 1 square inch
1 centiare = 1 square meter	= 10.764 square feet
1 are = 1 square decameter	= 1076.41 square feet
1 hectare = 100 ares	= 107641. square feet = 2.471 acres
1 square kilometer	= 0.3861 square miles = 247.1 acres

Volume

French	U. S. and British
1 cubic meter	= 35.314 cubic feet or 1.308 cubic yards
0.7646 cubic meter	= 1 cubic yard
0.02832 cubic meter	= 1 cubic foot
1 cubic decimeter	= 61.023 cubic inches or 0.0353 cubic foot
16.387 cubic centimeters	= 1 cubic inch
1 litre — 1 cubic decimeter	= 61.023 cubic inch = 1.05671 quarts (U. S.)
1 hectolitre or decistere	= 3.5314 cubic feet = 2.8375 bushels (U. S.)
1 stere, kilolitre, or cubic meter	= 1.308 cubic yards = 28.37 bushels (U. S.)

Weight

1 gram is the weight of 1 cubic centimeter of water at 4 degrees Centigrade.

French	U. S. and British
1 gram	= 15.432 grains
0.0648 gram	= 1 grain
28.35 gram	= 1 ounce avoirdupois
1 kilogram	= 2.2046 pounds
0.4536 kilogram	= 1 pound
1 tonne or metric ton or 1000 kilogram	= { 0.9842 long tons / 19.68 hundredweights (cwt.) / 2204.6 pounds }
1.016 metric tons 1016 kilograms	= 1 long ton of 2240 pounds

The metric system has in recent years been adopted as standard in engineering and technological work in China and the U.S.S.R.

ENGINEERING CONVERSION FACTORS

Multiply	by*	to obtain
Acres	.404687	hectares
"	4.04687×10^{-3}	square kilometers
Ares	1076.39	square feet
board feet	144 sq. in. $\times$ 1 in.	cubic inches
" "	.0833	cubic feet
centimeters	3.28083×10^{-2}	feet
"	.3937	inches
cubic centimeters	3.53145×10^{-5}	cubic feet
"	6.102×10^{-2}	cubic inches
cubic feet	2.8317×10^{4}	cubic centimeters
" "	2.8317×10^{-2}	cubic meters
" "	6.22905	gallons, British Imperial
" "	28.3170	liters
" "	2.38095×10^{-2}	tons, British Shipping
" "	.025	tons, U. S. Shipping
cubic inches	16.38716	cubic centimeters
cubic meters	35.3145	cubic feet
" "	1.30794	cubic yards
cubic yards	.764559	cubic meters
degrees, angular	.0174533	radians
degrees, Fahrenheit (less 32 F.)	.5556	degrees, Centigrade
" Centigrade	1.8	degrees, Fahrenheit (less 32 F.)
foot pounds	.13826	kilogram meters
feet	30.4801	centimeters
"	.304801	meters
"	304.801	millimeters
"	1.64468×10^{-4}	miles, nautical
gallons, British Imperial	.160538	cubic feet
" " "	1.20091	gallons, U. S.
" " "	4.54596	liters
gallons, U. S.	.832702	gallons, British Imperial
" "	.13368	cubic feet
" "	231.	cubic inches
" "	3.78543	liters
grams, metric	2.20462×10^{-3}	pounds, avoirdupois
hectares	2.47104	acres
"	1.076387×10^{-5}	square feet
"	3.86101×10^{-3}	square miles
horse-power, metric	.98632	horse-power, U. S.
horse-power, U. S.	1.01387	horse-power, metric
inches	2.54001	centimeters
"	2.54001×10^{-2}	meters
"	25.4001	millimeters
kilograms	2.20462	pounds
"	9.84206×10^{-4}	long tons
"	1.10231×10^{-3}	short tons
kilogram meters	7.233	foot pounds
kilograms per meter	.671972	pounds per foot
kilograms per square centimeter	14.2234	pounds per square inch
kilograms per square meter	.204817	pounds per square foot
" " " "	9.14362×10^{-5}	long tons per square foot
kilograms per square millimeter	1422.34	pounds per square inch
" " "	.634973	long tons per square inch
kilograms per cubic meter	6.24283×10^{-2}	pounds per cubic foot
kilometers	.62137	miles, statute
"	.53959	miles, nautical

* The expressions $\times 10^{-2}$, $\times 10^{-3}$, $\times 10^{-4}$, $\times 10^{-5}$, and $\times 10^{-6}$, following certain multipliers, indicate that the decimal point in the product — of left-column value times multiplier — is to be moved respectively 2, 3, 4, 5, or 6 places to the left.

ENGINEERING CONVERSION FACTORS

Multiply	by*	to obtain
liters	.219975	gallons, British Imperial
"	.26417	gallons, U. S.
"	3.53145×10^{-2}	cubic feet
meters	3.28083	feet
"	39.37	inches
"	1.09361	yards
miles, statute	1.60935	kilometers
" "	.8684	miles, nautical
miles, nautical	6080.204	feet
" "	1.85325	kilometers
" "	1.1516	miles, statute
millimeters	3.28083×10^{-3}	feet
"	3.937×10^{-2}	inches
pounds, avoirdupois	453.592	grams, metric
" "	.453592	kilograms
" "	4.464×10^{-4}	tons, long
" "	4.53592×10^{-4}	tons, metric
pounds per foot	1.48816	kilograms per meter
pounds per square foot	4.88241	kilograms per square meter
pounds per square inch	7.031×10^{-2}	kilograms per square centimeter
" " "	7.031×10^{-4}	kilograms per square millimeter
pounds per cubic foot	16.0184	kilograms per cubic meter
radians	57.29578	degrees, angular
square centimeters	.1550	square inches
square feet	9.29034×10^{-4}	ares
" "	9.29034×10^{-6}	hectares
" "	.0929034	square meters
square inches	6.45163	square centimeters
" "	645.163	square millimeters
square kilometers	247.104	acres
" "	.3861	square miles
square meters	10.7639	square feet
" "	1.19599	square yards
square miles	259.0	hectares
" "	2.590	square kilometers
square millimeters	1.550×10^{-3}	square inches
square yards	.83613	square meters
tons, long	1016.05	kilograms
" "	2240.	pounds
" "	1.01605	tons, metric
" "	1.120	tons, short
tons, long, per square foot	1.09366×10^{4}	kilograms per square meter
tons, long, per square inch	1.57494	kilograms per square millimeter
tons, metric	2204.62	pounds
" "	.98421	tons, long
" "	1.10231	tons, short
tons, short	907.185	kilograms
" "	.892857	tons, long
" "	.907185	tons, metric
tons, British Shipping	42.00	cubic feet
" " "	1.050	tons, U. S. Shipping
tons, U. S. Shipping	40.00	cubic feet
" " "	.952381	tons, British Shipping
yards	.914402	meters

* The expressions $\times 10^{-2}$, $\times 10^{-3}$, $\times 10^{-4}$, $\times 10^{-5}$, and $\times 10^{-6}$, following certain multipliers, indicate that the decimal point in the product — of left-column value times multiplier — is to be moved respectively 2, 3, 4, 5, or 6 places to the left.

CONVERSION TABLE

INCHES AND MILLIMETERS

The tables on these two pages are calculated on the newly adopted relation of 25.4 millimeters to the American inch.   This replaces the old ratio of 25.40005 : 1, a dif- ference of two parts in a million.   This ratio was approved at a meeting of American Standards Association on October 21, 1932.

The adoption of the new ratio simplifies calculations and eliminates errors caused by various interpretations of the decimal to be used.   The following tables are from the Bureau of Standards.

INCHES TO MILLIMETERS
Basis: 1 inch = 25.4 Millimeters

Inches	Milli-meters	Inches	Milli-meters	Inches	Milli-meters	Inches	Milli-meters
1	25.4	26	660.4	51	1295.4	76	1930.4
2	50.8	27	685.8	52	1320.8	77	1955.8
3	76.2	28	711.2	53	1346.2	78	1981.2
4	101.6	29	736.6	54	1371.6	79	2006.6
5	127.0	30	762.0	55	1397.0	80	2032.0
6	152.4	31	787.4	56	1422.4	81	2057.4
7	177.8	32	812.8	57	1447.8	82	2082.8
8	203.2	33	838.2	58	1473.2	83	2108.2
9	228.6	34	863.6	59	1498.6	84	2133.6
10	254.0	35	889.0	60	1524.0	85	2159.0
11	279.4	36	914.4	61	1549.4	86	2184.4
12	304.8	37	939.8	62	1574.8	87	2209.8
13	330.2	38	965.2	63	1600.2	88	2235.2
14	355.6	39	990.6	64	1625.6	89	2260.6
15	381.0	40	1016.0	65	1651.0	90	2286.0
16	406.4	41	1041.4	66	1676.4	91	2311.4
17	431.8	42	1066.8	67	1701.8	92	2336.8
18	457.2	43	1092.2	68	1727.2	93	2362.2
19	482.6	44	1117.6	69	1752.6	94	2387.6
20	508.0	45	1143.0	70	1778.0	95	2413.0
21	533.4	46	1168.4	71	1803.4	96	2438.4
22	558.8	47	1193.8	72	1828.8	97	2463.8
23	584.2	48	1219.2	73	1854.2	98	2489.2
24	609.6	49	1244.6	74	1879.6	99	2514.6
25	635.0	50	1270.0	75	1905.0	100	2540.0

Note. — The above table is exact.

CONVERSION TABLE

MILLIMETERS TO INCHES
Basis: 1 Inch = 25.4 Millimeters

Milli-meters	Inches	Milli-meters	Inches	Milli-meters	Inches	Milli-meters	Inches
1	0.039370	26	1.023622	51	2.007874	76	2.992126
2	0.078740	27	1.062992	52	2.047244	77	3.031496
3	0.118110	28	1.102362	53	2.086614	78	3.070866
4	0.157480	29	1.141732	54	2.125984	79	3.110236
5	0.196850	30	1.181102	55	2.165354	80	3.149606
6	0.236220	31	1.220472	56	2.204724	81	3.188976
7	0.275591	32	1.259843	57	2.244094	82	3.228346
8	0.314961	33	1.299213	58	2.283465	83	3.267717
9	0.354331	34	1.338583	59	2.322835	84	3.307087
10	0.393701	35	1.377953	60	2.362205	85	3.346457
11	0.433071	36	1.417323	61	2.401575	86	3.385827
12	0.472441	37	1.456693	62	2.440945	87	3.425197
13	0.511811	38	1.496063	63	2.480315	88	3.464567
14	0.551181	39	1.535433	64	2.519685	89	3.503937
15	0.590551	40	1.574803	65	2.559055	90	3.543307
16	0.629921	41	1.614173	66	2.598425	91	3.582677
17	0.669291	42	1.653543	67	2.637795	92	3.622047
18	0.708661	43	1.692913	68	2.677165	93	3.661417
19	0.748031	44	1.732283	69	2.716535	94	3.700787
20	0.787402	45	1.771654	70	2.755906	95	3.740157
21	0.826772	46	1.811024	71	2.795276	96	3.779528
22	0.866142	47	1.850394	72	2.834646	97	3.818898
23	0.905512	48	1.889764	73	2.874016	98	3.858268
24	0.944882	49	1.929134	74	2.913386	99	3.897638
25	0.984252	50	1.968504	75	2.952756	100	3.937008

Note. — The above table is approximate: 1/25.4 = 0.039370078740+.

TEMPERATURE CONVERSION TABLE

DEGREES FAHRENHEIT TO DEGREES CENTIGRADE

(Single boldface figures indicate recurring decimals.)

°F	0	20	40	60	80
	C	C	C	C	C
−400	−240.0	−251.1	−262.2	....	....
−300	−184.4	−195.5	−206.6	−217.7	−228.8
−200	−128.8	−140.0	−151.1	−162.2	−173.3
−100	−73.3	−84.4	−95.5	−106.6	−117.7
−0	−17.7	−28.8	−40.0	−51.1	−62.2
0	−17.7	−6.6	+4.4	+15.5	+26.6
100	37.7	48.8	60.0	71.1	82.2
200	93.3	104.4	115.5	126.6	137.7
300	148.8	160.0	171.1	182.2	193.3
400	204.4	215.5	226.6	237.7	248.8
500	260.0	271.1	282.2	293.3	304.4
600	315.5	326.6	337.7	348.8	360.0
700	371.1	382.2	393.3	404.4	415.5
800	426.6	437.7	448.8	460.0	471.1
900	482.2	493.3	504.4	515.5	526.6
1000	537.7	548.8	560.0	571.1	582.2
1100	593.3	604.4	615.5	626.6	637.7
1200	648.8	660.0	671.1	682.2	693.3
1300	704.4	715.5	726.6	737.7	748.8
1400	760.0	771.1	782.2	793.3	804.4
1500	815.5	826.6	837.7	848.8	860.0
1600	871.1	882.2	893.3	904.4	915.5
1700	926.6	937.7	948.8	960.0	971.1
1800	982.2	993.3	1004.4	1015.5	1026.6
1900	1037.7	1048.8	1060.0	1071.1	1082.2
2000	1093.3	1104.4	1115.5	1126.6	1137.7
2100	1148.8	1160.0	1171.1	1182.2	1193.3
2200	1204.4	1215.5	1226.6	1237.7	1248.8
2300	1260.0	1271.1	1282.2	1293.3	1304.4
2400	1315.5	1326.6	1337.7	1348.8	1360.0
2500	1371.1	1382.2	1393.3	1404.4	1415.5
2600	1426.6	1437.7	1448.8	1460.0	1471.1
2700	1482.2	1493.3	1504.4	1515.5	1526.6
2800	1537.7	1548.8	1560.0	1571.1	1582.2
2900	1593.3	1604.4	1615.5	1626.6	1637.7
3000	1648.8	1660.0	1671.1	1682.2	1693.3
°F	0	20	40	60	80

°F	°C
1	0.5
2	1.1
3	1.6
4	2.2
5	2.7
6	3.3
7	3.8
8	4.4
9	5.0

Examples: −246.0 °F = −151.11 °C − 3.33 °C = −154.44 °C.

3762 °F = 2071.1 °C + 1.1 °C = 2072.2 °C.

2423.5 °F = 1326.66 °C + 1.66 °C + 0.27 °C = 1328.61 °C.

TEMPERATURE CONVERSION TABLE
DEGREES FAHRENHEIT TO DEGREES CENTIGRADE — (CONTINUED)
(Single boldface figures indicate recurring decimals.)

°F	0	20	40	60	80		°F	°C
	C	C	C	C	C			
3100	1704.4	1715.5	1726.6	1737.7	1748.8			
3200	1760.0	1771.1	1782.2	1793.3	1804.4			
3300	1815.5	1826.6	1837.7	1848.8	1860.0			
3400	1871.1	1882.2	1893.3	1904.4	1915.5			
3500	1926.6	1937.7	1948.8	1960.0	1971.1			
3600	1982.2	1993.3	2004.4	2015.5	2026.6			
3700	2037.7	2048.8	2060.0	2071.1	2082.2			
3800	2093.3	2104.4	2115.5	2126.6	2137.7			
3900	2148.8	2160.0	2171.1	2182.2	2193.3			
4000	2204.4	2215.5	2226.6	2237.7	2248.8			
4100	2260.0	2271.1	2282.2	2293.3	2304.4			
4200	2315.5	2326.6	2337.7	2348.8	2360.0			
4300	2371.1	2382.2	2393.3	2404.4	2415.5			
4400	2426.6	2437.7	2448.8	2460.0	2471.1		°F	°C
4500	2482.2	2493.3	2504.4	2515.5	2526.6			
4600	2537.7	2548.8	2560.0	2571.1	2582.2			
							1	0.5
4700	2593.3	2604.4	2615.5	2626.6	2637.7		2	1.1
4800	2648.8	2660.0	2671.1	2682.2	2693.3		3	1.6
4900	2704.4	2715.5	2726.6	2737.7	2748.8			
							4	2.2
5000	2760.0	2771.1	2782.2	2793.3	2804.4		5	2.7
							6	3.3
5100	2815.5	2826.6	2837.7	2848.8	2860.0			
5200	2871.1	2882.2	2893.3	2904.4	2915.5		7	3.8
5300	2926.6	2937.7	2948.8	2960.0	2971.1		8	4.4
							9	5.0
5400	2982.2	2993.3	3004.4	3015.5	3026.6			
5500	3037.7	3048.8	3060.0	3071.1	3082.2			
5600	3093.3	3104.4	3115.5	3126.6	3137.7			
5700	3148.8	3160.0	3171.1	3182.2	3193.3			
5800	3204.4	3215.5	3226.6	3237.7	3248.8			
5900	3260.0	3271.1	3282.2	3293.3	3304.4			
6000	3315.5	3326.6	3337.7	3348.8	3360.0			
6100	3371.1	3382.2	3393.3	3404.4	3415.5			
6200	3426.6	3437.7	3448.8	3460.0	3471.1			
6300	3482.2	3493.3	3504.4	3515.5	3526.6			
6400	3537.7	3548.8	3560.0	3571.1	3582.2			
6500	3593.3	3604.4	3615.5	3626.6	3637.7			
6600	3648.8	3660.0	3671.1	3682.2	3693.3			
6700	3704.4	3715.5	3726.6	3737.7	3748.8			
6800	3760.0	3771.1	3782.2	3793.3	3804.4			
6900	3815.5	3826.6	3837.7	3848.8	3860.0			
7000	3871.1	3882.2	3893.3	3904.4	3915.5			
°F	0	20	40	60	80			

Examples: −246.0 °F = −151.11 °C − 3.33 °C = −154.44 °C.
3762 °F = 2071.1 °C + 1.1 °C = 2072.2 °C.
2423.5 °F = 1326.66 °C + 1.66 °C + 0.27 °C = 1328.61 °C.

TEMPERATURE CONVERSION TABLE

DEGREES CENTIGRADE TO DEGREES FAHRENHEIT

°C	0	20	40	60	80
	F	F	F	F	F
−200	−328	−364	−400	−436	. . . .
−100	−148	−184	−220	−256	−292
−0	+32	−4	−40	−76	−112
0	32	68	104	140	176
100	212	248	284	320	356
200	392	428	464	500	536
300	572	608	644	680	716
400	752	788	824	860	896
500	932	968	1004	1040	1076
600	1112	1148	1184	1220	1256
700	1292	1328	1364	1400	1436
800	1472	1508	1544	1580	1616
900	1652	1688	1724	1760	1796
1000	1832	1868	1904	1940	1976
1100	2012	2048	2084	2120	2156
1200	2192	2228	2264	2300	2336
1300	2372	2408	2444	2480	2516
1400	2552	2588	2624	2660	2696
1500	2732	2768	2804	2840	2876
1600	2912	2948	2984	3020	3056
1700	3092	3128	3164	3200	3236
1800	3272	3308	3344	3380	3416
1900	3452	3488	3524	3560	3596
2000	3632	3668	3704	3740	3776
2100	3812	3848	3884	3920	3956
2200	3992	4028	4064	4100	4136
2300	4172	4208	4244	4280	4316
2400	4352	4388	4424	4460	4496
2500	4532	4568	4604	4640	4676
2600	4712	4748	4784	4820	4856
2700	4892	4928	4964	5000	5036
2800	5072	5108	5144	5180	5216
2900	5252	5288	5324	5360	5396
3000	5432	5468	5504	5540	5576
3100	5612	5648	5684	5720	5756
3200	5792	5828	5864	5900	5936
3300	5972	6008	6044	6080	6116
°C	0	20	40	60	80

°C	°F
1	1.8
2	3.6
3	5.4
4	7.2
5	9.0
6	10.8
7	12.6
8	14.4
9	16.2
10	18.0

°F	°C
1	0.56
2	1.11
3	1.67
4	2.22
5	2.78
6	3.33
7	3.89
8	4.44
9	5.00
10	5.56
11	6.11
12	6.67
13	7.22
14	7.78
15	8.33
16	8.89
17	9.44
18	10.00

Examples: 1347 °C = 2444 °F + 12.6 °F = 2456.6 °F.   3366 °F = 1850 °C = 2.78 °C = 1852.78 °C.

DECIMALS OF AN INCH
FOR EACH 64TH OF AN INCH

WITH MILLIMETER EQUIVALENTS

Fraction	⅟₆₄ths	Decimal	Millimeters (approx.)	Fraction	⅟₆₄ths	Decimal	Millimeters (approx.)
....	1	.015625	0.397	....	33	.515625	13.097
¹⁄₃₂	2	.03125	0.794	¹⁷⁄₃₂	34	.53125	13.494
....	3	.046875	1.191	—	35	.546875	13.891
¹⁄₁₆	4	.0625	1.588	⁹⁄₁₆	36	.5625	14.288
....	5	.078125	1.984	....	37	.578125	14.684
³⁄₃₂	6	.09375	2.381	¹⁹⁄₃₂	38	.59375	15.081
....	7	.109375	2.778	....	39	.609375	15.478
¹⁄₈	8	.125	3.175	⁵⁄₈	40	.625	15.875
....	9	.140625	3.572	....	41	.640625	16.272
⁵⁄₃₂	10	.15625	3.969	²¹⁄₃₂	42	.65625	16.669
....	11	.171875	4.366	....	43	.671875	17.066
³⁄₁₆	12	.1875	4.763	¹¹⁄₁₆	44	.6875	17.463
....	13	.203125	5.159	....	45	.703125	17.859
⁷⁄₃₂	14	.21875	5.556	²³⁄₃₂	46	.71875	18.256
....	15	.234375	5.953	....	47	.734375	18.653
¹⁄₄	16	.250	6.350	³⁄₄	48	.750	19.050
....	17	.265625	6.747	....	49	.765625	19.447
⁹⁄₃₂	18	.28125	7.144	²⁵⁄₃₂	50	.78125	19.844
....	19	.296875	7.541	....	51	.796875	20.241
⁵⁄₁₆	20	.3125	7.938	¹³⁄₁₆	52	.8125	20.638
....	21	.328125	8.334	....	53	.828125	21.034
¹¹⁄₃₂	22	.34375	8.731	²⁷⁄₃₂	54	.84375	21.431
....	23	.359375	9.128	....	55	.859375	21.828
³⁄₈	24	.375	9.525	⁷⁄₈	56	.875	22.225
....	25	.390625	9.922	....	57	.890625	22.622
¹³⁄₃₂	26	.40625	10.319	²⁹⁄₃₂	58	.90625	23.019
....	27	.421875	10.716	....	59	.921875	23.416
⁷⁄₁₆	28	.4375	11.113	¹⁵⁄₁₆	60	.9375	23.813
....	29	.453125	11.509	....	61	.953125	24.209
¹⁵⁄₃₂	30	.46875	11.906	³¹⁄₃₂	62	.96875	24.606
....	31	.484375	12.303	....	63	.984375	25.003
¹⁄₂	32	.500	12.700	1	64	1.000	25.400

DECIMALS OF A FOOT

FOR EACH 32ND OF AN INCH

Inch	0″	1″	2″	3″	4″	5″
0	0	.0833	.1667	.2500	.3333	.4167
1/32	.0026	.0859	.1693	.2526	.3359	.4193
1/16	.0052	.0885	.1719	.2552	.3385	.4219
3/32	.0078	.0911	.1745	.2578	.3411	.4245
1/8	.0104	.0938	.1771	.2604	.3438	.4271
5/32	.0130	.0964	.1797	.2630	.3464	.4297
3/16	.0156	.0990	.1823	.2656	.3490	.4323
7/32	.0182	.1016	.1849	.2682	.3516	.4349
1/4	.0208	.1042	.1875	.2708	.3542	.4375
9/32	.0234	.1068	.1901	.2734	.3568	.4401
5/16	.0260	.1094	.1927	.2760	.3594	.4427
11/32	.0286	.1120	.1953	.2786	.3620	.4453
3/8	.0313	.1146	.1979	.2812	.3646	.4479
13/32	.0339	.1172	.2005	.2839	.3672	.4505
7/16	.0365	.1198	.2031	.2865	.3698	.4531
15/32	.0391	.1224	.2057	.2891	.3724	.4557
1/2	.0417	.1250	.2083	.2917	.3750	.4583
17/32	.0443	.1276	.2109	.2943	.3776	.4609
9/16	.0469	.1302	.2135	.2969	.3802	.4635
19/32	.0495	.1328	.2161	.2995	.3828	.4661
5/8	.0521	.1354	.2188	.3021	.3854	.4688
21/32	.0547	.1380	.2214	.3047	.3880	.4714
11/16	.0573	.1406	.2240	.3073	.3906	.4740
23/32	.0599	.1432	.2266	.3099	.3932	.4766
3/4	.0625	.1458	.2292	.3125	.3958	.4792
25/32	.0651	.1484	.2318	.3151	.3984	.4818
13/16	.0677	.1510	.2344	.3177	.4010	.4844
27/32	.0703	.1536	.2370	.3203	.4036	.4870
7/8	.0729	.1563	2396	.3229	.4063	.4896
29/32	.0755	.1589	.2422	.3255	.4089	.4922
15/16	.0781	.1615	.2448	.3281	.4115	.4948
31/32	.0807	.1641	.2474	.3307	.4141	.4974

DECIMALS OF A FOOT
FOR EACH 32ND OF AN INCH

Inch	6″	7″	8″	9″	10″	11″
0	.5000	.5833	.6667	.7500	.8333	.9167
1/32	.5026	.5859	.6693	.7526	.8359	.9193
1/16	.5052	.5885	.6719	.7552	.8385	.9219
3/32	.5078	.5911	.6745	.7578	.8411	.9245
1/8	.5104	.5938	.6771	.7604	.8438	.9271
5/32	.5130	.5964	.6797	.7630	.8464	.9297
3/16	.5156	.5990	.6823	.7656	.8490	.9323
7/32	.5182	.6016	.6849	.7682	.8516	.9349
1/4	.5208	.6042	.6875	.7708	.8542	.9375
9/32	.5234	.6068	.6901	.7734	.8568	.9401
5/16	.5260	.6094	.6927	.7760	.8594	.9427
11/32	.5286	.6120	.6953	.7786	.8620	.9453
3/8	.5313	.6146	.6979	.7813	.8646	.9479
13/32	.5339	.6172	.7005	.7839	.8672	.9505
7/16	.5365	.6198	.7031	.7865	.8698	.9531
15/32	.5391	.6224	.7057	.7891	.8724	.9557
1/2	.5417	.6250	.7083	.7917	.8750	.9583
17/32	.5443	.6276	.7109	.7943	.8776	.9609
9/16	.5469	.6302	.7135	.7969	.8802	.9635
19/32	.5495	.6328	.7161	.7995	.8828	.9661
5/8	.5521	.6354	.7188	.8021	.8854	.9688
21/32	.5547	.6380	.7214	.8047	.8880	.9714
11/16	.5573	.6406	.7240	.8073	.8906	.9740
23/32	.5599	.6432	.7266	.8099	.8932	.9766
3/4	.5625	.6458	.7292	.8125	.8958	.9792
25/32	.5651	.6484	.7318	.8151	.8984	.9818
13/16	.5677	.6510	.7344	.8177	.9010	.9844
27/32	.5703	.6536	.7370	.8203	.9036	.9870
7/8	.5729	.6563	.7396	.8229	.9063	.9896
29/32	.5755	.6589	.7422	.8255	.9089	.9922
15/16	.5781	.6615	.7448	.8281	.9115	.9948
31/32	.5807	.6641	.7474	.8307	.9141	.9974

AMERICAN INSTITUTE OF STEEL CONSTRUCTION

SQUARE AND ROUND BARS
WEIGHT AND AREA

Size Inches	Weight Lb. per Foot ■	Weight Lb. per Foot ●	Area Square Inches ▨	Area Square Inches ◎	Size Inches	Weight Lb. per Foot ■	Weight Lb. per Foot ●	Area Square Inches ▨	Area Square Inches ◎
0					3	30.60	24.03	9.000	7.069
1/16	.013	.010	.0039	.0031	1/16	31.89	25.05	9.379	7.366
1/8	.053	.042	.0156	.0123	1/8	33.20	26.08	9.766	7.670
3/16	.120	.094	.0352	.0276	3/16	34.54	27.13	10.160	7.980
1/4	.213	.167	.0625	.0491	1/4	35.91	28.21	10.563	8.296
5/16	.332	.261	.0977	.0767	5/16	37.31	29.30	10.973	8.618
3/8	.478	.376	.1406	.1105	3/8	38.73	30.42	11.391	8.946
7/16	.651	.511	.1914	.1503	7/16	40.18	31.55	11.816	9.281
1/2	.850	.668	.2500	.1963	1/2	41.65	32.71	12.250	9.621
9/16	1.076	.845	.3164	.2485	9/16	43.15	33.89	12.691	9.968
5/8	1.328	1.043	.3906	.3068	5/8	44.68	35.09	13.141	10.321
11/16	1.607	1.262	.4727	.3712	11/16	46.23	36.31	13.598	10.680
3/4	1.913	1.502	.5625	.4418	3/4	47.81	37.55	14.063	11.045
13/16	2.245	1.763	.6602	.5185	13/16	49.42	38.81	14.535	11.416
7/8	2.603	2.044	.7656	.6013	7/8	51.05	40.10	15.016	11.793
15/16	2.988	2.347	.8789	.6903	15/16	52.71	41.40	15.504	12.177
1	3.400	2.670	1.0000	.7854	4	54.40	42.73	16.000	12.566
1/16	3.838	3.015	1.1289	.8866	1/16	56.11	44.07	16.504	12.962
1/8	4.303	3.380	1.2656	.9940	1/8	57.85	45.44	17.016	13.364
3/16	4.795	3.766	1.4102	1.1075	3/16	59.62	46.83	17.535	13.772
1/4	5.313	4.172	1.5625	1.2272	1/4	61.41	48.23	18.063	14.186
5/16	5.857	4.600	1.7227	1.3530	5/16	63.23	49.66	18.598	14.607
3/8	6.428	5.049	1.8906	1.4849	3/8	65.08	51.11	19.141	15.033
7/16	7.026	5.518	2.0664	1.6230	7/16	66.95	52.58	19.691	15.466
1/2	7.650	6.008	2.2500	1.7671	1/2	68.85	54.07	20.250	15.904
9/16	8.301	6.519	2.4414	1.9175	9/16	70.78	55.59	20.816	16.349
5/8	8.978	7.051	2.6406	2.0739	5/8	72.73	57.12	21.391	16.800
11/16	9.682	7.604	2.8477	2.2365	11/16	74.71	58.67	21.973	17.257
3/4	10.413	8.178	3.0625	2.4053	3/4	76.71	60.25	22.563	17.721
13/16	11.170	8.773	3.2852	2.5802	13/16	78.74	61.85	23.160	18.190
7/8	11.953	9.388	3.5156	2.7612	7/8	80.80	63.46	23.766	18.665
15/16	12.763	10.024	3.7539	2.9483	15/16	82.89	65.10	24.379	19.147
2	13.600	10.681	4.0000	3.1416	5	85.00	66.76	25.000	19.635
1/16	14.463	11.359	4.2539	3.3410	1/16	87.14	68.44	25.629	20.129
1/8	15.353	12.058	4.5156	3.5466	1/8	89.30	70.14	26.266	20.629
3/16	16.270	12.778	4.7852	3.7583	3/16	91.49	71.86	26.910	21.135
1/4	17.213	13.519	5.0625	3.9761	1/4	93.71	73.60	27.563	21.648
5/16	18.182	14.280	5.3477	4.2000	5/16	95.96	75.36	28.223	22.166
3/8	19.178	15.062	5.6406	4.4301	3/8	98.23	77.15	28.891	22.691
7/16	20.201	15.866	5.9414	4.6664	7/16	100.53	78.95	29.566	23.221
1/2	21.250	16.690	6.2500	4.9087	1/2	102.85	80.78	30.250	23.758
9/16	22.326	17.534	6.5664	5.1572	9/16	105.20	82.62	30.941	24.301
5/8	23.428	18.400	6.8906	5.4119	5/8	107.58	84.49	31.641	24.850
11/16	24.557	19.287	7.2227	5.6727	11/16	109.98	86.38	32.348	25.406
3/4	25.713	20.195	7.5625	5.9396	3/4	112.41	88.29	33.063	25.967
13/16	26.895	21.123	7.9102	6.2126	13/16	114.87	90.22	33.785	26.535
7/8	28.103	22.072	8.2656	6.4918	7/8	117.35	92.17	34.516	27.109
15/16	29.338	23.042	8.6289	6.7771	15/16	119.86	94.14	35.254	27.688
3	30.600	24.033	9.0000	7.0686	6	122.40	96.13	36.000	28.274

SQUARE AND ROUND BARS
WEIGHT AND AREA

Size Inches	Weight Lb. per Foot ■	Weight Lb. per Foot ●	Area Square Inches ▨	Area Square Inches ◎	Size Inches	Weight Lb. per Foot ■	Weight Lb. per Foot ●	Area Square Inches ▨	Area Square Inches ◎
6	122.40	96.13	36.000	28.274	9	275.40	216.30	81.000	63.617
1/16	124.96	98.15	36.754	28.866	1/16	279.24	219.31	82.129	64.504
1/8	127.55	100.18	37.516	29.465	1/8	283.10	222.35	83.266	65.397
3/16	130.17	102.23	38.285	30.069	3/16	286.99	225.41	84.410	66.296
1/4	132.81	104.31	39.063	30.680	1/4	290.91	228.48	85.563	67.201
5/16	135.48	106.41	39.848	31.296	5/16	294.86	231.58	86.723	68.112
3/8	138.18	108.53	40.641	31.919	3/8	298.83	234.70	87.891	69.029
7/16	140.90	110.66	41.441	32.548	7/16	302.83	237.84	89.066	69.953
1/2	143.65	112.82	42.250	33.183	1/2	306.85	241.00	90.250	70.882
9/16	146.43	115.00	43.066	33.824	9/16	310.90	244.18	91.441	71.818
5/8	149.23	117.20	43.891	34.472	5/8	314.98	247.38	92.641	72.760
11/16	152.06	119.43	44.723	35.125	11/16	319.08	250.61	93.848	73.708
3/4	154.91	121.67	45.563	35.785	3/4	323.21	253.85	95.063	74.662
13/16	157.79	123.93	46.410	36.450	13/16	327.37	257.12	96.285	75.622
7/8	160.70	126.22	47.266	37.122	7/8	331.55	260.40	97.516	76.589
15/16	163.64	128.52	48.129	37.800	15/16	335.76	263.71	98.754	77.561
7	166.60	130.85	49.000	38.485	10	340.00	267.04	100.000	78.540
1/16	169.59	133.19	49.879	39.175	1/16	344.26	270.38	101.254	79.525
1/8	172.60	135.56	50.766	39.871	1/8	348.55	273.75	102.516	80.516
3/16	175.64	137.95	51.660	40.574	3/16	352.87	277.14	103.785	81.513
1/4	178.71	140.36	52.563	41.282	1/4	357.21	280.55	105.063	82.516
5/16	181.81	142.79	53.473	41.997	5/16	361.58	283.99	106.348	83.525
3/8	184.93	145.24	54.391	42.718	3/8	365.98	287.44	107.641	84.541
7/16	188.07	147.71	55.316	43.445	7/16	370.40	290.91	108.941	85.563
1/2	191.25	150.21	56.250	44.179	1/2	374.85	294.41	110.250	86.590
9/16	194.45	152.72	57.191	44.918	9/16	379.33	297.92	111.566	87.624
5/8	197.68	155.26	58.141	45.664	5/8	383.83	301.46	112.891	88.664
11/16	200.93	157.81	59.098	46.415	11/16	388.36	305.02	114.223	89.710
3/4	204.21	160.39	60.063	47.173	3/4	392.91	308.59	115.563	90.763
13/16	207.52	162.99	61.035	47.937	13/16	397.49	312.19	116.910	91.821
7/8	210.85	165.60	62.016	48.707	7/8	402.10	315.81	118.266	92.886
15/16	214.21	168.24	63.004	49.483	15/16	406.74	319.45	119.629	93.957
8	217.60	170.90	64.000	50.265	11	411.40	323.11	121.000	95.033
1/16	221.01	173.58	65.004	51.054	1/16	416.09	326.80	122.379	96.116
1/8	224.45	176.29	66.016	51.849	1/8	420.80	330.50	123.766	97.205
3/16	227.92	179.01	67.035	52.649	3/16	425.54	334.22	125.160	98.301
1/4	231.41	181.75	68.063	53.456	1/4	430.31	337.97	126.563	99.402
5/16	234.93	184.52	69.098	54.269	5/16	435.11	341.73	127.973	100.510
3/8	238.48	187.30	70.141	55.088	3/8	439.93	345.52	129.391	101.623
7/16	242.05	190.11	71.191	55.914	7/16	444.78	349.33	130.816	102.743
1/2	245.65	192.93	72.250	56.745	1/2	449.65	353.16	132.250	103.869
9/16	249.28	195.78	73.316	57.583	9/16	454.55	357.00	133.691	105.001
5/8	252.93	198.65	74.391	58.426	5/8	459.48	360.87	135.141	106.139
11/16	256.61	201.54	75.473	59.276	11/16	464.43	364.76	136.598	107.284
3/4	260.31	204.45	76.563	60.132	3/4	469.41	368.68	138.063	108.434
13/16	264.04	207.38	77.660	60.994	13/16	474.42	372.61	139.535	109.591
7/8	267.80	210.33	78.766	61.863	7/8	479.45	376.56	141.016	110.754
15/16	271.59	213.31	79.879	62.737	15/16	484.51	380.54	142.504	111.923
9	275.40	216.30	81.000	63.617	12	489.60	384.53	144.000	113.098

RELATIONS OF CHIEF AMERICAN GAUGES

WEIGHT GAUGES

Name of Gauge	United States Standard Gauge, U. S. S. G.		Galvanized Sheet Gauge, G. S. G.		Tin Plate Gauge, T. P. G.		
Principal Use	Uncoated Carbon Steel Sheets and Light Plates		Galvanized Sheet Steel		Tin Plate		
Gauge No.	Equivalent Thickness, Inch	Lb. per Sq. Ft.	Lb. per Sq. Ft.	Oz. per Sq. Ft.	Lb. per Sq. Ft.	Lb. per Base Bx.	Symbol
7/0's	.4902	20.0000					
6/0's	.4596	18.7500					
5/0's	.4289	17.5000					
4/0's	.3983	16.2500					
3/0's	.3676	15.0000					
2/0's	.3370	13.7500					
0	.3064	12.5000					
1	.2757	11.2500					
2	.2604	10.6250					
3	.2451	10.0000					
4	.2298	9.3750					
5	.2145	8.7500					
6	.1991	8.1250					
7	.1838	7.5000					
8	.1685	6.8750	7.0312	112.5			
9	.1532	6.2500	6.4062	102.5			
10	.1379	5.6250	5.7812	92.5			
11	.1225	5.0000	5.1562	82.5			
12	.1072	4.3750	4.5312	72.5			
13	.0919	3.7500	3.9062	62.5			
14	.0766	3.1250	3.2812	52.5			
15	.0689	2.8125	2.9687	47.5			
16	.0613	2.5000	2.6562	42.5			
17	.0551	2.2500	2.4062	38.5			
18	.0490	2.0000	2.1562	34.5			
19	.0429	1.7500	1.9062	30.5			
20	.0368	1.5000	1.6562	26.5			
21	.0337	1.3750	1.5312	24.5			
22	.0306	1.2500	1.4062	22.5			
23	.0276	1.1250	1.2812	20.5	1.1250		
					1.079	235	6X
					1.047	228	6XL
24	.0245	1.0000	1.1562	18.5	1.0000		
					.987	215	5X
					.964	210	D2X
					.955	208	5XL
					.895	195	4X
25	.0214	.8750	1.0312	16.5	.8750		
					.863	188	4XL
					.827	180	DX
					.804	175	3X
					.771	168	3XL

Table above is based on the theoretical weights, which make the weight of a plate one foot square and one inch thick 40.8 pounds. Sheets and light plates are gauged on the edge, as the spring in the rolls causes the centers to be slightly thicker than the edges. To have the estimated weights of sheets and light plates equal the actual weight, the average weight of a square foot one inch thick is taken as 41.82 pounds.

RELATIONS OF CHIEF AMERICAN GAUGES

(CONTINUED)

WEIGHT GAUGES
(CONTINUED)

Name of Gauge	United States Standard Gauge, U. S. S. G.		Galvanized Sheet Gauge, G. S. G.		Tin Plate Gauge, T. P. G.		
Principal Use	Uncoated Carbon Steel Sheets and Light Plates		Galvanized Sheet Steel		Tin Plate		
Gauge No.	Equivalent Thickness, Inch	Lb. per Sq. Ft.	Lb. per Sq. Ft.	Oz. per Sq. Ft.	Lb. per Sq. Ft.	Lb. per Base Bx.	Symbol
26	.0184	.7500	.9062	14.5	.7500		
					.748	163	
					.712	155	2X
27	.0169	.6875	.8437	13.5	.6875		
					.680	148	2XL
					.657	143	
					.638	139	DC
28	.0153	.6250	.7812	12.5	.6250		
					.620	135	IX
					.588	128	IXL
					.574	125	
					.565	123	
29	.0138	.5625	.7187	11.5	.5625		
					.542	118	
					.514	112	
					.505	110	
30	.0123	.5000	.6562	10.5	.5000		
					.491	107	IC
					.459	100	ICL
31	.0107	.4375	.5937	9.5	.4375		
					.436	95	
					.413	90	
32	.0100	.4062	.5625	9.0	.4062		
					.390	85	
33	.0092	.3750	.5312	8.5	.3750		
					.367	80	
34	.0084	.3437	.5000	8.0	.3437	75	
					.321	70	
35	.0077	.3125			.3125		
					.298	65	
36	.0069	.2812			.2812		
					.276	60	
37	.0065	.2656			.2656		
					.253	55	
38	.0061	.2500			.2500		
39	.0057	.2344			.2343		
40	.0054	.2187			.2187		
41	.0052	.2109			.2109		
42	.0050	.2031			.2031		
43	.0048	.1953			.1953		
44	.0046	.1875			.1875		

Table above is based on the theoretical weights, which make the weight of a plate one foot square and one inch thick 40.8 pounds. Sheets and light plates are gauged on the edge, as the spring in the rolls causes the centers to be slightly thicker than the edges. To have the estimated weights of sheets and light plates equal the actual weight, the average weight of a square foot one inch thick is taken as 41.82 pounds.

RELATIONS OF CHIEF AMERICAN GAUGES

(CONTINUED)

THICKNESS GAUGES

Name of Gauge	Steel Wire G. Washburn & Moen or W. & M. Wire G. U. S. Steel W. G. Steel W. G.	Music Wire Gauge, M. W. G.	Brown & Sharpe Gauge, B. & S. G., A. W. G.	Stubs' Iron Wire Gauge, W. W. G., B. W. G.
Principal Use	Steel Wire, except Music Wire	Steel Music Wire	Non-ferrous Sheets and Wire	Flats, Plates and Wire
Gauge No.	Thickness, Inch	Thickness, Inch	Thickness, Inch	Thickness, Inch
7/0's	.4900			
6/0's	.4615	.004	.5800	
5/0's	.4305	.005	.5165	.500
4/0's	.3938	.006	.4600	.454
3/0's	.3625	.007	.4096	.425
2/0's	.3310	.008	.3648	.380
0	.3065	.009	.3249	.340
1	.2830	.010	.2893	.300
2	.2625	.011	.2576	.284
3	.2437	.012	.2294	.259
4	.2253	.013	.2043	.238
5	.2070*	.014	.1819	.220
6	.1920*	.016	.1620	.203
7	.1770*	.018	.1443	.180
8	.1620*	.020	.1285	.165
9	.1483*	.022	.1144	.148
10	.1350*	.024	.1019	.134
11	.1205*	.026	.0907	.120
12	.1055*	.029	.0808	.109
13	.0915*	.031	.0720	.095
14	.0800*	.033	.0641	.083
15	.0720*	.035	.0571	.072
16	.0625*	.037	.0508	.065
17	.0540*	.039	.0453	.058
18	.0475*	.041	.0403	.049
19	.0410*	.043	.0359	.042
20	.0348	.045	.0320	.035
21	.0317	.047	.0285	.032
22	.0286	.049	.0253	.028
23	.0258	.051	.0226	.025
24	.0230	.055	.0201	.022
25	.0204	.059	.0179	.020
26	.0181	.063	.0159	.018
27	.0173	.067	.0142	.016
28	.0162	.071	.0126	.014
29	.0150	.075	.0113	.013
30	.0140	.080	.0100	.012
31	.0132	.085	.0089	.010
32	.0128	.090	.0080	.009
33	.0118	.095	.0071	.008
34	.0104	.100	.0063	.007
35	.0095	.106	.0056	.005
36	.0090	.112	.0050	.004
37	.0085	.118	.0045	
38	.0080	.124	.0040	

*Three intermediate fractional gauges sometimes used are omitted from this table.

FACTORS FOR ESTIMATING WEIGHTS OF CASTINGS*

PATTERN MATERIAL	CASTING MATERIAL					
	Aluminum	Brass	Cast Iron	Copper	Malleable Iron	Steel
Aluminum	1.0	3.3	2.8	3.5	2.9	3.1
Ash	3.3	11.3	9.6	11.8	9.8	10.5
Brass	0.3	1.0	0.8	1.0	0.86	0.9
Cast Iron	0.35	1.2	1.0	1.2	1.0	1.1
Cedar	4.5	14.8	12.1	15.5	12.8	14.0
Cherry	3.6	12.0	10.3	12.7	10.5	11.3
Copper	0.3	1.0	0.8	1.0	0.8	0.9
Cypress	4.25	14.0	12.0	14.7	12.2	13.2
Mahogany	2.8	9.4	8.0	9.8	8.1	8.8
Malleable Iron	0.35	1.1	1.0	1.2	1.0	1.1
Oak	3.2	10.5	9.0	11.2	9.1	9.9
Pine, White	5.1	16.9	14.4	17.6	14.6	15.8
Pine, Yellow	3.9	14.5	11.1	13.6	11.3	12.1
Spruce	5.9	18.8	16.0	19.6	16.3	17.5
Steel	0.3	1.1	0.9	1.1	0.9	1.0

*Pattern materials are shown at the left of the table. Casting materials are shown at the top of the table. The factor, at the intersection of any line representing pattern material and any column representing casting material, is the ratio of casting weight to pattern weight. Pattern weight multiplied by the proper factor equals casting weight.

Example: A cherry pattern weighs 2 ounces. How much will a malleable iron casting made from it weigh? The factor, at the intersection of the line "Cherry" and column "Malleable Iron," is 10.5. Therefore, the casting will weigh 10.5 × 2 = 21 ounces, or 1 pound, 5 ounces.

Note: The foregoing is correct only in the case of solid (not hollow) patterns where the entire pattern volume is replaced by metal in the casting.

DECIMAL EQUIVALENTS AND TAP DRILL SIZES

OF WIRE GAUGE AND FRACTIONAL SIZE DRILLS

(TAP DRILL SIZES BASED ON 75% MAXIMUM THREAD)

Fractional Size Drills Inches	Wire Gauge Drills	Decimal Equivalent Inches	Tap Sizes		Fractional Size Drills Inches	Wire Gauge Drills	Decimal Equivalent Inches	Tap Sizes	
			Size of Thread	Threads per Inch				Size of Thread	Threads per Inch
	80	.0135			3/32	. . . . . .	.0937		
	79	.0145				41	.0960		
1/64	. . . . . .	.0156				40	.0980		
	78	.0160				39	.0995		
	77	.0180				38	.1015	5	40
	76	.0200				37	.1040	5	44
	75	.0210				36	.1065	6	32
	74	.0225			7/64	. . . . . .	.1094		
	73	.0240				35	.1100		
	72	.0250				34	.1110		
	71	.0260				33	.1130	6	40
	70	.0280				32	.1160		
	69	.0292				31	.1200		
	68	.0310			1/8	. . . . . .	.1250		
1/32	. . . . . .	.0312				30	.1285		
	67	.0320				29	.1360	8	{32
						28	.1405		{36
	66	.0330			9/64	. . . . . .	.1406		
	65	.0350				27	.1440		
	64	.0360				26	.1470		
	63	.0370				25	.1495	10	24
	62	.0380				24	.1520		
	61	.0390				23	.1540		
	60	.0400			5/32	. . . . . .	.1562		
	59	.0410				22	.1570		
	58	.0420				21	.1590	10	32
	57	.0430				20	.1610		
	56	.0465				19	.1660		
3/64	. . . . . .	.0469	0	80		18	.1695		
	55	.0520			11/64	. . . . . .	.1719		
	54	.0550				17	.1730		
	53	.0595	1	{64		16	.1770	12	24
1/16	. . . . . .	.0625		{72		15	.1800		
	52	.0635				14	.1820	12	28
	51	.0670				13	.1850		
	50	.0700	2	{56	3/16	. . . . . .	.1875		
	49	.0730		{64		12	.1890		
	48	.0760				11	.1910		
5/64	. . . . . .	.0781				10	.1935		
	47	.0785	3	48		9	.1960		
	46	.0810				8	.1990		
	45	.0820	3	56		7	.2010	1/4	20
	44	.0860			13/64	. . . . . .	.2031		
	43	.0890	4	40		6	.2040		
	42	.0935	4	48					

DECIMAL EQUIVALENTS AND TAP DRILL SIZES
OF WIRE GAUGE, LETTER AND FRACTIONAL SIZE DRILLS
(TAP DRILL SIZES BASED ON 75% MAXIMUM THREAD)
(CONTINUED)

Fractional Size Drills Inches	Wire Gauge Drills	Decimal Equivalent Inches	Size of Thread	Threads per Inch	Fractional Size Drills Inches	Wire Gauge Drills	Decimal Equivalent Inches	Size of Thread	Threads per Inch
	5	.2055							
	4	.2090				Y	.4040		
	3	.2130	1/4	28	13/32		.4062		
7/32	....	.2187				Z	.4130		
	2	.2210			27/64	....	.4219	1/2	13
	1	.2280			7/16	....	.4375		
	A	.2340			29/64	....	.4531	1/2	20
15/64	....	.2344			15/32	....	.4687		
	B	.2380			31/64	....	.4844	9/16	12
	C	.2420			1/2	....	.5000		
	D	.2460			33/64	....	.5156	9/16	18
1/4	E	.2500			17/32	....	.5312	5/8	11
	F	.2570	5/16	18	35/64	....	.5469		
	G	.2610			9/16	....	.5625		
17/64	....	.2656			37/64	....	.5781	5/8	18
	H	.2660			19/32	....	.5937		
	I	.2720	5/16	24	39/64	....	.6094		
	J	.2770			5/8	....	.6250		
	K	.2810			41/64	....	.6406		
9/32	....	.2812			21/32	....	.6562	3/4	10
	L	.2900			43/64	....	.6719		
	M	.2950			11/16	....	.6875	3/4	16
19/64	....	.2969			45/64	....	.7031		
	N	.3020			23/32	....	.7187		
5/16	....	.3125	3/8	16	47/64	....	.7344		
	O	.3160			3/4	....	.7500		
	P	.3230			49/64	....	.7656	7/8	9
21/64	....	.3281			25/32	....	.7812		
	Q	.3320	3/8	24	51/64	....	.7969		
	R	.3390			13/16	....	.8125	7/8	14
11/32	....	.3437			53/64	....	.8281		
	S	.3480			27/32	....	.8437		
	T	.3580			55/64	....	.8594		
23/64	....	.3594			7/8	....	.8750	1	8
	U	.3680	7/16	14	57/64	....	.8906		
3/8	....	.3750			29/32	....	.9062		
	V	.3770			59/64	....	.9219		
	W	.3860			15/16	....	.9375	1	14
25/64	....	.3906	7/16	20	61/64	....	.9531		
	X	.3970			31/32	....	.9687		
					63/64	....	.9844	1-1/8	7
					1	....	1.0000		

SCREW THREADS

American Standard Free Fit-Class 2

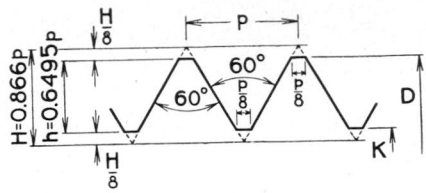

DIAMETER		AREA		Number of Threads per Inch
Total D In.	Net K In.	Total Dia., D Sq. In.	Net Dia., K Sq. In.	
¼	.185	.049	.027	20
⅜	.294	.110	.068	16
½	.400	.196	.126	13
⅝	.507	.307	.202	11
¾	.620	.442	.302	10
⅞	.731	.601	.419	9
1	.838	.785	.551	8
1⅛	.939	.994	.693	7
1¼	1.064	1.227	.890	7
1⅜	1.158	1.485	1.054	6
1½	1.283	1.767	1.294	6
1⅝	1.389	2.074	1.515	5½
1¾	1.490	2.405	1.744	5
1⅞	1.615	2.761	2.049	5
2	1.711	3.142	2.300	4½
2¼	1.961	3.976	3.021	4½

DIAMETER		AREA		Number of Threads per Inch
Total D In.	Net K In.	Total Dia., D Sq. In.	Net Dia., K Sq. In.	
2½	2.175	4.909	3.716	4
2¾	2.425	5.940	4.619	4
3	2.629	7.069	5.428	3½
3¼	2.879	8.296	6.509	3½
3½	3.100	9.621	7.549	3¼
3¾	3.317	11.045	8.641	3
4	3.567	12.566	9.993	3
4¼	3.798	14.186	11.330	2⅞
4½	4.028	15.904	12.741	2¾
4¾	4.255	17.721	14.221	2⅝
5	4.480	19.635	15.766	2½
5¼	4.730	21.648	17.574	2½
5½	4.953	23.758	19.268	2⅜
5¾	5.203	25.967	21.262	2⅜
6	5.423	28.274	23.095	2¼

LENGTH OF BOLT THREADS

Length of Bolt, Inches	Diameter of Bolt, Inches																	
	¼	⅜	½	⅝	¾	⅞	1	1⅛	1¼	1⅜	1½	1⅝	1¾	2	2¼	2½	2¾	3
1 to 1½	¾	¾	1	1¼														
1⅝ to 2	¾	¾	1	1¼	1½	1½												
2⅛ to 2½	¾	¾	1	1¼	1½	1¾	1¾											
2⅝ to 3	⅞	⅞	1	1¼	1½	1¾	1¾	2¼										
3⅛ to 4	⅞	⅞	1¼	1¼	1½	1¾	1¾	2¼	2½									
4⅛ to 8	1	1	1¼	1½	1¾	2	2¼	2½	2¾	3¼	3¾	4						
8⅛ to 12	1⅛	1⅛	1½	1¾	2	2¼	2½	3	3	3½	4	4¼	4½	5	5½	6¼	7	7¾
12⅛ to 20	1⅛	1⅛	1½	2	2	2¼	2½	3	3	3½	4	4¼	4½	5	5½	6¼	7	7¾

Bolts not listed are threaded about 3 times the diameter.

Standard bolts longer than 1¼ inches are in no case threaded closer to the head than ¼ inch.

BOLT HEADS AND NUTS

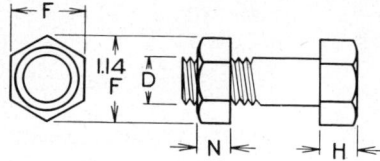
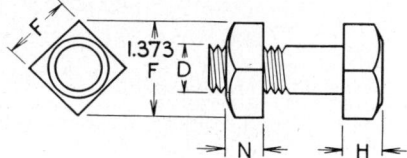

HEADS AND NUTS		American Standard Regular	American Standard Heavy
HEAD	Height, H.	$\frac{2}{3}$D	$\frac{3}{4}$D+$\frac{1}{16}$"
	Short Dia., F	$1\frac{1}{2}$D	$1\frac{1}{2}$D+$\frac{1}{8}$"
NUT	Height, N	$\frac{7}{8}$D	D
	Short Dia., F	$1\frac{1}{2}$D+$\frac{1}{16}$" (D = $\frac{5}{8}$" or less) / $1\frac{1}{2}$D (D greater than $\frac{5}{8}$")	$1\frac{1}{2}$D+$\frac{1}{8}$"

American Standard Bolt and Nut dimensions rounded to nearest $\frac{1}{16}$-inch, are those adopted by American Institute of Bolt, Nut and Rivet Manufacturers and approved by American Standards Association, March, 1933. "American Standard Regular" formerly called Manufacturers Standard, American Standard, etc. "American Standard Heavy" formerly called United States Standard. For bolts with countersunk heads the included angle is 78 degrees, same as for rivets.

STANDARD DIMENSIONS

Dia. of Bolt In.	Series	HEAD Hexagon Diameter, In. Long	Short	Height In.	Square Diameter, In. Long	Short	Dia. of Bolt In.	Series	NUT Hexagon Diameter, In. Long	Short	Height In.	Square Diameter, In. Long	Short
$\frac{1}{4}$	American Standard Regular	$\frac{7}{16}$	$\frac{3}{8}$	$\frac{3}{16}$	$\frac{1}{2}$	$\frac{3}{8}$	$\frac{1}{4}$	American Standard Regular	$\frac{1}{2}$	$\frac{7}{16}$	$\frac{1}{4}$	$\frac{5}{8}$	$\frac{7}{16}$
$\frac{3}{8}$		$\frac{5}{8}$	$\frac{9}{16}$	$\frac{1}{4}$	$\frac{3}{4}$	$\frac{9}{16}$	$\frac{3}{8}$		$\frac{11}{16}$	$\frac{5}{8}$	$\frac{5}{16}$	$\frac{7}{8}$	$\frac{5}{8}$
$\frac{1}{2}$		$\frac{7}{8}$	$\frac{3}{4}$	$\frac{5}{16}$	1	$\frac{3}{4}$	$\frac{1}{2}$		$\frac{15}{16}$	$\frac{13}{16}$	$\frac{7}{16}$	$1\frac{1}{8}$	$\frac{13}{16}$
$\frac{5}{8}$		$1\frac{1}{16}$	$\frac{15}{16}$	$\frac{7}{16}$	$1\frac{5}{16}$	$\frac{15}{16}$	$\frac{5}{8}$		$1\frac{1}{8}$	1	$\frac{9}{16}$	$1\frac{3}{8}$	1
$\frac{3}{4}$		$1\frac{5}{16}$	$1\frac{1}{8}$	$\frac{1}{2}$	$1\frac{9}{16}$	$1\frac{1}{8}$	$\frac{3}{4}$		$1\frac{5}{16}$	$1\frac{1}{8}$	$\frac{11}{16}$	$1\frac{9}{16}$	$1\frac{1}{8}$
$\frac{7}{8}$		$1\frac{1}{2}$	$1\frac{5}{16}$	$\frac{9}{16}$	$1\frac{13}{16}$	$1\frac{5}{16}$	$\frac{7}{8}$		$1\frac{1}{2}$	$1\frac{5}{16}$	$\frac{3}{4}$	$1\frac{13}{16}$	$1\frac{5}{16}$
1		$1\frac{11}{16}$	$1\frac{1}{2}$	$\frac{5}{8}$	$2\frac{1}{16}$	$1\frac{1}{2}$	1		$1\frac{11}{16}$	$1\frac{1}{2}$	$\frac{7}{8}$	$2\frac{1}{16}$	$1\frac{1}{2}$
$1\frac{1}{8}$		$1\frac{15}{16}$	$1\frac{11}{16}$	$\frac{3}{4}$	$2\frac{5}{16}$	$1\frac{11}{16}$	$1\frac{1}{8}$		$1\frac{15}{16}$	$1\frac{11}{16}$	1	$2\frac{5}{16}$	$1\frac{11}{16}$
$1\frac{1}{4}$		$2\frac{1}{8}$	$1\frac{7}{8}$	$\frac{13}{16}$	$2\frac{9}{16}$	$1\frac{7}{8}$	$1\frac{1}{4}$		$2\frac{1}{8}$	$1\frac{7}{8}$	$1\frac{1}{8}$	$2\frac{9}{16}$	$1\frac{7}{8}$
$1\frac{3}{8}$		$2\frac{3}{8}$	$2\frac{1}{16}$	$\frac{15}{16}$	$2\frac{13}{16}$	$2\frac{1}{16}$	$1\frac{3}{8}$		$2\frac{3}{8}$	$2\frac{1}{16}$	$1\frac{1}{4}$	$2\frac{13}{16}$	$2\frac{1}{16}$
$1\frac{1}{2}$		$2\frac{9}{16}$	$2\frac{1}{4}$	1	$3\frac{1}{16}$	$2\frac{1}{4}$	$1\frac{1}{2}$		$2\frac{9}{16}$	$2\frac{1}{4}$	$1\frac{5}{16}$	$3\frac{1}{16}$	$2\frac{1}{4}$
$1\frac{3}{8}$		$2\frac{3}{8}$	$2\frac{1}{16}$	$\frac{15}{16}$	$2\frac{13}{16}$	$2\frac{1}{16}$	$1\frac{3}{8}$		$2\frac{1}{2}$	$2\frac{3}{16}$	$1\frac{3}{8}$	3	$2\frac{3}{8}$
$1\frac{1}{2}$		$2\frac{9}{16}$	$2\frac{1}{4}$	1	$3\frac{1}{16}$	$2\frac{1}{4}$	$1\frac{1}{2}$		$2\frac{11}{16}$	$2\frac{3}{8}$	$1\frac{1}{2}$	$3\frac{1}{4}$	$2\frac{3}{8}$
$1\frac{5}{8}$		$2\frac{3}{4}$	$2\frac{7}{16}$	$1\frac{1}{16}$	$3\frac{3}{8}$	$2\frac{7}{16}$	$1\frac{5}{8}$		$2\frac{15}{16}$	$2\frac{9}{16}$	$1\frac{5}{8}$	$3\frac{1}{2}$	$2\frac{9}{16}$
$1\frac{3}{4}$		3	$2\frac{5}{8}$	$1\frac{3}{16}$	$3\frac{5}{8}$	$2\frac{5}{8}$	$1\frac{3}{4}$		$3\frac{1}{8}$	$2\frac{3}{4}$	$1\frac{3}{4}$	$3\frac{3}{4}$	$2\frac{3}{4}$
$1\frac{7}{8}$		$3\frac{3}{16}$	$2\frac{13}{16}$	$1\frac{1}{4}$	$3\frac{7}{8}$	$2\frac{13}{16}$	$1\frac{7}{8}$		$3\frac{3}{8}$	$2\frac{15}{16}$	$1\frac{7}{8}$	$4\frac{1}{16}$	$2\frac{15}{16}$
2	American Standard Regular	$3\frac{7}{16}$	3	$1\frac{5}{16}$	$4\frac{1}{8}$	3	2	American Standard Heavy	$3\frac{9}{16}$	$3\frac{1}{8}$	2	$4\frac{5}{16}$	$3\frac{1}{8}$
$2\frac{1}{4}$		$3\frac{7}{8}$	$3\frac{3}{8}$	$1\frac{1}{2}$	$4\frac{5}{8}$	$3\frac{3}{8}$	$2\frac{1}{4}$		4	$3\frac{1}{2}$	$2\frac{1}{4}$	$4\frac{13}{16}$	$3\frac{1}{2}$
$2\frac{1}{2}$		$4\frac{1}{4}$	$3\frac{3}{4}$	$1\frac{11}{16}$	$5\frac{1}{8}$	$3\frac{3}{4}$	$2\frac{1}{2}$		$4\frac{7}{16}$	$3\frac{7}{8}$	$2\frac{1}{2}$	$5\frac{5}{16}$	$3\frac{7}{8}$
$2\frac{3}{4}$		$4\frac{11}{16}$	$4\frac{1}{8}$	$1\frac{13}{16}$	$5\frac{11}{16}$	$4\frac{1}{8}$	$2\frac{3}{4}$		$4\frac{7}{8}$	$4\frac{1}{4}$	$2\frac{3}{4}$	$5\frac{13}{16}$	$4\frac{1}{4}$
3		$5\frac{1}{8}$	$4\frac{1}{2}$	2	$6\frac{3}{16}$	$4\frac{1}{2}$	3		$5\frac{1}{4}$	$4\frac{5}{8}$	3	$6\frac{3}{8}$	$4\frac{5}{8}$
$3\frac{1}{4}$		$5\frac{9}{16}$	$4\frac{7}{8}$	$2\frac{3}{16}$	$6\frac{11}{16}$	$4\frac{7}{8}$	$3\frac{1}{4}$		$5\frac{11}{16}$	5	$3\frac{1}{4}$	$6\frac{7}{8}$	5
$3\frac{1}{2}$		6	$5\frac{1}{4}$	$2\frac{5}{16}$	$7\frac{3}{16}$	$5\frac{1}{4}$	$3\frac{1}{2}$		$6\frac{1}{8}$	$5\frac{3}{8}$	$3\frac{1}{2}$	$7\frac{3}{8}$	$5\frac{3}{8}$
$3\frac{3}{4}$		$6\frac{7}{16}$	$5\frac{5}{8}$	$2\frac{1}{2}$	$7\frac{3}{4}$	$5\frac{5}{8}$	$3\frac{3}{4}$		$6\frac{9}{16}$	$5\frac{3}{4}$	$3\frac{3}{4}$	$7\frac{7}{8}$	$5\frac{3}{4}$
4		$6\frac{7}{8}$	6	$2\frac{11}{16}$	$8\frac{1}{4}$	6	4		7	$6\frac{1}{8}$	4	$8\frac{7}{16}$	$6\frac{1}{8}$
$4\frac{1}{4}$		$7\frac{1}{4}$	$6\frac{3}{8}$	$2\frac{13}{16}$	$8\frac{3}{4}$	$6\frac{3}{8}$	$4\frac{1}{4}$		$7\frac{7}{16}$	$6\frac{1}{2}$	$4\frac{1}{4}$	$8\frac{15}{16}$	$6\frac{1}{2}$
$4\frac{1}{2}$		$7\frac{11}{16}$	$6\frac{3}{4}$	3	$9\frac{1}{4}$	$6\frac{3}{4}$	$4\frac{1}{2}$		$7\frac{13}{16}$	$6\frac{7}{8}$	$4\frac{1}{2}$	$9\frac{7}{16}$	$6\frac{7}{8}$
$4\frac{3}{4}$		$8\frac{1}{8}$	$7\frac{1}{8}$	$3\frac{3}{16}$	$9\frac{13}{16}$	$7\frac{1}{8}$	$4\frac{3}{4}$		$8\frac{1}{4}$	$7\frac{1}{4}$	$4\frac{3}{4}$	$9\frac{15}{16}$	$7\frac{1}{4}$
5		$8\frac{9}{16}$	$7\frac{1}{2}$	$3\frac{5}{16}$	$10\frac{5}{16}$	$7\frac{1}{2}$	5		$8\frac{11}{16}$	$7\frac{5}{8}$	5	$10\frac{1}{2}$	$7\frac{5}{8}$

AMERICAN MALLEABLE IRON

WEIGHT OF BOLTS

WITH SQUARE HEADS AND HEXAGON NUTS
IN POUNDS PER 100

This head and nut combination, using "American Standard Regular" dimensions, is usual practice with many fabricators.

Length under head Inches	Diameter of Bolt in Inches										
	$\frac{1}{4}$	$\frac{5}{16}$	$\frac{3}{8}$	$\frac{7}{16}$	$\frac{1}{2}$	$\frac{5}{8}$	$\frac{3}{4}$	$\frac{7}{8}$	1	$1\frac{1}{8}$	$1\frac{1}{4}$
1	2.7	5.0	7.2	11.2	14.9	28	43				
$1\frac{1}{4}$	3.1	5.5	8.0	12.2	16.3	30	46	68			
$1\frac{1}{2}$	3.4	6.1	8.8	13.3	17.7	32	49	73	103	144	190
$1\frac{3}{4}$	3.8	6.6	9.6	14.4	19.0	35	52	77	109	151	199
2	4.1	7.2	10.4	15.4	20.4	37	55	81	115	158	208
$2\frac{1}{4}$	4.5	7.7	11.1	16.5	21.8	39	58	85	120	165	216
$2\frac{1}{2}$	4.8	8.2	11.9	17.5	23.2	41	61	90	126	172	225
$2\frac{3}{4}$	5.2	8.8	12.7	18.6	24.6	43	64	94	131	179	234
3	5.5	9.3	13.5	19.7	26.0	45	68	98	137	187	242
$3\frac{1}{4}$	5.9	9.9	14.3	20.7	27.4	48	71	102	142	194	251
$3\frac{1}{2}$	6.2	10.4	15.1	21.8	28.8	50	74	107	148	201	260
$3\frac{3}{4}$	6.6	11.0	15.8	22.9	30.2	52	77	111	153	208	268
4	6.9	11.5	16.6	23.9	31.6	54	80	115	159	215	277
$4\frac{1}{4}$	7.3	12.0	17.4	25.0	33.0	56	83	119	165	222	286
$4\frac{1}{2}$	7.6	12.6	18.2	26.1	34.4	58	86	124	170	229	294
$4\frac{3}{4}$	8.0	13.1	19.0	27.1	35.7	61	89	128	176	236	303
5	8.3	13.7	19.8	28.2	37.1	63	93	132	181	243	312
$5\frac{1}{4}$	8.6	14.2	20.5	29.3	38.5	65	96	136	187	250	321
$5\frac{1}{2}$	9.0	14.8	21.3	30.3	39.9	67	99	141	192	257	329
$5\frac{3}{4}$	9.3	15.3	22.1	31.4	41.3	69	102	145	198	264	338
6	9.7	15.9	22.9	32.4	42.7	71	105	149	204	271	347
$6\frac{1}{4}$	10.0	16.4	23.7	33.5	44.1	74	108	153	209	278	355
$6\frac{1}{2}$	10.4	16.9	24.5	34.6	45.5	76	111	158	215	285	364
$6\frac{3}{4}$	10.7	17.5	25.2	35.6	46.9	78	114	162	220	292	373
7	11.1	18.0	26.0	36.7	48.3	80	118	166	226	299	381
$7\frac{1}{4}$	11.4	18.6	26.8	37.8	49.7	82	121	170	231	306	390
$7\frac{1}{2}$	11.8	19.1	27.6	38.8	51.1	84	124	175	237	313	399
$7\frac{3}{4}$	12.1	19.7	28.4	39.9	52.4	87	127	179	242	320	407
8	12.5	20.2	29.2	41.0	53.8	89	130	183	248	327	416
$8\frac{1}{2}$	....	21.3	30.7	43.1	56.6	93	136	192	259	341	434
9	....	22.4	32.3	45.2	59.4	98	143	200	270	356	451
$9\frac{1}{2}$	....	23.5	33.9	47.4	62.2	102	149	209	281	370	468
10	....	.24.6	35.4	49.5	65.0	106	155	217	293	384	486
$10\frac{1}{2}$	....	....	37.0	51.6	67.8	111	161	226	304	398	503
11	....	....	38.6	53.7	70.5	115	168	234	315	412	520
$11\frac{1}{2}$	....	....	40.1	55.9	73.3	119	174	243	326	426	538
12	....	....	41.7	58.0	76.1	124	180	251	337	440	555
$12\frac{1}{2}$	....	....		60.1	78.9	128	186	260	348	454	573
13	....	....		62.3	81.7	132	193	268	359	468	590
$13\frac{1}{2}$	....	....		64.4	84.5	137	199	277	370	482	607
14	....	....		66.5	87.2	141	205	285	382	496	625
Per Inch additional	1.4	2.2	3.1	4.3	5.6	8.7	12.5	17.0	22.3	28.2	34.8

AMERICAN INSTITUTE OF STEEL CONSTRUCTION

WEIGHT OF BOLTS

SPECIAL CASES

IN POUNDS PER 100

VARIATIONS IN HEADS OR NUTS

As stated on opposite page, usual practice is Square Head and Hexagon Nut, "American Standard Regular." For other combinations of head and nut, or for "American Standard Heavy," make the appropriate deductions and additions of weights of heads and nuts as tabulated below, from the weights per 100 found on opposite page.

Weight of 100 each		Diameter of Bolt, Inches										
		1/4	5/16	3/8	7/16	1/2	5/8	3/4	7/8	1	1 1/8	1 1/4
Regular	Square Heads	.7	1.4	2.2	3.2	5.1	10	18	29	42	60	84
	Hexagon Heads	.6	1.2	1.9	2.8	4.5	9	15	25	36	52	73
	Square Nuts	.81	1.7	2.3	4.1	5.6	10	14	23	35	49	67
	Hexagon Nuts	.64	1.4	1.9	3.7	4.2	9	12	18	28	42	54
Heavy	Square Heads	....	....	....	....	9.5	17	28	42	61	84	112
	Hexagon Heads	....	....	....	....	8.2	14	24	36	53	73	94
	Square Nuts	....	....	....	....	7.9	14	23	35	50	66	92
	Hexagon Nuts	....	....	....	....	6.6	11	19	28	41	56	73

HEAVY BOLTS

Weights of bolts over 1 1/4 inches in diameter may be calculated from the following data. Standard practice is "American Standard Regular" head with "American Standard Regular" or "Heavy" nut, as specified.

Weight of 100 each		Diameter of Bolt, Inches										
		1 1/2	1 3/4	2	2 1/4	2 1/2	2 3/4	3	3 1/4	3 1/2	3 3/4	4
Regular	Square Heads	143	226	343	484	660	881	1148	1452	1830	2241	2710
	Hexagon Heads	124	196	297	419	577	764	994	1257	1585	1941	2350
	Square Nuts	116	184	276	391	539	666	874				
	Hexagon Nuts	102	162	231	337	472	606	825				
Heavy	Square Heads	190	295	432	608	825	1087	1401	1775	2115	2715	3312
	Hexagon Heads	162	254	377	538	727	890	1214	1526	1906	2344	2845
	Square Nuts	154	242	355	496	674	831	1082	1767	2043	2303	2969
	Hexagon Nuts	123	208	303	422	573	742	1008	1196	1485	1789	2184
Pounds per linear inch of Shank		.5007	.6815	.8900	1.127	1.391	1.683	2.003	2.348	2.723	3.126	3.556

STANDARD PIPES

Diameter in Inches			Weight per Foot, Pounds	Moment of Inertia, Inches[4]	Section Modulus, Inches[3]	Radius of Gyration, Inches
Nominal	External	Internal				
BLACK OR GALVANIZED STANDARD WEIGHT PIPE						
1/8	0.405	0.269	0.244	0.001	0.005	0.12
1/4	.540	.364	.424	.003	.012	.16
3/8	.675	.493	.567	.007	.022	.21
1/2	.840	.622	.850	.017	.041	.26
3/4	1.050	.824	1.130	.037	.071	.33
1	1.315	1.049	1.678	.09	.13	.42
1 1/4	1.660	1.380	2.272	.19	.23	.54
1 1/2	1.900	1.610	2.717	.31	.36	.62
2	2.375	2.067	3.652	.67	.56	.79
2 1/2	2.875	2.469	5.793	1.53	1.06	.95
3	3.500	3.068	7.575	3.02	1.72	1.16
3 1/2	4.000	3.548	9.109	4.79	2.39	1.34
4	4.500	4.026	10.790	7.23	3.21	1.51
4 1/2	5.000	4.506	12.538	10.4	4.2	1.68
5	5.563	5.047	14.617	15.2	5.5	1.88
6	6.625	6.065	18.974	28.1	8.5	2.25
7	7.625	7.023	23.544	46.5	12.2	2.59
8	8.625	8.071	24.696	63.4	14.7	3.31
9	9.625	8.941	33.907	107.6	22.4	3.28
10	10.750	10.192	31.201	125.9	23.4	3.70
10	10.750	10.020	40.483	160.9	29.9	3.67
11	11.750	11.000	45.557	217.0	36.9	4.02
12	12.750	12.090	43.773	248.5	40.0	4.39
12	12.750	12.000	49.562	285.4	44.7	4.38
13	14.000	13.250	54.568	372.8	53.3	4.82
14	15.000	14.250	58.573	461.0	61.5	5.23
15	16.000	15.250	62.579	562.0	70.3	5.53
STANDARD EXTRA STRONG PIPE						
1/8	0.405	0.215	0.314	0.001	0.006	0.11
1/4	.540	.302	.535	.004	.014	.15
3/8	.675	.423	.738	.009	.026	.20
1/2	.840	.546	1.087	.020	.048	.25
3/4	1.050	.742	1.473	.045	.085	.32

STANDARD PIPES
(CONTINUED)

Diameter in Inches			Weight per Foot, Pounds	Moment of Inertia, Inches^4	Section Modulus, Inches^3	Radius of Gyration, Inches
Nominal	External	Internal				

			STANDARD EXTRA STRONG PIPE (CONTINUED)			
1	1.315	0.957	2.171	0.11	0.16	0.41
1¼	1.660	1.278	2.996	.24	.29	.52
1½	1.900	1.500	3.631	.39	.46	.61
2	2.375	1.939	5.022	.87	.73	.77
2½	2.875	2.323	7.661	1.92	1.34	.92
3	3.500	2.900	10.252	3.89	2.23	1.14
3½	4.000	3.364	12.505	6.28	3.14	1.29
4	4.500	3.826	14.983	9.6	4.3	1.48
4½	5.000	4.290	17.611	14.1	5.6	1.65
5	5.563	4.813	20.778	20.7	7.4	1.84
6	6.625	5.761	28.573	40.5	12.2	2.19
7	7.625	6.625	38.048	71.4	18.7	2.53
8	8.625	7.625	43.388	105.7	24.5	2.88
9	9.625	8.625	48.728	149.4	31.0	3.23
10	10.750	9.750	54.735	212.0	39.3	3.63
11	11.750	10.750	60.075	280.1	47.7	3.98
12	12.750	11.750	65.415	360.7	56.6	4.33

			STANDARD DOUBLE EXTRA STRONG PIPE			
¾	1.050	0.434	2.440	0.058	0.11	0.28
1	1.315	.599	3.659	.14	.21	.36
1¼	1.660	.896	5.214	.34	.41	.47
1½	1.900	1.100	6.408	.57	.67	.55
2	2.375	1.503	9.029	1.31	1.10	.70
2½	2.875	1.771	13.695	2.87	2.00	.84
3	3.500	2.300	18.583	6.0	3.4	1.05
3½	4.000	2.728	22.850	9.8	4.9	1.21
4	4.500	3.152	27.541	15.3	6.8	1.37
4½	5.000	3.580	32.530	22.6	9.0	1.54
5	5.563	4.063	38.552	33.7	12.3	1.72
6	6.625	4.897	53.160	66.3	20.0	2.08
7	7.625	5.875	62.079	107.5	28.2	2.41
8	8.625	6.875	72.424	162.0	37.6	2.76

(CAMBRIA)

PIPE THREADS

NORMAL ENGAGEMENT BETWEEN MALE AND FEMALE THREADS TO MAKE TIGHT JOINTS

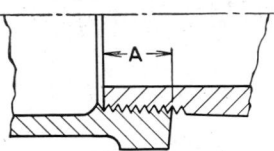

American Standard
Pipe Threads

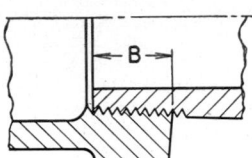

A.P.I. Line
Pipe Threads

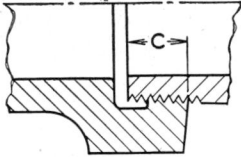

Shoulder Type
Drainage Fitting Threads

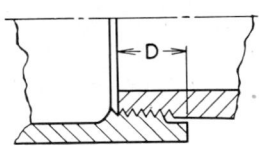

Railing Fitting
Threads

Size	$\frac{1}{8}$	$\frac{1}{4}$	$\frac{3}{8}$	$\frac{1}{2}$	$\frac{3}{4}$	1	$1\frac{1}{4}$	$1\frac{1}{2}$	2	$2\frac{1}{2}$	3	$3\frac{1}{2}$
A	$\frac{1}{4}$	$\frac{3}{8}$	$\frac{3}{8}$	$\frac{1}{2}$	$\frac{9}{16}$	$\frac{11}{16}$	$\frac{11}{16}$	$\frac{11}{16}$	$\frac{3}{4}$	$\frac{15}{16}$	1	$1\frac{1}{16}$
B*	$\frac{1}{4}$	$\frac{3}{8}$	$\frac{3}{8}$	$\frac{1}{2}$	$\frac{9}{16}$	$\frac{11}{16}$	$\frac{11}{16}$	$\frac{11}{16}$	$1\frac{1}{16}$	1	1	$1\frac{1}{4}$
C†						$\frac{9}{16}$	$\frac{5}{8}$	$\frac{5}{8}$	$\frac{5}{8}$	$\frac{7}{8}$	$\frac{15}{16}$	1
D§				$\frac{1}{2}$	$\frac{1}{2}$	$\frac{5}{8}$	$\frac{11}{16}$	$\frac{3}{4}$	$\frac{3}{4}$	1	$1\frac{1}{16}$	$1\frac{1}{8}$

Size	4	$4\frac{1}{2}$	5	6	7	8	9	10	11	12	14
A	$1\frac{1}{8}$	$1\frac{3}{16}$	$1\frac{1}{4}$	$1\frac{5}{16}$	$1\frac{3}{8}$	$1\frac{7}{16}$	$1\frac{1}{2}$	$1\frac{5}{8}$	$1\frac{11}{16}$	$1\frac{3}{4}$	
B*	$1\frac{1}{4}$		$1\frac{1}{2}$	$1\frac{9}{16}$		$1\frac{11}{16}$		$1\frac{7}{8}$		2	
C†	$1\frac{1}{16}$		$1\frac{3}{16}$	$1\frac{1}{4}$		$1\frac{3}{8}$		$1\frac{9}{16}$		$1\frac{11}{16}$	$1\frac{7}{8}$
D§	$1\frac{3}{16}$										

Dimensions given do not allow for variations in tapping or threading.

* Using an A.P.I. Line Pipe Male Thread and an American Standard Pipe Threaded Fitting. American Standard Pipe Threaded Fittings may be used provided there are no obstructions in the thread chambers to interfere with the longer A.P.I. Male Threads.

† Using American Standard Taper Male Thread with Crane shoulder type Drainage Fittings. The male thread, however, should not be threaded small to gauge and not more than one turn large.

§ Using a special male thread with Crane Railing Fittings. The male thread is basically the same as the American Standard Taper Pipe Thread except it is much shorter.

CODE FOR ARC AND GAS WELDING IN BUILDING CONSTRUCTION

AMERICAN WELDING SOCIETY (EDITION OF 1941)

Use of the fusion welding process (sometimes electric arc, sometimes oxyacetylene) plays an increasing part in the fabrication of structural steel: (a) as an aid to shop assembling processes (" tack-welding "), (b) as the final method of joining parts for transfer of stresses, in shop or field (" strength-welding ").

The art of designing and detailing for the safe and economical employment of strength-welding is a relatively new and changing one. At present it is suggested that strength-welding of structures be permitted only on condition that the designing, detailing, and erection are in the hands of personnel well trained in the best practice of the art. The best exposition of that art is to be found in the reports and recommendations of the American Welding Society, 33 West 39th St., New York City. The " Code for Arc and Gas Welding in Building Construction " of that Society, with Appendices, is authoritative.

The American Welding Society has compiled a code covering electric resistance welding, as applied to shop fabrication of building parts, such as bar joists.

LEGEND FOR USE ON DRAWINGS SPECIFYING FUSION WELDING

The symbols below are recommended by American Welding Society for incorporation on drawings specifying fusion welding. For more detailed instruction in the use of these symbols refer to " Welding Symbols and Instructions for Their Use " published by the American Welding Society.

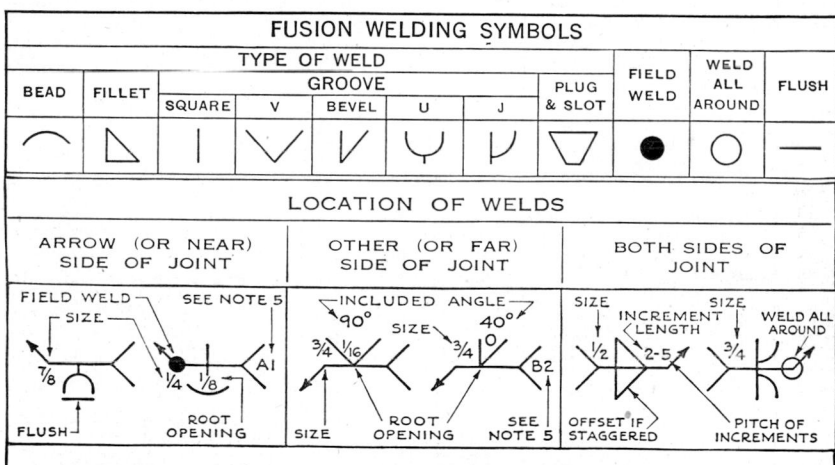

1. THE SIDE OF THE JOINT TO WHICH THE ARROW POINTS IS THE ARROW (OR NEAR) SIDE.

2. BOTH–SIDES WELDS OF SAME TYPE ARE OF SAME SIZE UNLESS OTHERWISE SHOWN.

3. SYMBOLS APPLY BETWEEN ABRUPT CHANGES IN DIRECTION OF JOINT OR AS DIMENSIONED (EXCEPT WHERE ALL AROUND SYMBOL IS USED).

4. ALL WELDS ARE CONTINUOUS AND OF USER'S STANDARD PROPORTIONS UNLESS OTHERWISE SHOWN.

5. TAIL OF ARROW USED FOR SPECIFICATION REFERENCE (TAIL MAY BE OMITTED WHEN REFERENCE NOT USED).

6. DIMENSIONS OF WELD SIZES, INCREMENT LENGTHS AND SPACINGS ARE IN INCHES.

AMERICAN INSTITUTE OF STEEL CONSTRUCTION

HARDNESS TESTS

Steels commonly used in construction work

Comparing Brinell hardness number scales for loads of 500 kg. and 3000 kg., with Vickers, Rockwell, and Shore hardness scales and tensile strength.

Brinell (10 mm. Ball) and M-1 Monotron			Vickers Hardness No.	Rockwell					Shore Sclero-scope No.	Tensile Strength p. s. i.
				C	B	Superficial Scale				
Diameter of Inden-tation, mm.	Hardness No.			150 kg. load 120° Diamond Brale	100 kg. load 1/16″ Diameter Ball	15-T	15-N			
	500 kg. load	3000 kg. load								
2.50	100	601	717	58	. . .	. . . .		89.0	81	298,000
2.55	96.3	578	675	57	. . .	. . . .		88.5	78	287,000
2.60	92.6	555	633	55	120	. . . .		87.5	75	276,000
2.65	89.0	534	598	53	119	. . . .		86.5	72	266,000
2.70	85.7	514	567	52	119	. . . .		86.0	70	256,000
2.75	82.6	495	540	50	117	. . . .		85.0	67	247,000
2.80	79.6	477	515	49	117	. . . .		84.5	65	238,000
2.85	76.8	461	494	47	116	. . . .		83.5	63	229,000
2.90	74.1	444	472	46	115	. . . .		83.0	61	220,000
2.95	71.5	429	454	45	115	. . . .		82.5	59	212,000
3.00	69.1	415	437	44	114	. . . .		82.0	57	204,000
3.05	66.8	401	420	42	113	. . . .		81.0	55	196,000
3.10	64.6	388	404	41	112	. . . .		80.5	54	189,000
3.15	62.5	375	389	40	112	. . . .		80.0	52	182,000
3.20	60.5	363	375	38	110	. . . .		79.0	51	176,000
3.25	58.6	352	363	37	110	. . . .		78.5	49	170,000
3.30	56.8	341	350	36	109	. . . .		78.0	48	165,000
3.35	55.1	331	339	35	109	. . . .		77.5	46	160,000
3.40	53.4	321	327	34	108	. . . .		77.0	45	155,000
3.45	51.8	311	316	33	108	. . . .		76.5	44	150,000
3.50	50.3	302	305	32	107	. . . .		76.0	43	146,000
3.55	48.9	293	296	31	106	. . . .		75.5	42	142,000
3.60	47.5	285	287	30	105	. . . .		75.0	40	138,000
3.65	46.1	277	279	29	104	. . . .		74.5	39	134,000
3.70	44.9	269	270	28	104	. . . .		74.0	38	131,000
3.75	43.6	262	263	26	103	. . . .		73.0	37	128,000
3.80	42.4	255	256	25	102	. . . .		72.5	37	125,000
3.85	41.3	248	248	24	102	. . . .		72.0	36	122,000
3.90	40.2	241	241	23	100	. . . .		71.5	35	119,000
3.95	39.1	235	235	22	99	92.5		71.0	34	116,000
4.00	38.1	229	229	21	98	. . . .		70.5	33	113,000
4.05	37.1	223	223	20	97	92.0		70.0	32	110,000
4.10	36.2	217	217	18	96	. . . .	. . . .		31	107,000
4.15	35.3	212	212	17	96	. . . .	. . . .		31	104,000
4.20	34.4	207	207	16	95	91.5	. . . .		30	101,000
4.25	33.6	202	202	15	94	91.0	. . . .		30	99,000

HARDNESS TESTS

(CONTINUED)

Steels commonly used in construction work

Comparing Brinell hardness number scales for loads of 500 kg. and 3000 kg., with Vickers, Rockwell, and Shore hardness scales and tensile strength.

Brinell (10 mm. Ball) and M-1 Monotron			Vickers Hardness No.	Rockwell				Shore Sclero-scope No.	Tensile Strength p. s. i.
Diameter of Inden-tation, mm.	Hardness No.			C	B	Superficial Scale			
	500 kg. load	3000 kg. load		150 kg. load 120° Diamond Brale	100 kg. load 1/16″ Diameter Ball	15-T	15-N		
4.30	32.8	197	197	13	93	. . . .	. . . .	29	97,000
4.35	32.0	192	192	12	92	90.5	. . . .	28	95,000
4.40	31.2	187	187	10	91	90.0	. . . .	28	93,000
4.45	30.5	183	183	9	90	. . . .	. . . .	27	91,000
4.50	29.8	179	179	8	89	89.5	. . . .	27	89,000
4.55	29.1	174	174	7	88	. . . .	. . . .	26	87,000
4.60	28.4	170	170	6	87	89.0	. . . .	26	85,000
4.65	27.8	166	166	4	86	. . . .	. . . .	25	83,000
4.70	27.1	163	163	3	85	88.5	. . . .	25	82,000
4.75	26.5	159	159	2	84	88.0	. . . .	24	80,000
4.80	25.9	156	156	1	83	. . . .	. . . .	24	78,000
4.85	25.4	153	153	. .	82	87.5	. . . .	23	76,000
4.90	24.8	149	149	. .	81	87.0	. . . .	23	75,000
4.95	24.3	146	146	. .	80	. . . .	. . . .	22	74,000
5.00	23.8	143	143	. .	79	86.5	. . . .	22	72,000
5.05	23.3	140	140	. .	78	. . . .	. . . .	21	71,000
5.10	22.8	137	137	. .	77	86.0	. . . .	21	70,000
5.15	22.3	134	134	. .	76	. . . .	. . . .	21	68,000
5.20	21.8	131	131	. .	74	85.0	. . . .	20	66,000
5.25	21.4	128	128	. .	73	. . . .	. . . .	20	65,000
5.30	20.9	126	126	. .	72	84.5	. . . .	. .	64,000
5.35	20.5	124	124	. .	71	84.0	. . . .	. .	63,000
5.40	20.1	121	121	. .	70	. . . .	. . . .	. .	62,000
5.45	19.7	118	118	. .	69	83.5	. . . .	. .	61,000
5.50	19.3	116	116	. .	68	. . . .	. . . .	. .	60,000
5.55	18.9	114	114	. .	67	83.0	. . . .	. .	59,000
5.60	18.6	112	112	. .	66	. . . .	. . . .	. .	58,000
5.65	18.2	109	109	. .	65	82.5	. . . .	. .	56,000
5.70	17.8	107	107	. .	64	82.0	. . . .	. .	55,000
5.75	17.5	105	105	. .	62	81.5	. . . .	. .	54,000
5.80	17.2	103	103	. .	61	81.0	. . . .	. .	53,000
5.85	16.8	101	101	. .	60	. . . .	. . . .	. .	52,000
5.90	16.5	99	99	. .	59	80.5	. . . .	. .	51,000
5.95	16.2	97	97	. .	57	80.0	. . . .	. .	50,000
6.00	15.9	95	95	. .	56	. . . .	. . . .	. .	49,000

APPROXIMATE SPECIFIC GRAVITIES AND DENSITIES

Water at 39° F and normal atmospheric pressure is taken as unity.
Data given are for usual room temperatures.

Substance	Specific Gravity	Avg Density lb. per cu. ft.	Substance	Specific Gravity	Avg Density lb. per cu. ft.
Metals, Alloys, Ores			Cork	0.22–0.26	15
Aluminum	2.56	165	Cotton, flax, hemp	1.47–1.50	93
Aluminum, bronze	7.7	481	Fats	0.90–0.97	58
Brass, cast-rolled	8.4–8.7	534	Flour, loose	0.40–0.50	28
Bronze	8.85	554	Flour, pressed	0.70–0.80	47
Copper	8.82	556	Glass, common	2.40–2.80	162
Copper ore, pyrites	4.1–4.3	262	Glass, plate or crown	2.45–2.72	161
German silver	8.58	536	Glass, crystal	2.90–3.00	184
Gold	19.32	1205	Glass, flint	3.2–4.7	247
Gold coin (U. S.)	17.18-17.2	1073	Hay and straw, bales	0.32	20
Iridium	22.42	1383	Leather	0.86–1.02	59
Iron, gray cast	7.20	442	Paper	0.70–1.15	58
Iron, cast, pig	7.2	450	Potatoes, piled	0.67	44
Iron, wrought	7.85	485	Rubber, caoutchouc	0.92–0.96	59
Iron, spiegel-eisen	7.5	468	Rubber goods	1.0–2.0	94
Iron, ferrosilicon	6.7–7.3	437	Salt, granulated, piled	0.77	48
Iron ore, hematite	5.2	325	Saltpeter	1.07	67
Iron ore, limonite	3.6–4.0	237	Starch	1.53	96
Iron ore, magnetite	4.9–5.2	315	Sulphur	1.93–2.07	125
Iron slag	2.5–3.0	172	Wool	1.32	82
Lead	11.37	710			
Lead ore, galena	7.3–7.6	465	**Timber, air-dry**		
Manganese	7.42	475	Apple	0.66–0.74	44
Manganese ore, pyro-			Ash, black	0.55	34
lusite	3.7–4.6	259	Ash, white	0.64–0.71	42
Mercury	13.546	847	Birch, sweet, yellow	0.71–0.72	44
Monel metal, rolled	8.97	555	Cedar, white, red	0.35	22
Nickel	8.80	537	Cherry, wild red	0.43	27
Platinum, cast-ham-			Chestnut	0.48	30
mered	21.5	1330	Cypress	0.45–0.48	29
Silver	10.53	656	Fir, Douglas	0.48–0.55	32
Steel, cold-drawn	7.83	489	Fir, balsam	0.40	25
Steel, machine	7.80	487	Elm, white	0.56	35
Steel, tool	7.70–7.73	481	Hemlock	0.45–0.50	29
Tin	7.29	459	Hickory	0.74–0.80	48
Tin ore, cassiterite	6.4–7.0	418	Locust	0.67–0.77	45
Tungsten	18.77	1200	Mahogany	0.56–0.85	44
Zinc, cast	6.86	440	Maple, sugar	0.68	43
Zinc, ore, blende	3.9–4.2	253	Maple, white	0.53	33
			Oak, chestnut	0.74	46
Various Solids			Oak, live	0.87	54
Cereals, oats, bulk	0.41	26	Oak, red, black	0.64–0.71	42
Cereals, barley, bulk	0.62	39	Oak, white	0.77	48
Cereals, corn, rye, bulk	0.73	45	Pine, Oregon	0.51	32
Cereals, wheat bulk	0.77	48			

APPROXIMATE SPECIFIC GRAVITIES AND DENSITIES

(CONTINUED)

Substance	Specific Gravity	Avg Density lb. per cu. ft.	Substance	Specific Gravity	Avg Density lb. per cu. ft.
Timber, air-dry			**Dry Rubble Masonry**		
Pine, red............	0.48	30	Granite, syenite, gneiss	1.9–2.3	130
Pine, white.........	0.43	27	Limestone, marble....	1.9–2.1	125
Pine, Southern.......	0.61–0.67	38–42	Sandstone, bluestone..	1.8–1.9	110
Pine, Norway........	0.55	34			
Poplar..............	0.43	27	**Brick Masonry**		
Redwood, California...	0.42	26	Hard brick...........	1.8–2.3	128
Spruce, white, red....	0.45	28	Medium brick........	1.6–2.0	112
Teak, African........	0.99	62	Soft brick...........	1.4–1.9	103
Teak, Indian.........	0.66–0.88	48	Sand-lime brick......	1.4–2.2	112
Walnut, black	0.59	37			
Willow..............	0.42–0.50	28	**Concrete Masonry**		
			Cement, stone, sand ..	2.2–2.4	144
Various Liquids			Cement, slag, etc.	1.9–2.3	130
Alcohol, ethyl (100%)..	0.789	49	Cement, cinder, etc. ..	1.5–1.7	100
Alcohol, methyl (100%)	0.796	50			
Acid, muriatic, 40%...	1.20	75	**Various Bldg. Mat'ls**		
Acid, nitric, 91%......	1.50	94	Ashes, cinders........	0.64–0.72	40–45
Acid, sulphuric, 87%..	1.80	112	Cement, Portland, loose	1.5	94
Chloroform..........	1.500	95	Portland cement......	3.1–3.2	196
Ether..............	0.736	46	Lime, gypsum, loose...	0.85–1.00	53–64
Lye, soda, 66%.......	1.70	106	Mortar, lime, set.....	1.4–1.9	103
Oils, vegetable.......	0.91–0.94	58	Mortar, Portland		94
Oils, mineral, lubricants	0.88–0.94	57	cement............	2.08–2.25	135
Turpentine..........	0.861–		Slags, bank slag......	1.1–1.2	67–72
	0.867	54	Slags, bank screenings.	1.5–1.9	98–117
Water, 4° C, max. den-			Slags, machine slag...	1.5	96
sity...............	1.0	62.428	Slags, slag sand.......	0.8–0.9	49–55
Water, 100° C........	0.9584	59.830			
Water, ice..........	0.88–0.92	56	**Earth, etc., Excavated**		
Water, snow, fresh fallen	0.125	8	Clay, dry...........	1.0	63
Water, sea water.....	1.02–1.03	64	Clay, damp plastic.....	1.76	110
			Clay and gravel, dry...	1.6	100
Ashlar Masonry			Earth, dry, loose......	1.2	76
Granite, syenite, gneiss	2.4–2.7	159	Earth, dry, packed....	1.5	95
Limestone...........	2.1–2.8	153	Earth, moist, loose....	1.3	78
Marble.............	2.4–2.8	162	Earth, moist, packed..	1.6	96
Sandstone...........	2.0–2.6	143	Earth, mud, flowing...	1.7	108
Bluestone...........	2.3–2.6	153	Earth, mud, packed...	1.8	115
			Riprap, limestone.....	1.3–1.4	80–85
Rubble Masonry			Riprap, sandstone.....	1.4	90
Granite, syenite, gneiss	2.3–2.6	153	Riprap, shale.........	1.7	105
Limestone...........	2.0–2.7	147	Sand, gravel, dry, loose	1.4–1.7	90–105
Sandstone...........	1.9–2.5	137	Sand, gravel, dry,		
Bluestone...........	2.2–2.5	147	packed............	1.6–1.9	100–120
Marble.............	2.3–2.7	156	Sand, gravel, wet.....	1.89–2.16	126

APPROXIMATE SPECIFIC GRAVITIES AND DENSITIES

(CONTINUED)

Substance	Specific Gravity	Avg Density lb. per cu. ft.	Substance	Specific Gravity	Avg Density lb. per cu. ft.
Excavations in Water			**Stone, Quarried, Piled**		
Sand or gravel........	0.96	60	Basalt, granite, gneiss.	1.5	96
Sand or gravel and clay	1.00	65	Limestone, marble,		
Clay................	1.28	80	quartz............	1.5	95
River mud..........	1.44	90	Sandstone..........	1.3	82
Soil................	1.12	70	Shale.............	1.5	92
Stone riprap........	1.00	65	Greenstone, hornblende	1.7	107
Minerals			**Bituminous**		
Asbestos...........	2.1–2.8	153	**Substances**		
Barytes............	4.50	281	Asphaltum.........	1.1–1.5	81
Basalt.............	2.7–3.2	184	Coal, anthracite......	1.4–1.8	97
Bauxite............	2.55	159	Coal, bituminous......	1.2–1.5	84
Bluestone..........	2.5–2.6	159	Coal, lignite.........	1.1–1.4	78
Borax.............	1.7–1.8	109	Coal, peat, turf, dry...	0.65–0.85	47
Chalk.............	1.8–2.8	143	Coal, charcoal, pine...	0.28–0.44	23
Clay, marl.........	1.8–2.6	137	Coal, charcoal, oak....	0.47–0.57	33
Dolomite..........	2.9	181	Coal, coke..........	1.0–1.4	75
Feldspar, orthoclase...	2.5–2.7	162	Graphite...........	1.64–2.7	135
Gneiss............	2.7–2.9	175	Paraffin...........	0.87–0.91	56
Granite...........	2.6–2.7	165	Petroleum..........	0.87	54
Greenstone, trap......	2.8–3.2	187	Petroleum, refined		
Gypsum, alabaster....	2.3–2.8	159	(kerosene).......	0.78–0.82	50
Hornblende.........	3.0	187	Petroleum, benzine....	0.73–0.75	46
Limestone..........	2.1–2.86	155	Petroleum, gasoline...	0.70–0.75	45
Marble............	2.6–2.86	170	Pitch..............	1.07–1.15	69
Magnesite..........	3.0	187	Tar, bituminous......	1.20	75
Phosphate rock, apatite	3.2	200			
Porphyry..........	2.6–2.9	172	**Coal and Coke, Piled**		
Pumice, natural......	0.37–0.90	40	Coal, anthracite......	0.75–0.93	47–58
Quartz, flint........	2.5–2.8	165	Coal, bituminous, lig-		
Sandstone..........	2.0–2.6	143	nite..............	0.64–0.87	40–54
Serpentine.........	2.7–2.8	171	Coal, peat, turf.......	0.32–0.42	20–26
Shale, Slate........	2.6–2.9	172	Coal, charcoal.......	0.16–0.23	10–14
Soapstone, talc.......	2.6–2.8	169	Coal, coke..........	0.37–0.51	23–32
Syenite............	2.6–2.7	165			

FIXED POINTS FOR
THERMOMETER CALIBRATION*

Substance	Point	Temperature	
		Thermo, °F.	Scale, °C.
Alcohol, ethyl.............................	Boils	173.0	78.3
Aluminum (Al), pure metal..................	Melts	1218.0	658.7
Antimony (Sb), pure metal..................	Melts	1166.0	630.0
Barium (chloride) (BaCl₂) salt...............	Melts	1760.0	960.0
Benzene....................................	Boils	176.0	80.0
Cadmium (Cd), pure metal..................	Melts	624.2	320.9
Cobalt (Co), pure metal....................	Melts	2696.0	1480.0
Copper (Cu), pure metal....................	Melts	1983.0	1083.0
Glycerine..................................	Boils	554.0	290.0
Gold (Au), pure metal......................	Melts	1945.4	1063.0
Iron (Fe), pure metal......................	Melts	2912.0	1600.0
Lead (Pb), pure metal......................	Melts	620.0	327.0
Mercury (Hg), pure metal..................	Solidifies	173.0	78.5
Mercury (Hg), pure metal..................	Boils	675.0	357.3
Nickel (Ni), pure metal....................	Melts	2645.6	1452.0
Platinum (Pt), pure metal..................	Melts	3191.0	1755.0
Potassium nitrate (KNO₃) salt..............	Melts	642.0	337.0
Silver (Ag), pure metal....................	Melts	1769.0	960.5
Sodium chloride (NaCl) salt.................	Melts	1481.0	805.0
Sodium nitrate (NaNO₃) salt	Melts	593.6	312.0
Sodium sulphate (Na₂SO₄) salt	Melts	1623.2	884.0
Sulphur (S), amorphous	Boils	833.0	444.7
Tin (Sn), pure metal.......................	Melts	450.0	232.0
Tungsten (W), pure metal	Melts	7052.0	3400.0
Water, distilled............................	Boils	212.0	100.0
Zinc (Zn), pure metal......................	Melts	786.2	419.0
Lead, 35% ⎫ lowest melting alloy of these two Tin, 65% ⎭ metals......................	Melts	358.0	181.0

Sodium ⎫
  chloride, 45% ⎪ lowest melting mixture of
Sodium ⎬ these two salts..........
  sulphate, 55% ⎭
	Melts	1154.0	623.0

Sodium ⎫
  nitrate, 50% ⎪ lowest melting mixture of
Potassium ⎬ these two salts..........
  nitrate, 50% ⎭
	Melts	424.0	218.0

* American Machinist's Handbook, seventh edition.

MELTING POINTS OF FOUNDRY MATERIALS

Material	Degrees F.	Notes
Alumina.	3725	
Aluminum.	1218	
Bauxite.	3308	
Brass (67% Cu–33% Zn)	1725	
Bronze (90% Cu–10% Sn) . . .	1850	
Calcium.	1490	
Calcium-Manganese-Silicon. .	1800–2000	16–20% Ca, 14–18% Mn, 55–60% Si
Calcium-Silicon.	1850–2100	28–35% Ca, 60–65% Si, 3–6% Fe.
Carbon.	Infusible	
Cast Iron.	2065–2400	
Chromite (FeO, Cr_2O_3)	3950	Also chrome brick.
Chromium.	2939	
Copper.	1981	
Dolomite.	. . . .	Dissociates at high temperatures.
Ferro-Chrome.	2200–2370	60–72% Cr, 4–8% C, 2–3% Si.
Ferro-Chrome (low carbon). . .	2300–2480	60–72% Cr, .06–2% C, 2–3% Si.
Ferro-Manganese.	2280–2325	78–82% Mn, 6–8% C, 1.00% Si.
Ferro-Molybdenum.	2965 approx.	55–65% Mo, 0.5–2.0% C.
Ferro-Silicon, 15% Si.	2180 approx.	
Ferro-Silicon, 50% Si.	2170 approx.	
Ferro-Silicon, 75% Si.	2150 approx.	
Ferro-Silicon, 90% Si.	2150 approx.	
Ferro-Carbon-Titanium.	2650	17% Ti, 7.5% C, 2.5% S, 1.00% C
Ferro-Tungsten.	3275–3450	78–83% Wo, 1.00% C.
Ferro-Vanadium.	2600–2700	35–40% V, 1.5–8.0% Si, 0.2–3.0% C
Fire-brick.	2800–3100	
Fluorspar.	. . . .	Decomposes at high temperature.
Fire Clay.	2730–3150	
Ganister.	2550	98% SiO_2.
Iron.	2786	
Iron Ore (Fe_2O_3)	2805	
Iron Ore (Fe_3O_4)	2800	
Lime (CaO).	. . . .	Decomposes at high temperature.
Magnesia (Periclase).	5070	
Magnesite.	3990–5070	Also magnesite brick.
Malleable Iron.	2375–2575	
Manganese.	2246	
Molybdenum.	4620	
Nickel.	2646	
Phosphorus.	111	
Pig Iron.	2066–2300	
Sand.	2900–3100	
Silica.	3100	Also silica brick.
Silica-Manganese.	2250	65–70% Mn, 20–25% Si, 1.00% C
Silicon.	2588	
Sillimanite ($Al_2O_3.SiO_2$)	3290	
Spiegeleisen.	1950–2265	15–30% Mn, 4.5–5% C.
Steel.	2500–2775	
Sulphur.	248	
Titanium.	3272	
Tungsten.	6152	
Vanadium.	3128	
Zircon.	4000–4600	
Zirconium.	3090	

SPECIFIC GRAVITIES AND PROPERTIES OF METALS

Metal	Specific Gravity	Weight per Cu. In., Pound	Weight per Cu. Ft., Pounds	Melting Point, Degrees F.
Aluminum	2.56	0.0924	159.7	1218
Antimony	6.71	0.2422	418.7	1166
Barium	3.75	0.1354	234.0	1562
Bismuth	9.80	0.3538	611.5	520
Boron	2.60	0.0939	162.2	4000–4500
Brass: 80% Cu 20% Zn	8.60	0.3105	536.6	
70% Cu 40% Zn	8.40	0.3032	524.1	1700–1850
60% Cu 40% Zn	8.36	0.3018	521.7	
50% Cu 50% Zn	8.20	0.2960	511.6	
Bronze	8.85	0.3195	552.2	1675
Cadmium	8.60	0.3105	536.6	610
Calcium	1.57	0.0567	98.0	1490
Chromium	6.50	0.2347	405.6	2939
Cobalt	8.65	0.3123	539.8	2696
Copper	8.82	0.3184	550.4	1981
Gold	19.32	0.6975	1205.6	1945
Iridium	22.42	0.8094	1399.0	4260
Iron, cast	7.20	0.2600	449.2	2065–2400
Iron, wrought	7.85	0.2834	489.8	2750
Lead	11.37	0.4105	709.5	621
Magnesium	1.74	0.0628	108.6	1204
Manganese	7.42	0.2679	463.0	2246
Mercury (60° F.)	13.58	0.4902	847.4	−38
Molybdenum	8.56	0.3090	534.2	4620
Nickel	8.80	0.3177	549.1	2646
Platinum, rolled	22.67	0.8184	1414.6	3191
Platinum, wire	21.04	0.7595	1312.9	3191
Potassium	0.87	0.0314	54.3	144
Silver	10.53	0.3802	657.1	1761
Sodium	0.98	0.0354	61.1	207
Steel	7.80	0.2816	486.7	2500
Tellurium	6.25	0.2256	390.0	846
Tin	7.29	0.2632	454.8	449
Titanium	3.54	0.1278	220.9	3272
Tungsten	18.77	0.6776	1171.2	6152
Vanadium	5.50	0.1986	343.2	3128
Zinc, cast	6.86	0.2476	428.1	787
Zinc, rolled	7.15	0.2581	446.1	787

EXPANSION OF BODIES BY HEAT

The coefficient of linear expansion (ϵ) is the change in length, per unit of length, for a change of one degree of temperature. The coefficient of surface expansion is approximately two times the linear coefficient, and the coefficient of volume expansion, for solids, is approximately three times the linear coefficient.

A bar, free to move, will increase in length with an increase in temperature and will decrease in length with a decrease in temperature. The change in length will be $\epsilon t l$, where ϵ is the coefficient of linear expansion, t the change in temperature, and l the length. If the ends of a bar are fixed, a change in temperature (t) will cause a change in the unit stress of $E\epsilon t$, and in the total (stress of) $AE\epsilon t$, where A is the cross sectional area of the bar and E the modulus of elasticity.

The following table gives the coefficient of linear expansion for 100°, or 100 times the value indicated above.

Example: A piece of medium steel is exactly 40 feet long at 60° F. Find the length at 90° F. assuming the ends free to move.

$$\text{Change of length} = \epsilon t l = \frac{.00067 \times 30 \times 40}{100} = .00804 \text{ foot.}$$

The length at 90° F. is 40.00804 feet.

Example: A piece of medium steel is exactly 40 feet long and the ends are fixed. If the temperature increases 30° F., what is the resulting change in the unit stress?

$$\text{Change in unit stress} = E\epsilon t = \frac{29,000,000 \times .00067 \times 30}{100} = 5830 \text{ lbs. per sq. in.}$$

COEFFICIENTS OF EXPANSION FOR 100 DEGREES = 100ϵ

Substances	Linear Expansion Centi-grade	Linear Expansion Fahren-heit	Substances	Linear Expansion Centi-grade	Linear Expansion Fahren-heit
METALS AND ALLOYS			Cement, portland	.00107	.00059
			Concrete	.00143	.00079
Aluminum, wrought	.00231	.00128	Granite	.00084	.00047
Brass	.00188	.00104	Limestone	.00080	.00044
Bronze	.00181	.00101	Marble	.00100	.00056
Copper	.00168	.00093	Plaster	.00166	.00092
Iron, cast, gray	.00106	.00059	Rubble masonry	.00063	.00035
Iron, wrought	.00120	.00067	Sandstone	.00110	.00061
Iron, wire	.00124	.00069	Slate	.00104	.00058
Lead	.00286	.00159			
Nickel	.00126	.00070	**TIMBER**		
Steel, cast	.00110	.00061			
Steel, hard	.00132	.00073	Fir	.00037	.00021
Steel, medium	.00120	.00067	Maple	.00064	.00036
Steel, soft	.00110	.00061	Oak } parallel to fiber	.00049	.00027
Zinc, rolled	.00311	.00173	Pine	.00054	.00030
			Fir	.0058	.0032
STONE AND MASONRY			Maple	.0048	.0027
			Oak } perpendicular to fiber	.0054	.0030
Ashlar masonry	.00063	.00035	Pine	.0034	.0019
Brick masonry	.00055	.00031			

EXPANSION OF WATER
MAXIMUM DENSITY = 1

C°	Volume	C°	Volume	C°	Volume	C°	Volume	C°	Volume	C°	Volume
0	1.000126	10	1.000257	30	1.004234	50	1.011877	70	1.022384	90	1.035829
4	1.000000	20	1.001732	40	1.007627	60	1.016954	80	1.029003	100	1.043116

STEELS*

Standard Steels. The General Technical Committee of the American Iron and Steel Institute selected certain chemical compositions as representing steels of proven merit and in extensive use for a wide variety of purposes. Such steels are termed Standard Steels.

When the many other grades of steel that have been used are critically compared with the equivalent standard grades listed in the tables herein, it is believed that in most cases the standard grades can successfully be used to replace them without detriment to fabricating method or impairment of quality of the article manufactured.

Carbon Steel. Steel is classed as carbon steel when no minimum content is specified or guaranteed for aluminum, chromium, cobalt, columbium, molybdenum, nickel, titanium, tungsten, vanadium or zirconium, or any other alloying element added to obtain a desired alloying effect; when the specified or guaranteed minimum content for copper does not exceed 0.40 per cent; or when the maximum content specified or guaranteed for any of the following elements does not exceed the percentages noted: manganese, 1.65 per cent; silicon, 0.60 per cent; copper, 0.60 per cent.

Alloy Steel. Steel is classed as alloy steel when the maximum of the range given for the content of alloying elements exceeds one or more of the following limits: manganese, 1.65 per cent; silicon, 0.60 per cent; copper, 0.60 per cent; or, in which a definite range or a definite minimum quantity of any of the following elements is guaranteed within the limits of the recognized commercial field of alloy steels: aluminum, chromium up to 3.99 per cent, cobalt, columbium, molybdenum, nickel up to 5.25 per cent, titanium, tungsten, vanadium, zirconium, or any other alloying element added to obtain a desired alloying effect.

The combined standard steel specifications of the American Iron and Steel Institute and the Society of Automotive Engineers, Inc., listed in the tables noted above, result in a simplification program aimed at greater efficiency in meeting steel needs.

These new specifications retain the more popular grades of steels included in the former SAE lists and include other widely used analyses not previously listed.

The differences in composition ranges between the various AISI steels are less than between SAE steels.

THE AISI numbering system, used to identify chemical compositions, is essentially similar to the former SAE system. This makes it possible to use numbers — partially descriptive of the chemistry of the steels specified — on drawings and prints.

SAE specifications now employ the same numerical designations as those employed in the AISI specifications but with the elimination of all letter prefixes.

Machinability ratings of various steels, together with approximate comparable steels, are given in Table 10, page 143.

* Data and excerpts on pages 331–345 inclusive compiled from various Steel Products Manuals of the American Iron and Steel Institute.

STEELS

(CONTINUED)

AISI SYSTEM OF IDENTIFICATION

A system of symbols is used to identify the grade classifications of standard steels. In those symbols a capital-letter prefix is used to denote the steelmaking process; and a second capital letter to denote a quality classification. Numbers are used to denote grades of steel by chemical composition or tensile properties. Lower-case letters are used, as suffixes, to denote various special requirements affecting quality.

Capital-Letter Prefixes (Denoting steelmaking process):

A   denotes basic open-hearth alloy steel.
B   denotes acid bessemer carbon steel.
C   denotes basic open-hearth carbon steel.
CB denotes either acid bessemer or basic open-hearth carbon steel at the option of the manufacturer.
D   denotes acid open-hearth carbon steel.
E   denotes electric furnace steel.
NE denotes National Emergency Standard Steel; designation adopted by Iron and Steel Branch of the War Production Board.
Q   denotes forging quality or special-requirement quality.
R   denotes re-rolling-quality billets.

Lower-Case Letter Suffixes (Denoting restrictive requirements affecting quality):

a   Restricted chemical composition.
b   Bearing quality.
c   Guaranteed segregation limits affected by methods of sampling.
d   Specified discard.
e   Homogeneity tests (macro-etch tests).
f   Rifle barrel, gun quality, or AP shot quality.
g   Limited austenitic grain size.
h   Guaranteed hardenability.
i   Nonmetallic inclusions requirement.
j   Fracture test.
t   Extensometer test.
v   Aircraft quality or magnaflux quality.

Numerical Designations of Grades. A four-numeral series is used to denote carbon and alloy steels specified to chemical composition ranges. A five-numeral series is used to denote a few certain alloy steels.

The last two digits of the four-numeral series are intended, so far as feasible, to indicate the approximate middle of the carbon range, i.e., 20 represents 0.18 to 0.23 per cent. It is necessary, however, to deviate from this rule and to interpolate numbers in the case of some carbon ranges; and for variations in manganese, sulphur, chromium, or other elements.

The basic numbers of the numerical series, together with their meaning, for the various grades of steel are shown on the next page.

STEELS

(CONTINUED)

AISI SYSTEM OF IDENTIFICATION

(CONTINUED)

CARBON STEELS

SERIES DESIGNATION	TYPES AND CLASSES
10xx	Basic and acid open-hearth and acid bessemer carbon steel grades, non-sulphurized and nonphosphorized.
11xx	Basic open-hearth and acid bessemer carbon steel grades; sulphurized but not phosphorized.
12xx	Basic open-hearth carbon steel grades; phosphorized.

ALLOY STEELS

SERIES DESIGNATION	TYPES AND CLASSES
13xx	Manganese 1.60 to 1.90 per cent
23xx	Nickel 3.50 per cent
25xx	Nickel 5.00 per cent
30xx	Nickel 0.70 per cent — Chromium 0.70 per cent
31xx	Nickel 1.25 per cent — Chromium 0.60 per cent
32xx	Nickel 1.75 per cent — Chromium 1.00 per cent
33xx	Nickel 3.50 per cent — Chromium 1.50 per cent
40xx	Molybdenum
41xx	Chromium-molybdenum
43xx	Nickel-chromium-molybdenum
46xx	Nickel 1.65 per cent — Molybdenum 0.25 per cent
48xx	Nickel 3.25 per cent — Molybdenum 0.25 per cent
50xx	Low chromium
51xx	Medium chromium
52xxx	Chromium, high-carbon
61xx	Chromium-vanadium
86xx	Nickel 0.55 per cent — Chromium 0.50 per cent — Molybdenum 0.20 per cent
87xx	Nickel 0.55 per cent — Chromium 0.50 per cent — Molybdenum 0.25 per cent
92xx	Manganese 0.80 per cent — Silicon 2.00 per cent
94xx	Manganese 0.95 to 1.15 per cent — Silicon 0.50 per cent — Nickel 0.35 per cent — Chromium 0.30 per cent — Molybdenum 0.12 per cent

COMBINED AISI AND SAE
STANDARD STEEL SPECIFICATIONS
BASIC OPEN-HEARTH AND ACID BESSEMER CARBON STEELS
(AS REVISED JUNE, 1943)

AISI Number	1943 SAE Number	C	Mn	P	S
C 1005	..	0.06 max.	0.35 max.	0.04	0.05
C 1006*	..	0.08 max.	0.25–0.40	0.04	0.05
C 1008*	1008	0.10 max.	0.30–0.50	0.04	0.05
CB 1008	..	0.10 max.	......	....	....
C 1009	..	0.07–0.12	0.25–0.40	0.04	0.05
C 1010*	1010	0.08–0.13	0.30–0.50	0.04	0.05
C 1011	..	0.08–0.13	0.40–0.60	0.04	0.05
C 1012	..	0.10–1.15	0.30–0.50	0.04	0.05
CB 1012	..	0.15 max.	......	....	....
C 1013	..	0.11–0.16	0.60–0.90	0.04	0.05
C 1014	..	0.13–0.18	0.40–0.60	0.04	0.05
C 1015*	1015	0.13–0.18	0.30–0.50	0 04	0.05
C 1016	1016	0.13–0.18	0.60–0.90	0.04	0.05
CB 1017	..	0.10–0.25	......	....	....
C 1017	..	0.15–0.20	0.40–0.60	0.04	0.05
C 1018	..	0.15–0.20	0.60–0.90	0.04	0.05
C 1019	..	0.15–0.20	0.70–1.00	0.04	0.05
C 1020*	1020	0.18–0.23	0.30–0.50	0.04	0.05
C 1021	..	0.18–0.23	0.40–0.60	0.04	0.05
C 1022	1022	0.18–0.23	0.70–1.00	0.04	0.05
C 1023	..	0.20–0.25	0.30–0.50	0.04	0.05
C 1024	1024	0.20–0.26	1.35–1.65	0.04	0.05
C 1025*	1025	0.22–0.28	0.30–0.50	0.04	0.05
C 1026	..	0.22–0.28	0.40–0.60	0.04	0.05
C 1027	..	0.24–0.30	0.40–0.60	0.04	0.05
C 1029	..	0.25–0.31	0.60–0.90	0.04	0.05
C 1030	1030	0.28–0.34	0.60–0.90	0.04	0.05
C 1031	..	0.28–0.34	0.40–0.60	0.04	0.05
CB 1032	..	0.25–0.40	......	....	....
C 1033	..	0.30–0.36	0.60–0.90	0.04	0.05
C 1034	..	0.32–0.38	0.50–0.70	0.04	0.05
D 1034	..	0.32–0.38	0.50–0.70	0.05	0.05
C 1035	1035	0.32–0.38	0.60–0.90	0.04	0.05
C 1036	1036	0.32–0.39	1.20–1.50	0.04	0.05
C 1037	..	0.32–0.38	0.40–0.60	0.04	0.05
C 1038	..	0.35–0.42	0.60–0.90	0.04	0.05
C 1039	..	0.37–0.44	0.40–0.60	0.04	0.05
C 1040	1040	0.37–0.44	0.60–0.90	0.04	0.05
C 1041	..	0.36–0.44	1.35–1.65	0.04	0.05
C 1042	..	0.40–0.47	0.60–0.90	0.04	0.05
C 1043	..	0.40–0.47	0.70–1.00	0.04	0.05
C 1044	..	0.43–0.50	0.50–0.70	0.04	0.05
C 1045	1045	0.43–0.50	0.60–0.90	0.04	0.05
C 1046	..	0.43–0.50	0.70–1.00	0.04	0.05

* Compositions given are for forging quality; re-rolling quality differs slightly in analysis.

Note 1.—When silicon is specified in standard basic open-hearth steels, silicon may be ordered only as 0.10% maximum; 0.10 to 0.20%; or 0.15 to 0.30%. In the case of many grades of basic open-hearth steel, special practice is necessary in order to comply with a specification including silicon.

Note 2.—Acid bessemer steel is not furnished with specified silicon content.

COMBINED AISI AND SAE
STANDARD STEEL SPECIFICATIONS
(CONTINUED)

BASIC OPEN-HEARTH AND ACID BESSEMER CARBON STEELS
(CONTINUED)

AISI Number	1943 SAE Number	Semi-finish	Bars†	Wire Rods†	Replaces 1941 SAE Number
C 1005	..	..	..	√	..
C 1006*	..	Q. R.	√	√	..
C 1008*	1008	Q. R.	√	√	..
CB 1008	..	..	√	√	..
C 1009	..	Q	..	..	..
C 1010*	1010	Q. R.	√	√	1010
C 1011	..	√	..	..	..
C 1012	..	Q	√	√	..
CB 1012	..	..	√	..	..
C 1013	..	..	..	√	..
C 1014	..	Q	√	√	..
C 1015*	1015	Q. R.	√	√	1015
C 1016	1016	Q	√	√	x1015
CB 1017	..	..	√	..	..
C 1017	..	Q	√	√	..
C 1018	..	Q	√	√	..
C 1019	..	Q	√	√	..
C 1020*	1020	Q. R.	√	√	1020
C 1021	..	Q	√	√	..
C 1022	1022	Q	√	√	x1020
C 1023	..	Q	√	√	..
C 1024	1024	..	√	..	..
C 1025*	1025	Q. R.	√	√	1025
C 1026	..	Q	√	√	..
C 1027	..	..	..	√	..
C 1029	..	Q	√	..	..
C 1030	1030	Q	√	√	1030
C 1031	..	Q	..	..	..
CB 1032	..	R	√	..	..
C 1033	..	Q	√	..	..
C 1034	..	..	..	√	..
D 1034	..	..	..	√	..
C 1035	1035	Q	..	..	1035
C 1036	1036	..	√	..	..
C 1037	..	C.r. strip	..	..	..
C 1038	..	Q	..	√	..
C 1039	..	C.r. strip	..	..	..
C 1040	1040	Q	√	√	1040
C 1041	..	..	..	√	..
C 1042	..	Q	√	..	..
C 1043	..	Q	√	..	..
C 1044	..	..	..	√	..
C 1045	1045	Q	√	..	1045
C 1046	..	Q	..	..	..

* Compositions given are for forging quality; re-rolling quality differs slightly in analysis.
† Check marks (√) in these columns indicate compositions applicable.

COMBINED AISI AND SAE
STANDARD STEEL SPECIFICATIONS

(CONTINUED)

BASIC OPEN-HEARTH AND ACID BESSEMER CARBON STEELS

(CONTINUED)

AISI Number	1943 SAE Number	C	Mn	P	S
C 1047	....	0.43–0.50	0.40–0.60	0.04	0.05
C 1049	....	0.48–0.55	0.40–0.60	0.04	0.05
D 1049	....	0.43–0.50	0.50–0.70	0.05	0.05
C 1050	1050	0.48–0.55	0.60–0.90	0.04	0.05
C 1051	....	0.45–0.56	0.85–1.15	0.04	0.05
C 1052	1052	0.47–0.55	1.20–1.50	0.04	0.05
C 1054	....	0.50–0.60	0.50–0.70	0.04	0.05
D 1054	....	0.50–0.60	0.50–0.70	0.05	0.05
C 1055	1055	0.50–0.60	0.60–0.90	0.04	0.05
C 1056	....	0.50–0.60	0.40–0.60	0.04	0.05
C 1057	....	0.50–0.61	0.85–1.15	0.04	0.05
C 1058	....	0.55–0.65	0.40–0.60	0.04	0.05
C 1059	....	0.55–0.65	0.50–0.70	0.04	0.05
D 1059	....	0.55–0.65	0.50–0.70	0.05	0.05
C 1060	1060	0.55–0.65	0.60–0.90	0.04	0.05
C 1061	....	0.54–0.65	0.75–1.05	0.04	0.05
C 1062	....	0.54–0.65	0.85–1.15	0.04	0.05
C 1064	....	0.60–0.70	0.50–0.70	0.04	0.05
D 1064	....	0.60–0.70	0.50–0.70	0.05	0.05
C 1065	....	0.60–0.70	0.60–0.90	0.04	0.05
C 1066	1066	0.60–0.71	0.80–1.10	0.04	0.05
C 1068	....	0.65–0.75	0.50 max.	0.04	0.05
C 1069	....	0.65–0.75	0.50–0.70	0.04	0.05
D 1069	....	0.65–0.75	0.40–0.60	0.05	0.05
C 1070	1070	0.65–0.75	0.70–1.00	0.04	0.05
C 1074	....	0.70–0.80	0.50–0.70	0.04	0.05
D 1074	....	0.70–0.80	0.40–0.60	0.05	0.05
C 1075	....	0.70–0.80	0.60–0.80	0.04	0.05
C 1076	....	0.65–0.85	0.60–0.85	0.04	0.05
C 1078	....	0.72–0.85	0.30–0.50	0.04	0.05
D 1078	....	0.70–0.85	0.30–0.50	0.05	0.05
C 1080	1080	0.75–0.88	0.60–0.90	0.04	0.05
D 1083	....	0.80–0.95	0.30–0.50	0.05	0.05
C 1084	....	0.80–0.93	0.60–0.90	0.04	0.05
C 1085	1085	0.80–0.93	0.70–1.10	0.04	0.05
C 1086	....	0.82–0.95	0.30–0.50	0.04	0.05
C 1090	....	0.85–1.00	0.60–0.90	0.04	0.05
C 1095	1095	0.90–1.05	0.30–0.50	0.04	0.05
D 1095	....	0.90–1.05	0.30–0.50	0.05	0.05
B 1006	....	0.08 max.	0.45 max.	0.11 max.	0.06 max.
B 1008	....	0.10 max.	0.30–0.50	0.11 max.	0.06 max.
B 1010	....	0.07–0.13	0.30–0.50	0.07–0.11	0.07 max.
B 1011	....	0.13 max.	0.50–0.70	0.11 max.	0.06 max.

Note 1.—When silicon is specified in standard basic open-hearth steels, silicon may be ordered only as 0.10% maximum; 0.10 to 0.20%; or 0.15 to 0.30%. In the case of many grades of basic open-hearth steel, special practice is necessary in order to comply with a specification including silicon.

Note 2.—Acid bessemer steel is not furnished with specified silicon content.

COMBINED AISI AND SAE
STANDARD STEEL SPECIFICATIONS
(CONTINUED)

BASIC OPEN-HEARTH AND ACID BESSEMER CARBON STEELS
(CONTINUED)

AISI Number	1943 SAE Number	Semi-Finish	Bars†	Wire Rods†	Replaces 1941 SAE Number
C 1047	....	C.r. strip			....
C 1049	....	C.r. strip			....
D 1049	....	..		√	
C 1050	1050	Q	√	..	1050
C 1051	....	..	..	√	....
C 1052	1052	..	√	..	....
C 1054	....	..	..	√	....
D 1054	....	..	..	√	....
C 1055	1055	Q	√	..	1055
C 1056	....	C.r. strip			....
C 1057	....	..	..	√	....
C 1058	....	C.r. strip			....
C 1059	....	..	..	√	....
D 1059	....	..	..	√	....
C 1060	1060	..	√	√	1060
C 1061	....	..	√	..	....
C 1062	....	..	..	√	....
C 1064	....	..	√	√	....
D 1064	....	..	..	√	....
C 1065	....	Strip			....
C 1066	1066	..	√	√	x1065
C 1068	....	..	√	..	....
C 1069	....	..	..	√	....
D 1069	....	..	..	√	....
C 1070	1070	..	√	..	1070
C 1074	....	..	√	√	....
D 1074	....	..	..	√	....
C 1075	....	..	..	√	....
C 1076	....	Q	..	..	....
C 1078	....	..	√	√	....
D 1078	....	..	..	√	....
C 1080	1080	..	√	..	1080
D 1083	....	..	..	√	....
C 1084	....	Q	..	..	....
C 1085	1085	Q	√	..	1085
C 1086	....	..	√	√	....
C 1090	....	Q	..	..	....
C 1095	1095	..	√	√	1095
D 1095	....	..	..	√	....
B 1006	....	..	..	√	....
B 1008	....	R	√	..	....
B 1010	....	..	√	..	....
B 1011	....	..	√	√	....

† Check marks (√) in these columns indicate compositions applicable.

COMBINED AISI AND SAE
STANDARD STEEL SPECIFICATIONS

(CONTINUED)

SULPHURIZED OR PHOSPHORIZED CARBON STEELS
(FREE-CUTTING STEELS)

(AS REVISED JUNE, 1943)

AISI Number	1943 SAE Number	C	Mn	P	S
B 1106	....	0.09 max	0.50 max.	0.11 max.	0.04–0.09
C 1108	....	0.08–0.13	0.50–0.70	0.045 max.	0.07–0.12
C 1109	....	0.08–0.13	0.60–0.90	0.045 max.	0.08–0.13
B 1110	....	0.13 max.	0.60 max.	0.11 max.	0.045–0.075
C 1110	....	0.08–0.13	0.60–0.90	0.045 max.	0.10–0.15
B 1111	1111	0.08–0.13	0.60–0.90	0.09–0.90	0.10–0.15
C 1111	....	0.08–0.13	0.60–0.90	0.045 max.	0.16–0.23
B 1112	1112	0.08–0.13	0.60–0.90	0.09–0.13	0.16–0.23
C 1112	....	0.10–0.16	1.00–1.30	0.045 max.	0.08–0.13
B 1113	1113	0.08–0.13	0.60–0.90	0.09–0.13	0.24–0.33
C 1113	....	0.10–0.16	1.00–1.30	0.045 max.	0.24–0.33
C 1114	....	0.12–0.18	0.45–0.65	0.045 max.	0.075–0.15
C 1115	1115	0.13–0.18	0.70–1.00	0.045 max.	0.10–0.15
C 1116	....	0.14–0.20	1.10–1.40	0.045 max.	0.16–0.23
C 1117	1117	0.14–0.20	1.00–1.30	0.045 max.	0.08–0.13
C 1118	1118	0.14–0.20	1.30–1.60	0.045 max.	0.08–0.13
C 1119	....	0.14–0.20	1.35–1.65	0.045 max.	0.16–0.23
C 1120*	....	0.18–0.23	0.60–0.90	0.045 max.	0.08–0.13
C 1121	....	0.18–0.23	0.70–1.00	0.045 max.	0.08–0.13
C 1122	....	0.17–0.23	1.35–1.65	0.045 max.	0.08–0.13
C 1132	1132	0.27–0.34	1.35–1.65	0.045 max.	0.08–0.13
C 1137	1137	0.32–0.39	1.35–1.65	0.045 max.	0.08–0.13
C 1140‡	....	0.37–0.44	0.60–0.90	0.045 max.	0.04–0.07
C 1141	1141	0.37–0.45	1.35–1.65	0.045 max.	0.08–0.13
C 1144	....	0.40–0.48	1.35–1.65	0.045 max.	0.24–0.33
C 1145‡	1145	0.42–0.49	0.70–1.00	0.045 max.	0.04–0.07
C 1205	....	0.08 max.	0.25–0.40	0.04–0.07	0.05 max.
C 1206	....	0.08 max.	0.05–0.40	0.04–0.07	0.05 max.
C 1209	....	0.08–0.13	0.30–0.50	0.05–0.10	0.05 max.
C 1210	....	0.08–0.13	0.30–0.50	0.06–0.10	0.05 max.
C 1211	....	0.08–0.13	0.60–0.90	0.09–0.13	0.10–0.15
C 1217	....	0.14–0.19	0.70–1.00	0.09–0.13	0.20–0.29

* Compositions given are for forging quality; re-rolling quality differs slightly in analysis.
‡ Standard steels C1140 and C1145 may be ordered with silicon content either as 0.10% max., 0.10 to 0.20%, or 0.15 to 0.30%.
Note 1.—Sulphurized steel is not subject to check analysis for sulphur.
Note 2.—Acid bessemer steel is not furnished with specified silicon content.

COMBINED AISI AND SAE
STANDARD STEEL SPECIFICATIONS
(CONTINUED)

SULPHURIZED OR PHOSPHORIZED CARBON STEELS
(FREE-CUTTING STEELS)
(CONTINUED)

AISI Number	1943 SAE Number	Semi-Finish	Bars†	Wire Rods†	Replaces 1941 SAE Number
B 1106	. . . .	. .	. .	√	. . . .
C 1108	. . . .	. .	. .	√	. . . .
C 1109	. . . .	Q	√	√	. . . .
B 1110	. . . .	. .	√	√	. . . .
C 1110	. . . .	. .	√	√	. . . .
B 1111	1111	. .	√	√	. . . .
C 1111	. . . .	. .	. .	√	. . . .
B 1112	1112	. .	√	√	. . . .
C 1112	. . . .	. .	√	. .	. . . .
B 1113	1113	. .	√	√	. . . .
C 1113	. . . .	Q	√	. .	. . . .
C 1114	. . . .	R	. .		. . . .
C 1115	1115	Q	√	√	1115
C 1116	. . . .	Q	√	√	. . . .
C 1117	1117	. .	√	√	x1314
C 1118	1118	Q	√	√	x1315
C 1119	. . . .	. .	. .	√	. . . .
C 1120	. . . .	Q. R.	√	√	. . . .
C 1121	. . . .	Q	√	√	. . . .
C 1122	. . . .	Q	√	√	. . . .
C 1132	1132	Q	√	√	x1330
C 1137	1137	Q	√	√	x1335
C 1140	. . . .	Q	√	. .	. . . .
C 1141	1141	. .	√	. .	x1340
C 1144	. . . .	. .	√	. .	. . . .
C 1145	1145	Q	√	. .	. . . .
C 1205	. . . .	Q	. .	√	. . . .
C 1206	. . . .	R	. .	√	. . . .
C 1209	. . . .	R	. .	√	. . . .
C 1210	. . . .	Q	. .	√	. . . .
C 1211	. . . .	. .	. .	√	. . . .
C 1217	. . . .	. .	√	. .	. . . .

† Check marks (√) in these columns indicate compositions applicable.

COMBINED AISI AND SAE
STANDARD STEEL SPECIFICATIONS
(CONTINUED)

OPEN-HEARTH AND ELECTRIC FURNACE ALLOY STEELS
(NE STEELS CORRECTED TO MAY 26, 1944)

AISI Number	1943 SAE Number	C	Mn	P Max.**	S Max.**
. . . .	1320	0.18–0.23	1.60–1.90	0.040	0.040
*A 1330	1330	0.28–0.33	1.60–1.90	0.040	0.040
*A 1335	1335	0.33–0.38	1.60–1.90	0.040	0.040
*A 1340	1340	0.38–0.43	1.60–1.90	0.040	0.040
*A 1345	. . . .	0.43–0.48	1.60–1.90	0.040	0.040
*A 1350	. . . .	0.48–0.53	1.60–1.90	0.040	0.040
A 2317	2317	0.15–0.20	0.40–0.60	0.040	0.040
A 2330	2330	0.28–0.33	0.60–0.80	0.040	0.040
A 2335	. . . .	0.33–0.38	0.60–0.80	0.040	0.040
A 2340	2340	0.38–0.43	0.70–0.90	0.040	0.040
A 2345	2345	0.43–0.48	0.70–0.90	0.040	0.040
E 2512	. . . .	0.09–0.14	0.45–0.60	0.025	0.025
A 2515	2515	0.12–0.17	0.40–0.60	0.040	0.040
E 2517	. . . .	0.15–0.20	0.45–0.60	0.025	0.025
A 3045	. . . .	0.43–0.48	0.75–0.95	0.040	0.040
A 3115	3115	0.13–0.18	0.40–0.60	0.040	0.040
A 3120	3120	0.17–0.22	0.60–0.80	0.040	0.040
A 3130	3130	0.28–0.33	0.60–0.80	0.040	0.040
A 3135	3135	0.33–0.38	0.60–0.80	0.040	0.040
A 3140	3140	0.38–0.43	0.70–0.90	0.040	0.040
A 3141	3141	0.38–0.43	0.70–0.90	0.040	0.040
A 3145	3145	0.43–0.48	0.70–0.90	0.040	0.040
A 3150	3150	0.48–0.53	0.70–0.90	0.040	0.040
A 3240	. . . .	0.38–0.43	0.40–0.60	0.040	0.040
. . . .	3240	0.38–0.45	0.40–0.60	0.040	0.040
E 3310	3310	0.08–0.13	0.45–0.60	0.025	0.025
E 3316	. . . .	0.14–0.19	0.45–0.60	0.025	0.025
A 4023	4023	0.20–0.25	0.70–0.90	0.040	0.040
A 4024	. . . .	0.20–0.25	0.70–0.90	0.040	0.035–0.050
A 4027	4027	0.25–0.30	0.70–0.90	0.040	0.040
A 4028	. . . .	0.25–0.30	0.70–0.90	0.040	0.035–0.050
A 4032	4032	0.30–0.35	0.70–0.90	0.040	0.040
A 4037	4037	0.35–0.40	0.75–1.00	0.040	0.040
A 4042	4042	0.40–0.45	0.75–1.00	0.040	0.040
A 4047	4047	0.45–0.50	0.75–1.00	0.040	0.040
A 4063	4063	0.60–0.67	0.75–1.00	0.040	0.040
A 4068	4068	0.64–0.72	0.75–1.00	0.040	0.040
A 4119	4119	0.17–0.22	0.70–0.90	0.040	0.040
A 4120	. . . .	0.17–0.22	0.70–0.90	0.040	0.040
A 4125	4125	0.23–0.28	0.70–0.90	0.040	0.040
A 4130	4130	0.28–0.33	0.40–0.60	0.040	0.040
A 4131	. . . .	0.28–0.33	0.50–0.70	0.040	0.040
E 4132	. . . .	0.30–0.35	0.40–0.60	0.025	0.025

* These are also NE steels.
** Lowest standard maximum phosphorus or sulphur content for acid open-hearth or acid electric furnace alloy steel is 0.05% each; silicon is 0.15% minimum.

COMBINED AISI AND SAE
STANDARD STEEL SPECIFICATIONS
(CONTINUED)

OPEN-HEARTH AND ELECTRIC FURNACE ALLOY STEELS
(CONTINUED)

AISI Number	1943 SAE Number	Si**	Ni	Cr	Mo	Replaces 1941 SAE Number
. . . .	1320	0.20–0.35	. . . .	. . . .	. . . .	. . . .
*A 1330	1330	0.20–0.35	. . . .	. . . .	. . . .	1330
*A 1335	1335	0.20–0.35	. . . .	. . . .	. . . .	1335
*A 1340	1340	0.20–0.35	. . . .	. . . .	. . . .	1340
*A 1345	. . . .	0.20–0.35	. . . .	. . . .	. . . .	1345
*A 1350	. . . .	0.20–0.35	. . . .	. . . .	. . . .	1350
A 2317	2317	0.20–0.35	3.25–3.75	. . . .	. . . .	2315
A 2330	2330	0.20–0.35	3.25–3.75	. . . .	. . . .	2330
A 2335	. . . .	0.20–0.35	3.25–3.75	. . . .	. . . .	. . . .
A 2340	2340	0.20–0.35	3.25–3.75	. . . .	. . . .	2340
A 2345	2345	0.20–0.35	3.25–3.75	. . . .	. . . .	2345
E 2512	. . . .	0.20–0.35	4.75–5.25	. . . .	. . . .	. . . .
A 2515	2515	0.20–0.35	4.75–5.25	. . . .	. . . .	2515
E 2517	. . . .	0.20–0.35	4.75–5.25	. . . .	. . . .	. . . .
A 3045	. . . .	0.20–0.35	0.60–0.80	0.60–0.80	. . . .	. . . .
A 3115	3115	0.20–0.35	1.10–1.40	0.55–0.75	. . . .	3115
A 3120	3120	0.20–0.35	1.10–1.40	0.55–0.75	. . . .	3120
A 3130	3130	0.20–0.35	1.10–1.40	0.55–0.75	. . . .	3130
A 3135	3135	0.20–0.35	1.10–1.40	0.55–0.75	. . . .	3135
A 3140	3140	0.20–0.35	1.10–1.40	0.55–0.75	. . . .	3140
A 3141	3141	0.20–0.35	1.10–1.40	0.70–0.90	. . . .	x3140
A 3145	3145	0.20–0.35	1.10–1.40	0.70–0.90	. . . .	3145
A 3150	3150	0.20–0.35	1.10–1.40	0.70–0.90	. . . .	3150
A 3240	. . . .	0.20–0.35	1.65–2.00	0.90–1.20	. . . .	3240
. . . .	3240	0.20–0.35	1.65–2.00	0.90–1.20	. . . .	3240
E 3310	3310	0.20–0.35	3.25–3.75	1.40–1.75	. . . .	3312
E 3316	. . . .	0.20–0.35	3.25–3.75	1.40–1.75	. . . .	. . . .
A 4023	4023	0.20–0.35	. . . .	. . . .	0.20–0.30	. . . .
A 4024	. . . .	0.20–0.35	. . . .	. . . .	0.20–0.30	. . . .
A 4027	4027	0.20–0.35	. . . .	. . . .	0.20–0.30	. . . .
A 4028	. . . .	0.20–0.35	. . . .	. . . .	0.20 0.30	. . . .
A 4032	4032	0.20–0.35	. . . .	. . . .	0.20–0.30	. . . .
A 4037	4037	0.20–0.35	. . . .	. . . .	0.20–0.30	. . . .
A 4042	4042	0.20–0.35	. . . .	. . . .	0.20–0.30	. . . .
A 4047	4047	0.20–0.35	. . . .	. . . .	0.20–0.30	. . . .
A 4063	4063	0.20–0.35	. . . .	. . . .	0.20–0.30	. . . .
A 4068	4068	0.20–0.35	. . . .	. . . .	0.20–0.30	. . . .
A 4119	4119	0.20–0.35	. . . .	0.40–0.60	0.20–0.30	. . . .
A 4120	. . . .	0.20–0.35	. . . .	0.60–0.80	0.20–0.30	. . . .
A 4125	4125	0.20–0.35	. . . .	0.40–0.60	0.20–0.30	. . . .
A 4130	4130	0.20–0.35	. . . .	0.80–1.10	0.15–0.25	x4130
A 4131	. . . .	0.20–0.35	. . . .	0.80–1.00	0.14–0.19	. . . .
E 4132	. . . .	0.20–0.35	. . . .	0.80–1.10	0.18–0.25	. . . .

* These are also NE steels.
** Lowest standard maximum phosphorus or sulphur content for acid open-hearth or acid electric furnace alloy steel is 0.05% each; silicon is 0.15% minimum.

COMBINED AISI AND SAE
STANDARD STEEL SPECIFICATIONS

(CONTINUED)

OPEN-HEARTH AND ELECTRIC FURNACE ALLOY STEELS

(CONTINUED)

AISI Number	1943 SAE Number	C	Mn	P Max.**	S Max.**
A 4134	....	0.32–0.37	0.40–0.60	0.040	0.040
E 4135	....	0.33–0.38	0.70–0.90	0.025	0.025
A 4137	4137	0.35–0.40	0.70–0.90	0.040	0.040
E 4137	....	0.35–0.40	0.70–0.90	0.025	0.025
A 4140	4140	0.38–0.43	0.75–1.00	0.040	0.040
A 4141	....	0.38–0.43	0.75–1.00	0.040	0.040
A 4142	....	0.40–0.45	0.75–1.00	0.040	0.040
A 4143	....	0.40–0.45	0.75–1.00	0.040	0.040
A 4145	4145	0.43–0.48	0.75–1.00	0.040	0.040
A 4147	....	0.45–0.50	0.75–1.00	0.040	0.040
A 4150	4150	0.46–0.53	0.75–1.00	0.040	0.040
E 4150	....	0.48–0.53	0.70–0.90	0.025	0.025
A 4317	....	0.15–0.20	0.45–0.65	0.040	0.040
A 4320	4320	0.17–0.22	0.45–0.65	0.040	0.040
A 4337	....	0.35–0.40	0.60–0.80	0.040	0.040
E 4337	....	0.35–0.40	0.60–0.80	0.025	0.025
A 4340	4340	0.38–0.43	0.60–0.80	0.040	0.040
E 4342	....	0.40–0.45	0.60–0.80	0.025	0.025
A 4608	....	0.06–0.11	0.40 max.	0.040	0.040
A 4615	4615	0.13–0.18	0.45–0.65	0.040	0.040
E 4617	....	0.15–0.20	0.45–0.65	0.025	0.025
A 4620	4620	0.17–0.22	0.45–0.65	0.040	0.040
E 4620	....	0.17–0.22	0.45–0.60	0.025	0.025
A 4621	....	0.18–0.23	0.70–0.90	0.040	0.040
A 4640	4640	0.38–0.43	0.60–0.80	0.040	0.040
E 4640	....	0.38–0.43	0.60–0.80	0.025	0.025
A 4645	....	0.43–0.48	0.60–0.80	0.040	0.040
A 4815	4815	0.13–0.18	0.40–0.60	0.040	0.040
A 4820	4820	0.18–0.23	0.50–0.70	0.040	0.040
A 5045	....	0.43–0.48	0.70–0.90	0.040	0.040
A 5120	5120	0.17–0.22	0.70–0.90	0.040	0.040
A 5130	....	0.28–0.33	0.70–0.90	0.040	0.040
A 5140	5140	0.38–0.43	0.70–0.90	0.040	0.040
A 5145	....	0.43–0.48	0.70–0.90	0.040	0.040
A 5150	5150	0.48–0.55	0.70–0.90	0.040	0.040
A 5152	....	0.45–0.55	0.70–0.90	0.040	0.040
*E 52095	....	0.95–1.10	0.25–0.45	0.025	0.025
*E 52098	....	0.95–1.10	0.25–0.45	0.025	0.025
*E 52100	....	0.95–1.10	0.25–0.45	0.025	0.025
....	52100	0.95–1.10	0.30–0.50	0.025	0.025
NE 52100A	....	0.95–1.10	0.25–0.45	0.025	0.025
NE 52100B	....	0.95–1.10	0.25–0.45	0.025	0.025
NE 52100C	....	0.95–1.10	0.25–0.45	0.025	0.025
*E 52101	....	0.95–1.10	0.25–0.45	0.025	0.025

* These are also NE steels.
** Lowest standard maximum phosphorus or sulphur content for acid open-hearth or acid electric furnace alloy steel is 0.05% each; silicon is 0.15% minimum.

COMBINED AISI AND SAE
STANDARD STEEL SPECIFICATIONS
(CONTINUED)
OPEN-HEARTH AND ELECTRIC FURNACE ALLOY STEELS
(CONTINUED)

AISI Number	1943 SAE Number	Si**	Ni	Cr	Mo	Replaces 1941 SAE Number
A 4134	....	0.20–0.35	....	0.80–1.10	0.15–0.25	....
E 4135	....	0.20–0.35	....	0.80–1.10	0.18–0.25	....
A 4137	4137	0.20–0.35	....	0.80–1.10	0.15–0.25	....
E 4137	....	0.20–0.35	....	0.80–1.10	0.18–0.25	....
A 4140	4140	0.20–0.35	....	0.80–1.10	0.15–0.25	4140
A 4141	....	0.20–0.35	....	0.80–1.10	0.14–0.19	....
A 4142	....	0.20–0.35	....	0.80–1.10	0.15–0.25	....
A 4143	....	0.20–0.35	....	0.80–1.10	0.30–0.40	....
A 4145	4145	0.20–0.35	....	0.80–1.10	0.15–0.25	....
A 4147	....	0.20–0.35	....	0.80–1.10	0.15–0.25	....
A 4150	4150	0.20–0.35	....	0.80–1.10	0.15–0.25	4150
E 4150	....	0.20–0.35	....	0.80–1.10	0.20–0.27	....
A 4317	....	0.20–0.35	1.65–2.00	0.40–0.60	0.20–0.30	....
A 4320	4320	0.20–0.35	1.65–2.00	0.40–0.60	0.20–0.30	4320
A 4337	....	0.20 0.35	1.65–2.00	0.60–0.80	0.30–0.40	....
E 4337	....	0.20–0.35	1.65–2.00	0.70–0.90	0.23–0.30	....
A 4340	4340	0.20–0.35	1.65–2.00	0.70–0.90	0.20–0.30	x4340
E 4342	....	0.20–0.35	1.65–2.00	0.70–0.90	0.23–0.30	....
A 4608	....	0.25 max.	1.40–1.75	....	0.15–0.25	....
A 4615	4615	0.20–0.35	1.65–2.00	....	0.20–0.30	4615
E 4617	....	0.20–0.35	1.65–2.00	....	0.20–0.27	....
A 4620	4620	0.20–0.35	1.65–2.00	....	0.20–0.30	4620
E 4620	....	0.20 0.25	1.65 2.00	....	0.20–0.27	....
A 4621	....	0.20–0.35	1.65–2.00	....	0.20–0.30	....
A 4640	4640	0.20–0.35	1.65–2.00	....	0.20–0.30	4640
E 4640	....	0.20–0.35	1.65–2.00	....	0.20–0.27	....
A 4645	....	0.20–0.35	1.65–2.00	....	0.20–0.30	....
A 4815	4815	0.20–0.35	3.25–3.75	....	0.20–0.30	4815
A 4820	4820	0.20–0.35	3.25–3.75	....	0.20–0.30	4820
A 5045	....	0.20–0.35	....	0.55–0.75	....	....
A 5120	5120	0.20–0.35	....	0.70–0.90	....	5120
A 5130	....	0.20–0.35	....	0.80–1.10	....	....
A 5140	5140	0.20–0.35	....	0.70–0.90	....	5140
A 5145	....	0.20–0.35	....	0.70–0.90	....	....
A 5150	5150	0.20–0.35	....	0.70–0.90	....	5150
A 5152	....	0.20–0.35	....	0.90–1.20	....	....
*E 52095	....	0.20–0.35	....	0.40–0.60	....	....
*E 52098	....	0.20–0.35	....	0.90–1.15	....	....
*E 52100	....	0.20–0.35	....	1.20–1.50	....	52100
....	52100	0.20–0.35	....	1.20–1.50	....	52100
NE 52100A	....	0.20–0.35	0.35 max.	1.30–1.60	0.08 max.	....
NE 52100B	....	0.20–0.35	0.35 max.	0.90–1.15	0.08 max.	....
NE 52100C	....	0.20–0.35	0.35 max.	0.40–0.60	0.08 max.	....
*E 52101	....	0.20–0.35	....	1.30–1.60	....	....

* These are also NE steels.
** Lowest standard maximum phosphorus or sulphur content for acid open-hearth or acid electric furnace alloy steel is 0.05% each; silicon is 0.15% minimum.

COMBINED AISI AND SAE
STANDARD STEEL SPECIFICATIONS
(CONTINUED)

OPEN-HEARTH AND ELECTRIC FURNACE ALLOY STEELS
(CONTINUED)

AISI Number	1943 SAE Number	C	Mn	P Max.**	S Max.**
A 6120	....	0.17–0.22	0.70–0.90	0.040	0.040
A 6145	....	0.43–0.48	0.70–0.90	0.040	0.040
....	6150	0.48–0.55	0.65–0.90	0.040	0.040
E 6150	....	0.47–0.53	0.70–0.90	0.025	0.025
A 6152	....	0.48–0.55	0.70–0.90	0.040	0.040
NE 8612	....	0.10–0.15	0.70–0.90	0.040	0.040
NE 8615	....	0.13–0.18	0.70–0.90	0.040	0.040
NE 8617	....	0.15–0.20	0.70–0.90	0.040	0.040
NE 8620	....	0.18–0.23	0.70–0.90	0.040	0.040
NE 8622	....	0.20–0.25	0.70–0.90	0.040	0.040
NE 8625	....	0.23–0.28	0.70–0.90	0.040	0.040
NE 8627	....	0.25–0.30	0.70–0.90	0.040	0.040
NE 8630	....	0.28–0.33	0.70–0.90	0.040	0.040
NE 8632	....	0.30–0.35	0.70–0.90	0.040	0.040
NE 8635	....	0.33–0.38	0.75–1.00	0.040	0.040
NE 8637	....	0.35–0.40	0.75–1.00	0.040	0.040
NE 8640	....	0.38–0.43	0.75–1.00	0.040	0.040
NE 8642	....	0.40–0.45	0.75–1.00	0.040	0.040
NE 8645	....	0.43–0.48	0.75–1.00	0.040	0.040
NE 8647	....	0.45–0.50	0.75–1.00	0.040	0.040
NE 8650	....	0.48–0.53	0.75–1.00	0.040	0.040
NE 8712	....	0.10–0.15	0.70–0.90	0.040	0.040
NE 8715	....	0.13–0.18	0.70–0.90	0.040	0.040
NE 8717	....	0.15–0.20	0.70–0.90	0.040	0.040
NE 8720	....	0.18–0.23	0.70–0.90	0.040	0.040
NE 8722	....	0.20–0.25	0.70–0.90	0.040	0.040
NE 8725	....	0.23–0.28	0.70–0.90	0.040	0.040
NE 8727	....	0.25–0.30	0.70–0.90	0.040	0.040
NE 8730	....	0.28–0.33	0.70–0.90	0.040	0.040
NE 8732	....	0.30–0.35	0.70–0.90	0.040	0.040
NE 8735	....	0.33–0.38	0.75–1.00	0.040	0.040
NE 8737	....	0.35–0.40	0.75–1.00	0.040	0.040
NE 8740	....	0.38–0.43	0.75–1.00	0.040	0.040
NE 8742	....	0.40–0.45	0.75–1.00	0.040	0.040
NE 8745	....	0.43–0.48	0.75–1.00	0.040	0.040
NE 8747	....	0.45–0.50	0.75–1.00	0.040	0.040
NE 8750	....	0.48–0.53	0.75–1.00	0.040	0.040
*A 9255	....	0.50–0.60	0.70–0.95	0.040	0.040
*A 9260	....	0.55–0.65	0.70–1.00	0.040	0.040
....	9260	0.55–0.65	0.70–0.90	0.040	0.040
NE 9261	....	0.55–0.65	0.70–1.00	0.040	0.040
*A 9262	....	0.55–0.65	0.70–1.00	0.040	0.040

* These are also NE steels.
** Lowest standard maximum phosphorus or sulphur content for acid open-hearth or acid electric furnace alloy steel is 0.05% each; silicon is 0.15% minimum.
    For NE Steels, when electric furnace steel is specified, phosphorus and sulphur contents are to be 0.025% maximum each.

COMBINED AISI AND SAE
STANDARD STEEL SPECIFICATIONS
(CONTINUED)
OPEN-HEARTH AND ELECTRIC FURNACE ALLOY STEELS
(CONTINUED)

AISI Number	1943 SAE Number	Si**	Ni	Cr	Mo	Replaces 1941 SAE Number
A 6120	....	0.20–0.35	....	0.70–0.90	0.10 min. ▲	....
A 6145	....	0.20–0.35	....	0.80–1.10	0.15 min. ▲	....
....	6150	0.20–0.35	....	0.80–1.10	0.15 min. ▲	6150
E 6150	....	0.20–0.35	....	0.80–1.10	0.15 min. ▲	....
A 6152	....	0.20–0.35	....	0.80–1.10	0.10 min. ▲	....
NE 8612	....	0.20–0.35	0.40–0.70	0.40–0.60	0.15–0.25	....
NE 8615	....	0.20–0.35	0.40–0.70	0.40–0.60	0.15–0.25	....
NE 8617	....	0.20–0.35	0.40–0.70	0.40–0.60	0.15–0.25	....
NE 8620	....	0.20–0.35	0.40–0.70	0.40–0.60	0.15–0.25	....
NE 8622	....	0.20–0.35	0.40–0.70	0.40–0.60	0.15–0.25	....
NE 8625	....	0.20–0.35	0.40–0.70	0.40–0.60	0.15–0.25	....
NE 8627	....	0.20–0.35	0.40–0.70	0.40–0.60	0.15–0.25	....
NE 8630	....	0.20–0.35	0.40–0.70	0.40–0.60	0.15–0.25	....
NE 8632	....	0.20–0.35	0.40–0.70	0.40–0.60	0.15–0.25	....
NE 8635	....	0.20–0.35	0.40–0.70	0.40–0.60	0.15–0.25	....
NE 8637	....	0.20–0.35	0.40–0.70	0.40–0.60	0.15–0.25	....
NE 8640	....	0.20–0.35	0.40–0.70	0.40–0.60	0.15–0.25	....
NE 8642	....	0.20–0.35	0.40–0.70	0.40–0.60	0.15–0.25	....
NE 8645	....	0.20–0.35	0.40–0.70	0.40–0.60	0.15–0.25	....
NE 8647	....	0.20–0.35	0.40–0.70	0.40–0.60	0.15–0.25	....
NE 8650	....	0.20–0.35	0.40–0.70	0.40–0.60	0.15–0.25	....
NE 8712	....	0.20–0.35	0.40–0.70	0.40–0.60	0.20–0.30	....
NE 8715	....	0.20–0.35	0.40–0.70	0.40–0.60	0.20–0.30	....
NE 8717	....	0.20–0.35	0.40–0.70	0.40–0.60	0.20–0.30	....
NE 8720	....	0.20–0.35	0.40–0.70	0.40–0.60	0.20–0.30	....
NE 8722	....	0.20–0.35	0.40–0.70	0.40–0.60	0.20–0.30	....
NE 8725	....	0.20–0.35	0.40–0.70	0.40–0.60	0.20–0.30	....
NE 8727	....	0.20–0.35	0.40–0.70	0.40–0.60	0.20–0.30	....
NE 8730	....	0.20–0.35	0.40–0.70	0.40–0.60	0.20–0.30	....
NE 8732	....	0.20–0.35	0.40–0.70	0.40–0.60	0.20–0.30	....
NE 8735	....	0.20–0.35	0.40–0.70	0.40–0.60	0.20–0.30	....
NE 8737	....	0.20–0.35	0.40–0.70	0.40–0.60	0.20–0.30	....
NE 8740	....	0.20–0.35	0.40–0.70	0.40–0.60	0.20–0.30	....
NE 8742	....	0.20–0.35	0.40–0.70	0.40–0.60	0.20–0.30	....
NE 8745	....	0.20–0.35	0.40–0.70	0.40–0.60	0.20–0.30	....
NE 8747	....	0.20–0.35	0.40–0.70	0.40–0.60	0.20–0.30	....
NE 8750	....	0.20–0.35	0.40–0.70	0.40–0.60	0.20–0.30	....
*A 9255	....	1.80–2.20	....	....	....	....
*A 9260	....	1.80–2.20	....	....	....	....
....	9260	1.80–2.20	....	....	....	9260
NE 9261	....	1.80–2.20	....	0.10–0.25	....	....
*A 9262	....	1.80–2.20	....	0.25–0.40	....	....

* These are also NE steels.
** Lowest standard maximum phosphorus or sulphur content for acid open-hearth or acid electric furnace alloy steel is 0.05% each; silicon is 0.15% minimum.
▲ These values for the 6100 series are for vanadium instead of molybdenum.

COMBINED AISI AND SAE
STANDARD STEEL SPECIFICATIONS
(CONTINUED)

OPEN-HEARTH AND ELECTRIC FURNACE ALLOY STEELS
(CONTINUED)

AISI Number	1943 SAE Number	C	Mn	P Max.**	S Max.**
NE 9415	....	0.13–0.18	0.80–1.10	0.040	0.040
NE 9417	....	0.15–0.20	0.80–1.10	0.040	0.040
NE 9420	....	0.18–0.23	0.80–1.10	0.040	0.040
NE 9422	....	0.20–0.25	0.80–1.10	0.040	0.040
NE 9425	....	0.23–0.28	0.90–1.20	0.040	0.040
NE 9427	....	0.25–0.30	0.90–1.20	0.040	0.040
NE 9430	....	0.28–0.33	0.90–1.20	0.040	0.040
NE 9432	....	0.30–0.35	0.90–1.20	0.040	0.040
NE 9435	....	0.33–0.38	0.90–1.20	0.040	0.040
NE 9437	....	0.35–0.40	0.90–1.20	0.040	0.040
NE 9440	....	0.38–0.43	0.90–1.20	0.040	0.040
NE 9442	....	0.40–0.45	1.00–1.30	0.040	0.040
NE 9445	....	0.43–0.48	1.00–1.30	0.040	0.040
NE 9447	....	0.45–0.50	1.20–1.50	0.040	0.040
NE 9450	....	0.48–0.53	1.20–1.50	0.040	0.040
NE 9722	....	0.20–0.25	0.50–0.80	0.040	0.040
NE 9727	....	0.25–0.30	0.50–0.80	0.040	0.040
NE 9732	....	0.30–0.35	0.50–0.80	0.040	0.040
NE 9737	....	0.35–0.40	0.50–0.80	0.040	0.040
NE 9742	....	0.40–0.45	0.50–0.80	0.040	0.040
NE 9745	....	0.43–0.48	0.50–0.80	0.040	0.040
NE 9747	....	0.45–0.50	0.50–0.80	0.040	0.040
NE 9750	....	0.48–0.53	0.50–0.80	0.040	0.040
NE 9763	....	0.60–0.67	0.50–0.80	0.040	0.040
NE 9768	....	0.64–0.72	0.50–0.80	0.040	0.040
NE 9830	....	0.28–0.33	0.70–0.90	0.040	0.040
NE 9832	....	0.30–0.35	0.70–0.90	0.040	0.040
NE 9835	....	0.33–0.38	0.70–0.90	0.040	0.040
NE 9837	....	0.35–0.40	0.70–0.90	0.040	0.040
NE 9840	....	0.38–0.43	0.70–0.90	0.040	0.040
NE 9842	....	0.40–0.45	0.70–0.90	0.040	0.040
NE 9845	....	0.43–0.48	0.70–0.90	0.040	0.040
NE 9847	....	0.45–0.50	0.70–0.90	0.040	0.040
NE 9850	....	0.48–0.53	0.70–0.90	0.040	0.040
NE 9912	....	0.10–0.15	0.50–0.70	0.040	0.040
NE 9915	....	0.13–0.18	0.50–0.70	0.040	0.040
NE 9917	....	0.15–0.20	0.50–0.70	0.040	0.040
NE 9920	....	0.18–0.23	0.50–0.70	0.040	0.040
NE 9922	....	0.20–0.25	0.50–0.70	0.040	0.040
NE 9925	....	0.23–0.28	0.50–0.70	0.040	0.040

** Lowest standard maximum phosphorus or sulphur content for acid open-hearth or acid electric furnace alloy steel is 0.05% each; silicon is 0.15% minimum.
For NE Steels, when electric furnace steel is specified, phosphorus and sulphur contents are to be 0.025% maximum each.

COMBINED AISI AND SAE
STANDARD STEEL SPECIFICATIONS
(CONTINUED)

OPEN-HEARTH AND ELECTRIC FURNACE ALLOY STEELS
(CONTINUED)

AISI Number	1943 SAE Number	Si**	Ni	Cr	Mo	Replaces 1941 SAE Number
NE 9415	....	0.20–0.35	0.30–0.60	0.30–0.50	0.08–0.15	....
NE 9417	....	0.20–0.35	0.30–0.60	0.30–0.50	0.08–0.15	....
NE 9420	....	0.20–0.35	0.30–0.60	0.30–0.50	0.08–0.15	....
NE 9422	....	0.20–0.35	0.30–0.60	0.30–0.50	0.08–0.15	....
NE 9425	....	0.20–0.35	0.30–0.60	0.30–0.50	0.08–0.15	....
NE 9427	....	0.20–0.35	0.30–0.60	0.30–0.50	0.08–0.15	....
NE 9430	....	0.20–0.35	0.30–0.60	0.30–0.50	0.08–0.15	....
NE 9432	....	0.20–0.35	0.30–0.60	0.30–0.50	0.08–0.15	....
NE 9435	....	0.20–0.35	0.30–0.60	0.30–0.50	0.08–0.15	....
NE 9437	....	0.20–0.35	0.30–0.60	0.30–0.50	0.08–0.15	....
NE 9440	....	0.20 0.35	0.30 0.60	0.30 0.50	0.08 0.15	....
NE 9442	....	0.20–0.35	0.30–0.60	0.30–0.50	0.08–0.15	....
NE 9445	....	0.20–0.35	0.30–0.60	0.30–0.50	0.08–0.15	....
NE 9447	....	0.20–0.35	0.30–0.60	0.30–0.50	0.08–0.15	....
NE 9450	....	0.20–0.35	0.30–0.60	0.30–0.50	0.08–0.15	....
NE 9722	....	0.20–0.35	0.40–0.70	0.10–0.25	0.15–0.25	....
NE 9727	....	0.20–0.35	0.40–0.70	0.10–0.25	0.15–0.25	....
NE 9732	....	0.20–0.35	0.40–0.70	0.10–0.25	0.15–0.25	....
NE 9737	....	0.20–0.35	0.40–0.70	0.10–0.25	0.15–0.25	....
NE 9742	....	0.20–0.35	0.40–0.70	0.10–0.25	0.15–0.25	....
NE 9745	....	0.20–0.35	0.40–0.70	0.10–0.25	0.15–0.25	....
NE 9747	....	0.20–0.35	0.40–0.70	0.10 0.25	0.15 0.25	....
NE 9750	....	0.20–0.35	0.40–0.70	0.10–0.25	0.15–0.25	....
NE 9763	....	0.20–0.35	0.40–0.70	0.10–0.25	0.15–0.25	....
NE 9768	....	0.20–0.35	0.40–0.70	0.10–0.25	0.15–0.25	....
NE 9830	....	0.20–0.35	0.85–1.15	0.70–0.90	0.20–0.30	....
NE 9832	....	0.20–0.35	0.85–1.15	0.70–0.90	0.20–0.30	....
NE 9835	....	0.20–0.35	0.85–1.15	0.70–0.90	0.20–0.30	....
NE 9837	....	0.20–0.35	0.85–1.15	0.70–0.90	0.20–0.30	....
NE 9840	....	0.20–0.35	0.85–1.15	0.70–0.90	0.20–0.30	....
NE 9842	....	0.20–0.35	0.85–1.15	0.70–0.90	0.20–0.30	....
NE 9845	....	0.20–0.35	0.85–1.15	0.70–0.90	0.20–0.30	....
NE 9847	....	0.20–0.35	0.85–1.15	0.70–0.90	0.20–0.30	....
NE 9850	....	0.20–0.35	0.85–1.15	0.70–0.90	0.20–0.30	....
NE 9912	....	0.20–0.35	1.00–1.30	0.40–0.60	0.20–0.30	....
NE 9915	....	0.20–0.35	1.00–1.30	0.40–0.60	0.20–0.30	....
NE 9917	....	0.20–0.35	1.00–1.30	0.40–0.60	0.20–0.30	....
NE 9920	....	0.20–0.35	1.00–1.30	0.40–0.60	0.20–0.30	....
NE 9922	....	0.20–0.35	1.00–1.30	0.40–0.60	0.20–0.30	....
NE 9925	....	0.20–0.35	1.00–1.30	0.40–0.60	0.20–0.30	....

** Lowest standard maximum phosphorus or sulphur content for acid open-hearth or acid electric furnace alloy steel is 0.05% each; silicon is 0.15% minimum.

PROPERTIES OF POPULAR STAINLESS STEELS

American Iron and Steel Inst. Type No. →	403 and 410	416
Approximate Chemical Composition	C .12% Max. Mn .50% Max. Si .50% Max. S and P .03% Max. Cr 11.5–14.0%	C .12% Max. Mn .50% Max. Si .50% Max. S .20–.40% P .03% Max. Cr 12–15% Mo .45–.65%
Magnetic Properties	Ferromagnetic	Ferromagnetic
Nominal Values of Mechanical Properties Hardness, Brinell Number Annealed............ Heat-Treated.......	 135–165 293–390	 145–185 180–300
Ultimate Tensile Strength, lbs./sq. in. Annealed............ Heat-Treated.......	 65,000–85,000 100,000–200,000	 70,000–85,000 80,000–160,000
Yield Point, lbs./sq. in. Annealed............ Heat-Treated.......	 35,000–45,000 60,000–180,000	 40,000–50,000 60,000–130,000
Elongation in 2 in. Annealed............ Heat-Treated.......	 35–25% 25–10%	 35–25% 25–15%
Reduction of Area Annealed............ Heat-Treated.......	 65–60% 60–25%	 65–60% 60–40%
Creep Strength for a Life of 10,000 Hours with 1% Elongation At 1000°F., lbs./sq. in. At 1100°F., lbs./sq. in. At 1300°F., lbs./sq. in. At 1500°F., lbs./sq. in.	 13,000 5,000 1,500	 13,000 5,000 1,500 ......
Strength at Elevated Temp. Short Time Tests At 1300°F........... At 1500°F........... At 1700°F...........	 15,000 8,000 8,000	 15,000 8,000 8,000
Heat-Resistance, Scaling Temperature Continuous Service .. Intermittent Service..	 1250°F. 1400°F.	 1250°F. 1400°F.

(REPUBLIC)

PROPERTIES OF POPULAR STAINLESS STEELS

American Iron and Steel Inst. Type No. ⟶	302—(18-8)	302B	501
Approximate Chemical Composition	C .20% Max. Mn .60% Max. Si .75% Max. S and P .03% Max. Cr 17–19% Ni 7–9.5%	C .20% Max. Mn 1.50% Max. Si 2.0–3.0% S and P .03% Max. Cr 17–19% Ni 7–9.5%	C .10% Min. Mn .50% Max. S and P .04% Max. Cr 4–6%
Magnetic Properties	Non-Magnetic	Non-Magnetic	
Nominal Values of Mechanical Properties Hardness, Brinell Number Annealed........... Heat-Treated.......	135–185 Non-Hardening	150–180 Non-Hardening	131–165 180–418
Ultimate Tensile Strength, lbs./sq. in. Annealed........... Heat-Treated.......	80,000–90,000 Non-Hardening	80,000–100,000 Non-Hardening	60,000–80,000 80,000–180,000
Yield Point, lbs./sq. in. Annealed........... Heat-Treated.......	35,000–45,000 Non-Hardening	40,000–50,000 Non-Hardening	30,000–40,000 60,000–150,000
Elongation in 2 in. Annealed........... Heat-Treated.......	60–55% Non-Hardening	60–50% Non-Hardening	
Reduction of Area Annealed........... Heat-Treated.......	65–55% Non-Hardening	70–50% Non-Hardening	
Creep Strength for a Life of 10,000 Hours with 1% Elongation At 1000°F., lbs./sq. in. At 1100°F., lbs./sq. in. At 1300°F., lbs./sq. in. At 1500°F., lbs./sq. in.	17,000 12,000 4,000 850	....	3,500 2,000 1,200 ......
Strength at Elevated Temp. Short Time Tests At 1300°F........... At 1500°F........... At 1700°F...........	42,000 28,000 18,000	60,000 32,000 24,000	
Heat-Resistance, Scaling Temperature Continuous Service... Intermittent Service..	1600°F. 1450°F.	1700°F. 1600°F.	

(REPUBLIC)

STRENGTH OF MATERIALS

AVERAGE STRENGTH DATA FOR IRON AND STEEL

Material Letters (a) etc. Indicate Footnotes	Ultimate Strength, Pounds per Square Inch			Yield Point, Pounds per Square Inch	Modulus of Elasticity, Tension	Elongation in 2 Inches, Per Cent
	Tension	Compression Footnote (m)	Shear			
Cast Iron, Soft............	16,000	80,000	17,000	....	12,000,000	....
Cast Iron, Average.......	22,000	100,000	24,000	....	16,000,000	....
Cast Iron, Hard (a)......	35,000	150,000	38,000	....	20,000,000	....
Cast Iron, High-test (b)...	45,000	200,000	50,000	....	....	....
Castings, Malleable......	54,000	....	48,000	36,000	25,000,000	18
Castings, Steel (c).......	70,000	70,000	60,000	40,000	30,000,000	25
Carbon Steel (d).........	56,000	56,000	42,000	28,000	29,000,000	30
Cold worked (e).........	75,000	75,000	55,000	38,000	30,000,000	....
Casehardened (f).......	80,000	80,000	60,000	50,000	30,000,000	20
Hardened, drawn (g)....	120,000	120,000	90,000	90,000	30,000,000	15
Machinery Steel (h)......	60,000	60,000	45,000	40,000	30,000,000	....
Nickel Steel (i)...........	130,000	130,000	98,000	100,000	30,000,000	18
S.A.E. No. 2330.......	145,000	145,000	110,000	120,000	30,000,000	18
S.A.E. No. 2340.......	165,000	165,000	125,000	150,000	30,000,000	12
Nickel-Chromium (j).....	125,000	125,000	95,000	95,000	30,000,000	18
S.A.E. No. 3130......	150,000	150,000	110,000	125,000	30,000,000	15
S.A.E. No. 3140......	175,000	175,000	130,000	150,000	30,000,000	....
S.A.E. No. 3230.......	180,000	180,000	135,000	150,000	30,000,000	15
S.A.E. No. 3240.......	200,000	200,000	150,000	180,000	30,000,000	15
S.A.E. No. 3250.......	220,000	220,000	165,000	200,000	30,000,000	12
Rivet Steel.............	57,000	57,000	44,000	36,000	29,000,000	....
Stainless Steel (k).......	225,000	225,000	....	185,000	....	9
Drawn 1290° F.........	120,000	120,000	....	90,000	....	22
Structural Steel..........	60,000	60,000	45,000	30,000	29,000,000	....
Steel Wire (l)...........	120,000	....	....	60,000	30,000,000	....
Annealed.............	80,000	....	....	40,000	29,000,000	....
Plow Steel............	275,000	....	....	....	....	....
Music Wire...........	300,000	....	....	....	....	....
Wrought Iron...........	48,000	46,000	40,000	25,000	27,000,000	....

(a) Compressive strength of "white" and "high-test" irons may range from 175,000 to 250,000 lbs. per sq. in.

(b) Tensile strength may range from 40,000 to 70,000 or even higher.

(c) Heat-treated *alloy-steel* castings may have tensile strength up to 200,000 lbs. per sq. in.

(d) Soft open-hearth annealed steel.

(e) Yield-point range up to 60,000 according to amount of cold-working.

(f) Strength data for S.A.E. No. 1020 casehardened steel water-quenched and drawn to 400 deg. F.

(g) S.A.E. No. 1045, hardened in water, drawn to 800 deg. F.

(h) Some "machinery" steels have tensile strengths ranging up to 100,000 lbs. per sq. in.

(i) S.A.E. No. 2320. Strength data for all nickel steels listed based upon a drawing temperature of 800 deg. F. and oil-quenching.

(j) S.A.E. No. 3120. Nickel-chromium steels listed drawn to 800 deg. F.

(k) Strength data for steel drawn to 390 deg. F. Note data for 1290 deg. F.

(l) Strength varies over wide range depending upon size and composition.

(m) For columns made of soft or medium steels, subjected to compressive and bending stresses combined, use yield point as value for ultimate compressive strength.

INDEX

	Date Due	
NO 17 '87		
OC 23 '89		
1508-155		